I. C. S.
REFERENCE LIBRARY

A SERIES OF TEXTBOOKS PREPARED FOR THE STUDENTS OF THE
INTERNATIONAL CORRESPONDENCE SCHOOLS AND CONTAINING
IN PERMANENT FORM THE INSTRUCTION PAPERS,
EXAMINATION QUESTIONS, AND KEYS USED
IN THEIR VARIOUS COURSES

GEOMETRICAL DRAWING
MECHANICAL DRAWING
SKETCHING
PRACTICAL PROJECTION
DEVELOPMENT OF SURFACES

SCRANTON
INTERNATIONAL TEXTBOOK COMPANY
39

Press of
International Textbook Company
Scranton, Pa.

71762

PREFACE

Formerly it was our practice to send to each student entitled to receive them a set of volumes printed and bound especially for the Course for which the student enrolled. In consequence of the vast increase in the enrolment, this plan became no longer practicable and we therefore concluded to issue a single set of volumes, comprising all our textbooks, under the general title of I. C. S. Reference Library. The students receive such volumes of this Library as contain the instruction to which they are entitled. Under this plan some volumes contain one or more Papers not included in the particular Course for which the student enrolled, but in no case are any subjects omitted that form a part of such Course. This plan is particularly advantageous to those students who enroll for more than one Course, since they no longer receive volumes that are, in some cases, practically duplicates of those they already have. This arrangement also renders it much easier to revise a volume and keep each subject up to date.

Each volume in the Library contains, in addition to the text proper, the Examination Questions and (for those subjects in which they are issued) the Answers to the Examination Questions.

In preparing these textbooks, it has been our constant endeavor to view the matter from the student's standpoint, and try to anticipate everything that would cause him trouble. The utmost pains have been taken to avoid and correct any and all ambiguous expressions—both those due to faulty rhetoric and those due to insufficiency of statement or explanation. As the best way to make a statement, explanation, or description clear is to give a picture or a

iii

diagram in connection with it, illustrations have been used almost without limit. The illustrations have in all cases been adapted to the requirements of the text, and projections and sections or outline, partially shaded, or full-shaded perspectives have been used, according to which will best produce the desired results.

The method of numbering pages and articles is such that each part is complete in itself; hence, in order to make the indexes intelligible, it was necessary to give each part a number. This number is placed at the top of each page, on the headline, opposite the page number; and to distinguish it from the page number, it is preceded by a section mark (§). Consequently, a reference, such as §3, page 10, can be readily found by looking along the inside edges of the headlines until §3 is found, and then through §3 until page 10 is found.

INTERNATIONAL CORRESPONDENCE SCHOOLS

CONTENTS

CONTENTS

GEOMETRICAL DRAWING

INSTRUMENTS AND MATERIALS

1. A **drawing** is a representation of objects on a plane surface by means of lines or lines and shades. When done by the use of free hand only, it is called **freehand drawing** or **sketching;** when instruments are used, so that greater exactness may be obtained, it is called **instrumental,** or **mechanical, drawing.**

2. All the instruments and materials required for the courses in drawing are mentioned in the following descriptions:

The **drawing board** should be made of well-seasoned, straight-grained pine, the grain running lengthwise. For this Course, the student will need a board of the following dimensions: length over all, about 21 inches; width, about 16 inches.

The drawing board illustrated in Fig. 1 is the one furnished in our students' drawing outfits and can be recommended as meeting all the requirements of the drawing work of this Course. It is made of several pieces of pine wood glued together to the required width of the board. A pair of hardwood cleats is screwed to the back of the board. Grooves are cut through half the thickness of the board over the entire back side. These grooves take the transverse resistance out of the wood and thus keep the board from warping, at the same time leaving the longitudinal strength nearly unimpaired. The cleats also raise the board from the table, thus making it easier to change the

position of the board.   When in use, the board is placed so
that one of the short edges is at the left of the draftsman,
as shown in Fig. 2.

The wood of which the board is made is very carefully

FIG. 1

and thoroughly dried, a necessary precaution to keep the
boards from warping.   Nevertheless, if kept near a source
of heat, as a stove, a radiator, etc. it may warp in spite of

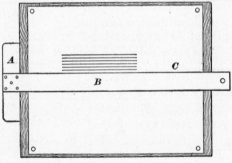

FIG. 2

the slots, on account of absorbing moisture from the air
and the uneven distribution of heat from the stove,
radiator, etc.

3.   The **T square** is used for drawing horizontal straight
lines.   The head A is placed against the left-hand edge of
the board, as shown in Fig. 2.   The upper edge C of the
blade B is brought very near to the point through which it
is desired to pass a line, so that the straight edge C of the
blade may be used as a guide for the pen or pencil.   It is
evident that all lines drawn in this manner will be parallel.

Vertical lines are drawn by means of triangles. The triangles most generally used are shown in Figs. 3 and 4, each of which has one right angle. The triangle shown in **Fig. 3**

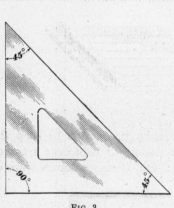

FIG. 3

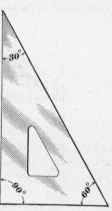

FIG. 4

has two angles of 45° each, and that in Fig. 4 one of 60° and one of 30°. They are called *45*° and *60*° *triangles,* respectively.

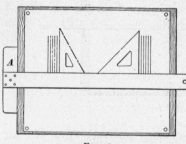

FIG. 5

To draw a vertical line, place the **T** square in position to draw a horizontal line, and lay the triangle against it, so as to form a right angle. Hold both **T** square and triangle lightly with the left hand, so as to keep them from slipping, and draw the line with the pen or pencil held in the right hand, and against the edge of the triangle. Fig. 5 shows the triangles and **T** square in position.

4. For drawing parallel lines that are neither vertical nor horizontal, the simplest and best way, when the lines are near together, is to place one edge of a triangle, as *a b*, Fig. 6, on the given line *c d*, and lay the other triangle, as *B*, against one of the two edges, holding it **fast**

with the left hand; then move the triangle *A* along the
edge of *B*.   The edge *a b* will be parallel to the line *c d*;
and when the edge *a b* reaches the point *g*, through which it
is desired to draw the parallel line, hold both triangles

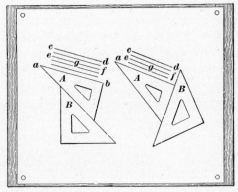

FIG. 6

stationary with the left hand and draw the line *e f* by pass·
ing the pencil along the edge *a b*.   Should the triangle *A*
extend too far beyond the edge of the triangle *B* after a
number of lines have been drawn, hold *A* stationary with
the left hand and shift *B* along the edge of *A* with the
right hand and then proceed as before.

5. A line may be drawn at right angles to another line
which is neither vertical nor horizontal, as illustrated in
Fig. 7.   Let *c d* be the given line (shown at the left-hand
side).   Place one of the shorter edges, as *a b*, of the triangle *B*
so that it will coincide with the line *c d*; then, keeping the
triangle in this position, place the triangle *A* so that its
long edge will come against the long edge of *B*.   Now,
holding *A* securely in place with the left hand, slide *B* along
the edge of *A* with the right hand, when the lines *h i*, *m n*,
etc. may be drawn perpendicular to *c d* along the edge *b f*
of the triangle *B*.   The dotted lines show the position of the
triangle *B* when moved along the edge of *A*.

6. The right-hand portion of Fig. 7 shows another
.method of accomplishing the same result, and illustrates

how the triangles may be used for drawing a rectangular figure, when the sides of the figure make an angle with the T square such that the latter cannot be used.

Let the side cd of the figure be given. Place the *long* side of the triangle B so as to coincide with the line cd, and bring the triangle A into position against the lower side of B, as shown. Now, holding the triangle A in place with the left hand, revolve B so that its other short edge will rest against the long edge of A, as shown in the dotted position at B'. The parallel lines ce and df may now be drawn

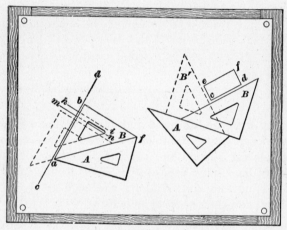

FIG. 7

through the points c and d by sliding the triangle B on the triangle A, as described in connection with Fig. 6. Measure off the required width of the figure on the line ce, reverse the triangle B again to its original position, still holding the triangle A in a fixed position with the left hand, and slide B upon A until the long edge of B passes through e. Draw the line ef through the point e, and ef will be parallel to cd. The student should practice with his triangles before beginning drawing.

7. The **compasses,** next to the T square and triangles, are used more than any other instrument. A pencil and pen point are provided, as shown in Fig. 8, either of which may be inserted into a socket in one leg of the instrument, for the drawing of circles in pencil or ink.   The other leg is fitted with a needle point, which acts as the center about which the circle is drawn.   In all good instruments, the needle point itself is a separate piece of round steel wire, held in place in a socket provided at the end of the leg. The wire should have a square shoulder at its lower end, below which a fine, needle-like point projects.   The *lengthening bar*, also shown in the figure, is used to extend the leg carrying the pen and pencil points when circles of large radii are to be drawn.

The joint at the top of the compasses should hold the legs firmly in any position, and at the same time should permit

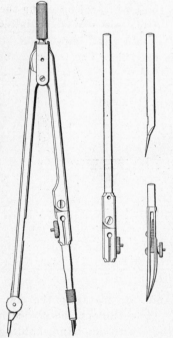

their being opened or closed with one hand.   The joint may be tightened or loosened by means of a screwdriver or wrench, which accompanies the compasses.

It will be noticed in Fig. 8 that each leg of the compasses is jointed; this is done so that the compass points may always be kept perpendicular to the paper when drawing circles, as in Fig. 11.

The common style of joint, Figs. 8 and 9, is the *pivot joint*, in which the head of each leg is shaped like a disk and the two disks are held together in a fork-shaped brace either by means of two pivot screws or by one screw penetrating both disks.   The brace that forms a part of this joint

FIG. 8

is generally provided with a handle, as the shape of the joint makes it rather awkward to hold the compasses by the head, as is usual with instruments provided with tongue joints. Another common style of compass has what is

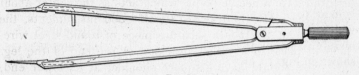

Fig. 9

called a *tongue joint*, in which the head of one leg has a tongue, generally of steel, which moves between two lugs on the other leg. In Fig. 9 is shown a common style of spacing dividers.

8. The following suggestions for handling the compasses should be carefully observed by those who are beginning the subject of mechanical drawing. Any draftsman who handles his instruments awkwardly will create a bad impression, no matter how good a workman he may be. The tendency of

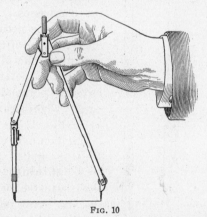

Fig. 10

all beginners is to use both hands for operating the compasses. This is to be avoided. The student should learn at the start to open and close them with one hand, holding them as shown in Fig. 10, with the needle-point leg resting between the thumb and fourth finger, and the other leg between the middle and forefinger. When drawing circles, hold the compasses lightly at the top between the thumb and forefinger, or thumb, forefinger, and middle finger, as in Fig. 11.   Another case where both hands should not be used is in locating the needle point at a point on the drawing about which the circle is to be drawn, unless the left hand is used merely to steady the needle point.   Hold the compasses as shown in Fig. 10, and incline them until the under side of the

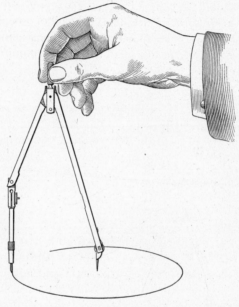

FIG. 11

hand rests upon the paper.   This will steady the hand so that the needle point can be brought to exactly the right place on the drawing.   Having placed the needle at the desired point, and with it still resting on the paper, the pen or pencil point may be moved out or in to any desired radius, as indicated in Fig. 10.   When the lengthening bar is used, both hands must be employed.

9.   The compasses must be handled in such a manner that the needle point will not dig large holes in the paper.   Keep the needle point adjusted so that it will be perpendicular to the paper, when drawing circles, and *do not bear upon it.* A slight pressure will be necessary on the pen or pencil point, *but not on the needle point.*

10. The **dividers,** shown in Figs. 9 and 12, are used for laying off distances upon a drawing, or for dividing straight lines or circles into parts. The points of the dividers should be *very* sharp, so that they will not punch holes in the paper larger than is absolutely necessary to be seen. Compasses are sometimes furnished with two steel divider points, besides the pen and pencil points, so that the instrument may be used either as compasses or dividers. This is the kind illustrated in Fig. 12. When using the

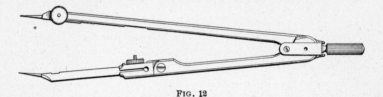

FIG. 12

dividers to space a line or circle into a number of equal parts, hold them at the top between the thumb and forefinger, as when using the compasses, and step off the spaces, turning the instrument alternately to the right and left. If the line or circle does not space exactly, vary the distance between the divider points and try again; so continue until it is spaced equally. When spacing in this manner, great care must be exercised not to press the divider points into the paper; for, if the points enter the paper, the spacing can never be accurately done. The student should satisfy himself of the truth of this statement by actual trial.

11. The **bow-pencil** and **bow-pen,** shown in Fig. 13, are convenient for describing small circles. The two points of the instruments must be adjusted to the same length; otherwise, very small circles cannot be drawn. To open or close either of these instruments, support it in a vertical position by resting the needle point on the paper and bearing slightly on the top of it with the forefinger of one hand,

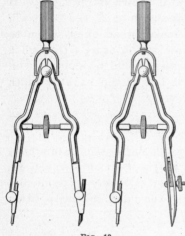

and turn the adjusting nut with the thumb and middle finger of the same hand.

12. Drawing Paper and Pencils.—The drawing paper recommended for this series of lessons is T. S. Co.'s cold-pressed demy, the size of which is $15'' \times 20''$. It takes ink well and withstands considerable erasing. The paper is secured to the drawing board by means of **thumbtacks.** Four are usually sufficient — one at

FIG. 13

each corner of the sheet (see Fig. 7). Place a piece of paper on the drawing board, and press a thumbtack through one of the corners about $\frac{1}{4}$ or $\frac{3}{8}$ of an inch from each edge. Place the **T** square in position for drawing a horizontal line, as before explained, and straighten the paper so that its upper edge will be parallel to the edge of the **T**-square blade. Pull the corner diagonally opposite that in which the thumbtack was placed, so as to stretch the paper slightly, and push in another thumbtack. Do the same with the remaining two corners. For drawing in pencil, an HHHH pencil of any reputable make should be used. The pencil should be sharpened as shown at A, Fig. 14. Cut the wood away so as to leave about $\frac{1}{4}$ or $\frac{3}{8}$ of an inch of the lead projecting; then

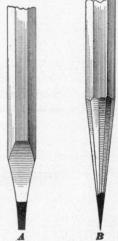

FIG. 14

sharpen it flat by rubbing it against a fine file or a piece of fine emery cloth or sandpaper that has been fastened to a flat stick. Grind it to a sharp edge like a knife blade, and round the corners very slightly, as shown in the figure. If sharpened to a round point, as shown at *B*, the point will wear away very quickly and make broad lines; when so sharpened it is difficult to draw a line exactly through a point. The lead for the compasses should be sharpened in the same manner as the pencil, but should have its width narrower. *Be sure that the compass lead is so secured that when circles are struck in either direction, but one line will be drawn with the same radius and center.*

13. Inking.—For drawing ink lines other than arcs of circles, the **ruling pen** (or *right-line pen*, as it is sometimes called) is used. It should be held as nearly perpendicular to the board as possible, with the hand in the position

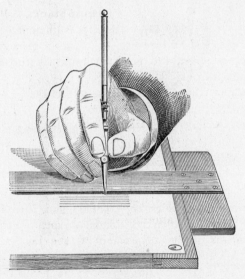

FIG. 15

shown in Figs. 15 and 16, bearing lightly against the **T** square or triangle, along the edge of which the line is drawn. After a little practice, this position will become natural, and no difficulty will be experienced.

14. The beginner will find that it is not always easy to make smooth lines. If the pen is held so that only one blade bears on the paper when drawing, the line will almost invariably be ragged on the edge where the blade does not bear. When held at right angles to the paper, as in Fig. 16, however, both blades will rest on the paper, and if the pen is in good condition, smooth lines will result. The pen must not be pressed against the edge of the **T** square or triangle, as the blades will then close together, making the line uneven. The edge should serve as a guide simply.

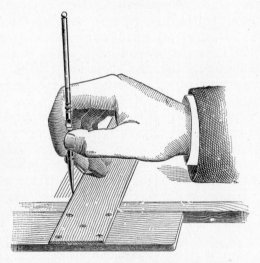

FIG. 16

In drawing circles with the compass pen, the same care should be taken to keep the blades perpendicular to the paper by means of the adjustment at the joint. In both the ruling pen and compass pen, the width of the lines can be altered by means of the screw which holds the blades together. The handles of most ruling pens can be unscrewed, and are provided with a needle point intended for use when copying maps by pricking through the original and the underlying paper, thus locating a series of points through which the outline may be drawn.

15. Drawing Ink.—The ink we recommend for the
work in this Course is the T. S. Co.'s superior waterproof
liquid India ink. A quill is attached to the cork of every
bottle of this ink, by means of which the pen may be filled.
Dip the quill into the ink and then pass the end of it
between the blades of the drawing pen. Do not put too
much ink in the pen, not more than enough to fill it for a
quarter of an inch along the blades, otherwise the ink is
liable to drop. Many draftsmen prefer to use stick India
ink; and for some purposes this is to be preferred to the
prepared liquid ink recommended above. In case the stick
ink is bought, put enough water in a shallow dish (a common individual butter plate will do) to make enough ink for
the drawing, then place one end of the stick in the water,
and grind by giving the stick a circular motion. Do not
bear hard upon the stick. Test the ink occasionally to see
if it is black. Draw a fine line with the pen and hold the
paper in a strong light. If it shows brown (or gray), grind
a while longer, and test again. Keep grinding until a fine
line shows *black*, which will usually take from fifteen minutes to half an hour, depending on the quantity of water
used. The ink should always be kept well covered with a
flat plate of some kind, to keep out the dust and prevent
evaporation. The drawing pen may be filled by dipping an
ordinary writing pen into the ink and drawing it through
the blades, as previously described when using the quill. If
liquid ink is used, all the lines on all the drawings will be of
the same color, and no time will be lost in grinding. If
stick ink is used, it is poor economy to buy a cheap stick.
A small stick of the best quality, costing, say, a dollar, will
last as long, perhaps, as five dollars' worth of liquid ink.
The only reason for using liquid ink is that all lines are then
sure to be of equal blackness and time is saved in grinding.

India ink will dry quickly on the drawing, which is desirable, but it also causes trouble by drying between the blades
and refusing to flow, especially when drawing fine lines.
The only remedy is to wipe out the pen frequently with a cloth.
Do not lay the pen down for any great length of time when

it contains ink; wipe it out first.   The ink may sometimes be started by moistening the end of the finger and touching it to the point, or by drawing a slip of paper between the ends of the blade.   *Always keep the bottle corked.*

16.   To Sharpen the Drawing Pen.—When the ruling, or compass, pen becomes badly worn, it must be sharpened.   For this purpose a fine oilstone should be used.   If an oilstone is to be purchased, a small, flat, close-grained stone should be obtained, those having a triangular section being preferable, as the narrow edge can be used on the inside of the blades in case the latter are not made to swing apart so as to permit the use of a thicker edge.

The first step in sharpening is to screw the blades together, and, holding the pen perpendicular to the oilstone, to draw it back and forth over the stone, changing the slope of the pen from downwards and to the right to downwards and to the left for each movement of the pen to the right and left. The object of this is to bring the blades to exactly the same length and shape, and to round them nicely at the point.

This process, of course, makes the edges even duller than before.   To sharpen, separate the points by means of the screw, and rub one of the blades to and from the operator in a straight line, giving the pen a slight twisting motion at the same time, and holding it at an angle of about 15° with the face of the stone.   Repeat the process for the other blade.   To be in good condition, the edges should be fairly sharp and smooth, but not sharp enough to cut the paper. *All the sharpening must be done on the outside of the blades.* The inside of the blades should be rubbed on the stone only enough to remove any burr that may have been formed. Anything more than this will be likely to injure the pen. The whole operation must be done very carefully, bearing on lightly, as it is easy to spoil a pen in the process. Examine the points frequently, and keep at work until the pen will draw both *fine* lines and *smooth* heavy lines.   Many draftsmen prefer to send the pens to be sharpened to the dealer who sold them, and who is generally willing to do such sharpening at a trifling cost.

17. Irregular Curves.—Curves other than arcs of circles are drawn with the pencil or ruling pen by means of curved or irregular-shaped rulers, called **irregular curves** (see Fig. 17). A series of points is first determined through which the curved line is to pass. The line is then drawn through these points by using such parts of the irregular curve as will pass through several of the points at once, the curve being shifted from time to time as required.

It is usually difficult to draw a smooth, continuous curve. The tendency is to make it curve out too much between the points, thus giving it a wavy appearance, or else to cause it to change its direction abruptly where the different lines join, making angles at these points. These defects may largely be avoided by always fitting the curve to at least three points, and, when moving it to a new position, by setting it so that it will coincide with part of the line already drawn. It will be found to be a great help if the line be first sketched in freehand, in pencil. It can then be penciled over neatly, or inked,

FIG. 17

without much difficulty, with the aid of the irregular curve, since the original pencil line will show the general direction in which the curve should be drawn. Whenever the given points are far apart, or fall in such positions that the irregular curve cannot always be made to pass through three of them, the line must invariably be sketched in at first.

As an example, let it be required to draw a curved line through the points *a*, *b*, *c*, *d*, etc., Fig. 18. As just stated, a part of the irregular curve must be used which will pass through at least three points. With the curve set in the first position *A*, its edge is found to coincide with four points *a*, *b*, *c*, and *d*. The line may then be drawn from *a* around to *d*, or, better, to a point between *c* and *d*, since, by not continuing it quite to *d*, there is less liability of there being an angle where the next section joins on.   For the next section of the line, the curve should be adjusted so as to coincide with a part of the section already drawn; that is, instead of adjusting it to points *d*, *e*, *f*, etc., it should be placed so as to

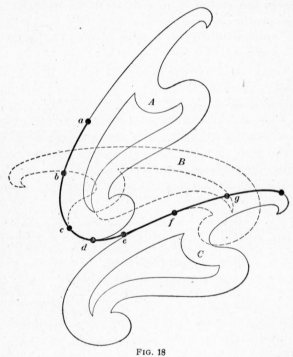

FIG. 18

pass through the point *c*, the part from *c* to *d* being coincident with the corresponding part of the first line drawn.   The irregular curve is shown dotted in this position at *B*. Its edge passes through four points *c*, *d*, *e*, and *f*, and the line should be made to stop midway between the last two, as before.

Now, it will be noticed that the points *f* and *g* are so situated that the remainder of the line must curve up, instead of down, as heretofore, the change in curvature occurring at a point between *e* and *f*. In this case, therefore, it is not necessary for the curve to extend back to *e*, through which point the line has already been drawn, but it may be placed in position *C* with its edge just tangent to the line at the point where the curvature changes.

It is to be noticed that in inking with the irregular curve, the blades of the pen must be kept tangent to its edge (i. e., the inside flat surface of the blades must have the same direction as the curve at the point where the pen touches the paper), which requires that the direction of the pen be continually changed.

18. The **scale** is used for obtaining measurements for drawings. The most convenient forms are the usual flat and triangular boxwood scales, having beveled edges, each of which is graduated for a distance of 12 inches. The beveled edges serve to bring the lines of division close to the paper when the scale is lying flat, so that the drawing may be accurately measured, or distances laid off correctly. The use of the graduations on scales will be explained when it is necessary to use the scale.

19. A **protractor** is shown in Fig. 19. The outer edge is a semicircle, with center at *O*, and is divided into

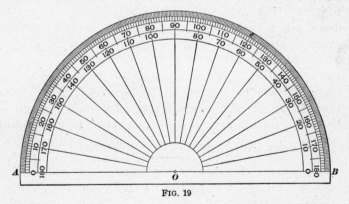

FIG. 19

360 parts. Each division is one-half of one degree, and, for convenience, the degrees are numbered from 0° to 180° from

both *A* and *B*. The protractor is used for laying off or measuring angles. Protractors are often made of metal, in which case the central part is cut away to make the drawing under it visible. When using the protractor, it must be placed so that the line *O B*, Fig. 19, will coincide with the line forming one side of the angle to be laid off or measured, and the center *O* must be at the vertex of the angle.

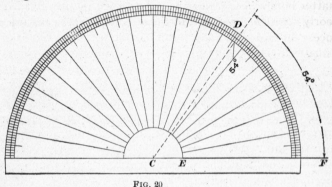

FIG. 20

For example, let it be required to draw a line through the point *C*, making an angle of 54° with the line *E F*, Fig. 20. Place the protractor upon the line *E F*, as just described, with the center *O* upon the point *C*. With a sharp-pointed pencil, make a mark on the paper at the 54° division, as indicated at *D*. A line drawn through *C* and *D* will then make an angle of 54° with *E F*. Greater exactness will be secured if the line *E F* be extended to the left, so that both zero marks (*A* and *B*, Fig. 19) can be placed on the line. This should always be done when possible.

LETTERING

20. In mechanical drawing, all headings, explanatory matter, and dimensions should be neatly printed on the drawing. Ordinary script writing is not permissible.

It is usually difficult for beginners to letter well, and unless the student is skilful at it, he should devote some time to practicing lettering before commencing the drawing. In correcting the plates, the lettering will be considered as well as the drawing. Many students think that it is only necessary to exercise special care when drawing the views on a plate, and that it is not necessary to take particular pains in lettering. This, however, is not the case, for, no matter how well the views may be drawn, if the lettering is poorly done, the finished drawing will not have a neat appearance. In fact, generally speaking, more time is required to make well-executed letters than to make well-executed drawings of objects. We earnestly request the student to practice lettering, and not to think that that part of the work is of no importance. The student should not be too hasty in doing the lettering. It takes an experienced draftsman considerable time to do good lettering, and no draftsman can perform this work as quickly as he can ordinary writing; therefore, no beginner should attempt to do what experienced draftsmen cannot do. In order to letter well, the work must be done slowly. Very frequently more time is spent in lettering a drawing than in inking in the objects represented. Instructions will be given in two styles of freehand lettering, both extensively used in American drafting rooms.

With the exception of the large headings or titles of the plates, the style and size of all lettering used on the original drawing plates of this Course are shown in Fig. 21. This

ABCDEFGHIJKLMNOPQRSTUVWXYZ
abcdefghijklmnopqrstuvwxyz &
1234567890 1234567890 2″-6¼″dia.Cast Iron

FIG. 21

style, although a little more elaborate and difficult in execution, was selected on account of its greater neatness and legibleness. The two styles are very similar in the formation of the letters, and although the student is advised to select and use only one of the two on his drawings in this Course, he will find, after having mastered one of the styles, little difficulty in practicing the other.

When lettering, a Gillott's No. 303 pen should be used. The height of the capital letters should be $\frac{3}{32}''$, and of the small letters two-thirds of this, or $\frac{1}{16}''$. This applies to both styles of freehand lettering. *Do not make them larger than this.*

21. Before beginning to letter, horizontal guide lines should be drawn with the **T** square, to serve as a guide for the tops and bottoms of the letters (see Fig. 22). The out-

Mechanical Mechanical

FIG. 22

side lines should be $\frac{3}{32}''$ apart for the capitals, and the two lower lines $\frac{1}{16}''$ apart for the small letters. The letters should be made to extend fully up to the top, and down to the bottom, guide lines. They must not fall short of the guide lines, nor extend beyond them. Failure to observe this point will cause the lettering to look ragged, as in the second word in Fig. 22.

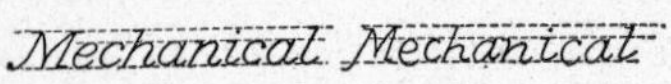

22. It is very important that all the letters have the same inclination. For example, by referring to Fig. 23 (*a*), it will be seen that the backs of letters like *B, E, l, g, d, i, t*, etc.

BElgdit HMnuhy

FIG. 23 (*a*)

are parallel and slant the same way. This is also true of both sides of letters like *H, M, n, u, h, y*, etc. To aid in keeping the slant uniform, draw

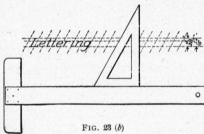

parallel slanting lines across the guide lines with the 60° triangle, as in Fig. 23 (*b*), and, in lettering, make the backs or sides of the letters parallel with these lines.

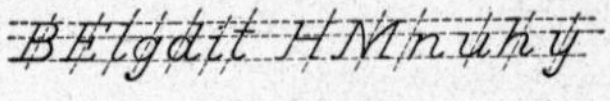

FIG. 23 (*b*)

23. A few points regarding the construction of the letters are illustrated in Fig. 24, in which the letters are shown upon an enlarged scale.   The capital letters A, V, Y, M, and W must be printed so that their general inclination will be the same as for the other letters.   To print the A, draw the center line $a\,d$, having the common slant; from a draw the sides $a\,c$ and $a\,b$, so that points c and b will each be $\frac{3}{64}''$ distant from point d.   The side $a\,b$ will be nearly perpendicular to the guide lines.   The V is like an inverted A, and is drawn in the same way, the line $b\,d$ being nearly perpendicular.

To make the Y, draw the center line $a\,d$, having the common slant, which gives the slant for the base of the letter. The upper part of the Y begins a little below its center, and is similar to the V, though somewhat narrower, as the letter should be only $\frac{5}{64}''$ wide at the top.   Points b and c should be at equal distances from point a.

The two sides $b\,c$ and $e\,f$ of the M are parallel, and have the common slant.   The M is made as broad as it is high, or $\frac{3}{32}''$.   Having drawn the two sides, mark the point d, midway between the points c and f, and connect it with points b and e.   The lines $b\,d$ and $e\,d$ should be slightly curved, as shown.

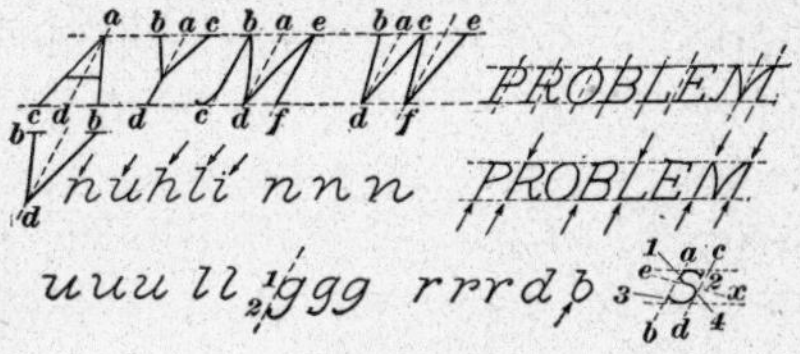

FIG. 24

In the W the two outside lines are not parallel, as in the M, but are farther apart at the top than at the bottom. Draw the line $a\,d$, having the common slant.   Mark points b and c, which are exactly $\frac{1}{32}''$ from the point a.   From b and c, draw lines $b\,d$ and $c\,d$.   The other half of the W is like the first part, $c\,f$ being parallel to $b\,d$ and $e\,f$ parallel to $c\,d$.   It will be seen that the W is composed of two narrow V's, each $\frac{1}{16}''$ wide, the width of the whole letter being $\frac{1}{8}''$.

24.   Capital letters like P, R, B, L, E, etc. should be printed so that their top and bottom lines will be *exactly horizontal*.   This is illustrated in the two examples of the word *problem* in Fig. 24.   In the first example, it will be noticed that the tops of the P and R, the bottom of the L, and the tops and bottoms of the *B* and *E*, all run in the same direction as the guide lines, and coincide with them.   In the second example, these lines are not horizontal, which makes the word look very uneven.   It is also to be noticed that these lines extend beyond the upright lines in the first word, and that cross-lines are used on the bottom of the *P* and *R*, on the top of the *L*, and on the *M*.   In the second word, these lines are omitted at the points indicated by the arrows.   These features are found on most of the other capitals.

The small letters *n*, *u*, *h*, *l*, *i*, etc. should have sharp corners at the points indicated by the arrows in Fig. 24.   They look much better that way, and are less difficult to make, than when they have round corners.   Following these letters are five groups of letters containing *n*, *u*, *l*, *g*, and *r*.   The first letter of each group is printed correctly, while the letters following show ways in which they should *not* be printed. In the case of the *g*, point *2* should fall in a slanting direction under point *1*, the slant being the same as *a d* of the preceding letters.   The difference between *d* and *b* and the construction of the *s* are also shown in the same figure.   The *b* should be made rounding at the point indicated.   As a guide in making the *s*, draw the two lines *a b* and *c d*, having the common slant.   The *s* should now be drawn so that it will touch these lines at points *1*, *3*, and *4*, but *not* at point *2*.   It will be an additional help if the line *e x* is also drawn as a guide for the middle portion of the *s*; but care should be taken not to have it slant more than shown in the copy.

The letters *a*, *o*, *b*, *g*, etc. should be full and round; do not cramp them.   It will be necessary to follow the copy closely until familiar with it.   Notice that the figures are not made as in writing, particularly the *6*, *4*, *8*, and *9* (see Fig. 21). Try to space the letters evenly.   Letter in pencil first, and, if not right, erase and try again.

25. Another style of freehand lettering is shown in Fig. 25.   This style is extensively used for the lettering of working drawings. It is more easily and rapidly made than the style previously described, and although not productive

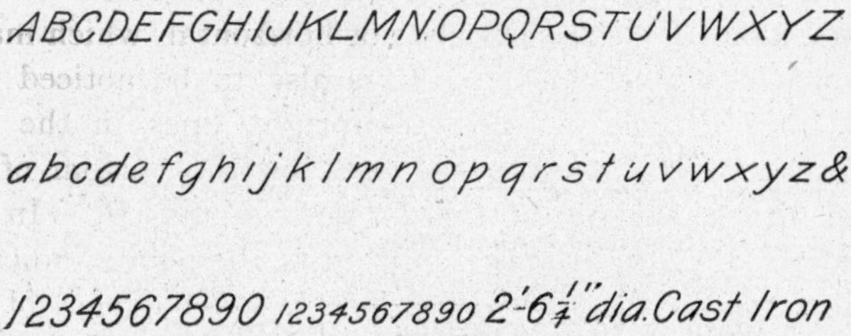

ABCDEFGHIJKLMNOPQRSTUVWXYZ

abcdefghijklmn opqrstuvwxyz&

1234567890 1234567890 2'-6¼" dia. Cast Iron

FIG. 25

of as high degree of neatness in appearance will be found very useful and acceptable for general office work.

A comparison between the two systems will disclose a great similarity in the detail formation of the letters.

26. The horizontal and slanting guide lines are drawn exactly in the same manner as for the style previously described, and if not followed, the results will be similar. See the uneven appearance of the second word in Fig. 26.

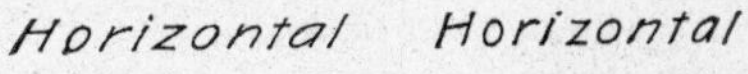

Horizontal   Horizontal

FIG. 26

27. By studying the formation of the letters carefully, it will be found that many of them are formed on the same principle, as shown in Fig. 27.

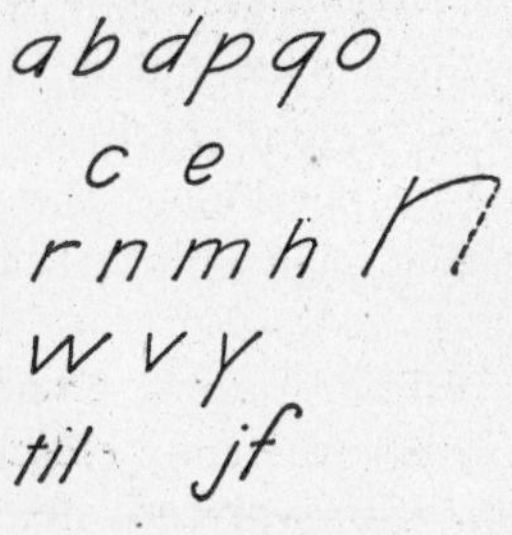

abdpqo
ce
rnmh
wvy
til jf

FIG. 27

The ovals of the letters *a*, *b*, *d*, *g*, *p*, and *q* are formed exactly alike and have a slant of 45° with the horizontal. These ovals should be made a little wider at the top than at the bottom. Care should be taken that the straight downward strokes are made parallel to the slanting guide lines. The letters *c* and *e* are commenced in the same way, but the upper loop in *e* should be formed in such a manner that its axis will be at an angle of 45° with the horizontal. The *r* is made by having the down stroke parallel to the slanting guide line and the up stroke slightly curved in the same way as in the letter *n* (see Fig. 27). The strokes in the letters *j* and *f* are the same, with the position of the hook part reversed.

28. The capital letters shown in Fig. 28 are formed very nearly in the same manner as those shown in Art. **23,** but differ slightly by omitting the short spurs that give to the letters a more finished appearance.

In the capital *M*, however, there is a decided variation. The *M* is made with four strokes, putting in the parallel sides first. The two other strokes should join midway

$$A \quad Y \quad M \quad W$$

$$V \quad PROBLEM$$

FIG. 28

between these sides and at a distance from the top of about ⅖ of the height of the letter. These strokes, as will be seen, are straight and not curved.

29. The *numerals* should be $\frac{3}{32}''$ high and of the style shown in Fig. 25; fractions should be $\frac{1}{8}''$ high over all. In

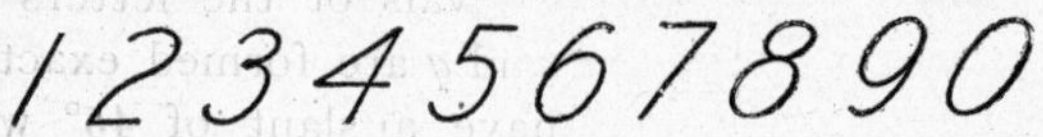

$$1 \, 2 \, 3 \, 4 \, 5 \, 6 \, 7 \, 8 \, 9 \, 0$$

FIG. 29

Fig. 29 the numerals are illustrated to a larger scale, and a comparison with the style shown in Fig. 21 will disclose several variations.

The loops of the *2, 3, 5, 6,* and *9* should be formed so that their axes will be at an angle of 45° with the horizontal. It will be noted that the *7* differs widely from the style shown in Fig. 21, the down stroke not curving but having a straight slant of 45°. The axis of the *0* and the loops of the *8* should slant at an angle of 60°.

Diligent practice for a short time and careful observation of the forms of letters and numerals, as shown in Figs. 21–29, will soon enable the student to acquire skill and speed in this branch of drawing.

30. The alphabet shown in Fig. 30, called the **block letter,** is to be used for the large headings or titles of plates, as shown on the copy plates. This alphabet is *not* to be used on the first five geometrical drawing plates. The letters and figures are to be made $\frac{5}{16}''$ high and $\frac{1}{4}''$ wide, except M, which is $\frac{5}{16}''$ wide, and W, which is $\frac{3}{8}''$ wide. The thickness of all the lines forming the letters is $\frac{1}{16}''$, measured horizontally. The distance between any two letters of a word is $\frac{1}{16}''$, except where A follows P or F:

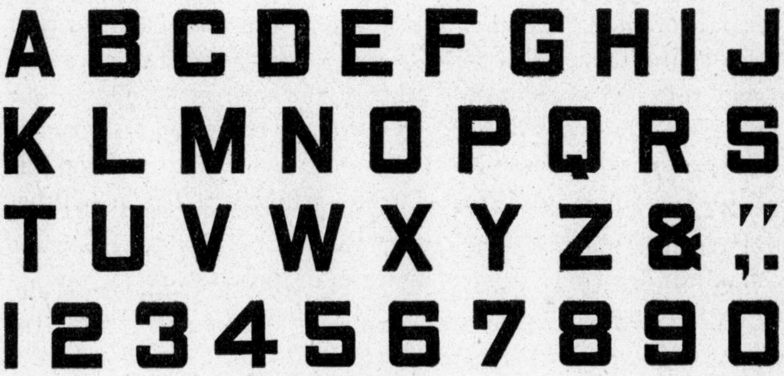

ABCDEFGHIJ
KLMNOPQRS
TUVWXYZ&;.
1234567890

FIG. 30

where V, W, or Y follows L; where J follows F, P, T, V, W, or Y; where T and A are adjacent, or A and V, W, or Y are adjacent; in this case, the bottom extremity of A and the top extremity of P, T, V, W are in the same vertical line, etc.

Since these letters are composed of straight lines, they can be made with the **T** square and triangle. In lettering the title of the drawing plates, the student should draw six horizontal lines $\frac{1}{16}''$ apart in lead pencil, to represent the thickness of the letters at the top, center, and bottom; then, by use of the triangle, he should draw in the width of the letters and the spaces between them in lead pencil. Having the letters all laid out, he can very easily ink them in. Use the ruling pen for inking in the straight outlines of the letters, and the lettering pen for rounding the corners and filling in between the outlines. It is well to ink in all the perpendicular lines first, next the horizontal lines, and then the oblique lines.

PLATES

31. Preliminary Directions.—The size of each plate over all will be $14'' \times 18''$, having a border line $\frac{1}{2}''$ from each edge all around, thus making the size of the space on which the drawing is to be made $13'' \times 17''$. The sheet itself must be larger than this when first placed upon the board, so that the thumbtack holes may be cut out; the extra margin is also very convenient for testing the pen, in order to see whether the ink is flowing well and whether the lines are of the proper thickness.

32. The first five plates will consist of practical geometrical problems which constantly arise in practice when making drawings. The method of solving every one of these problems should be carefully memorized, so that they can be instantly applied when the occasion requires, without being obliged to refer to the text for help. Particular attention should be paid to the lettering. Whenever any dimensions are specified, they should be laid off as accurately as possible. All drawings should be made as neat as possible, and the penciling entirely finished before inking in any part of it. Great care should be taken in distributing the different views, parts, details, etc. on the drawing, so that when the drawing is completed, one view will not be so near to another as to mar the appearance of the drawing. The hands should be perfectly clean, and should not touch the paper except when necessary. No lines should be erased except when *absolutely* necessary; for, whenever a line has once been erased, the dirt flying around in the air and constantly falling on the drawing will stick to any spot where an erasure has been made, and it is then very difficult, if not impossible, to entirely remove it. For this reason, all construction lines that are to be removed, or that are liable to be changed, should be drawn lightly, that the finish of the paper may not be destroyed when erasing them. When it is found necessary to erase an ink blot or a line that has been inked in, only an *ink eraser* or *sand rubber* should be used. After the erasure has been made, the roughened part of the surface of the paper can be smoothed by rubbing with some hard, smooth substance, as a piece of ivory or the handle of a knife.

PLATE I

33. Fasten a sheet of drawing paper to the board, as previously described, and draw the outlines of the size of the plate $14'' \times 18''$. Draw the border line all around $\frac{1}{2}''$ from the edge of the outline, leaving the space inside for the drawing $13'' \times 17''$. When the word *drawing* is used hereafter, it refers only to the space inside the border lines and the objects drawn upon it. Remove the folded sheet at the end of this Paper, and spread it open, so as to keep it constantly before the eye. On it is drawn Plate I to a reduced scale. Divide the drawing into two equal parts by means of a faint horizontal line. This line is shown dotted in Plate I. Divide each of these halves into three equal parts, as shown by the dotted lines; this divides the drawing into six rectangular spaces. *These division lines are not to be inked in, but must be erased when the plate is completed.* On the first five plates, space for the lettering must be taken into account. For each of the six equal spaces, the lettering will take up one or two lines. The height of all capital letters on these plates will be $\frac{3}{32}''$, and of the small letters $\frac{2}{3}$ of this, or $\frac{1}{16}''$. The distance between any two lines of lettering will also be $\frac{3}{32}''$. The distance between the tops of the letters on the first line of lettering and the top line of the equal divisions of the drawing is to be $\frac{1}{2}''$; and the space between the bottoms of the letters and the topmost point of the figure represented on the drawing within one of these six divisions must also be not less than $\frac{1}{2}''$. This makes a very neat arrangement, if the figure is so placed that the outermost points of the bounding lines are equally distant from the sides of one of the equal rectangular spaces. Consequently, if there is one line of lettering, no point of the figure drawn should come nearer than $\frac{1}{2}'' + \frac{3}{32}'' + \frac{1}{2}'' = 1\frac{3}{32}''$ to the top line of the space within which it is represented; or, if there are two lines of lettering, nearer than $\frac{1}{2}'' + \frac{3}{32}''$ $+ \frac{3}{32}'' + \frac{3}{32}'' + \frac{1}{2}'' = 1\frac{9}{32}''$. The letter heading for each figure on the first five plates will be printed in heavy-faced type at the beginning of the directions explaining each problem. The student must judge for himself by the length of the heading whether it will take up one line or two, and make due allowance for the space it takes up. This is a necessary precaution, because the lettering should never be done until the rest of the drawing is entirely finished and inked in.

PROBLEM 1.—**To bisect a straight line.**

See Fig. 31; also 1 of Plate I.

CONSTRUCTION. — Draw a straight line $A\,B$, $3\frac{1}{2}''$ long. With one extremity A as a center, and a radius greater than

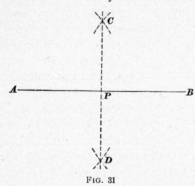

one-half of the length of the line, describe an arc of a circle on each side of the given line; with the other extremity B as a center, and the same radius, describe arcs intersecting the first two in the points C and D. Join C and D by the line $C\,D$, and the point P, where it

FIG. 31

intersects $A\,B$, will be the required point; that is, $A\,P = P\,B$, and P is the middle point of *A B*. Since *C D* is perpendicular to *A B*, this construction also gives a *perpendicular to a straight line at its middle point.*

PROBLEM 2.—**To draw a perpendicular to a straight line from a given point in that line.**

NOTE.—As there are two cases of this problem, requiring two figures on the plate, the line of letters will be run clear across both figures, as shown in Plate I.

Case I.—*When the point is at or near the center of the line.* See Fig. 32; also 2, Case I, of Plate I.

CONSTRUCTION. — Draw *A B* $3\frac{1}{2}''$ long. Let *P* be the given point. With *P* as a center, and any radius, as *P D*, describe two short arcs cutting *A B* in the points *C* and *D*. With *C*

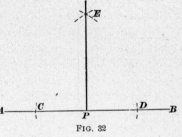

FIG. 32

and *D* as centers, and any convenient radius greater than *P D*, describe two arcs intersecting in *E*. Draw *P E*, and it will be perpendicular to *A B* at the point *P*.

Case II.—*When the point is near the end of the line.* See Fig. 33; also 2, Case II, of Plate I.

Draw *A B* $3\frac{1}{2}''$ long. Take the given point *P* about $\frac{3}{8}''$ from the end of the line. With any point *O* as a center, and a radius *O P*, describe an arc cutting *A B* in *P* and *D*. Draw *D O*, and prolong it until it intersects the arc in the

FIG. 33

point *C*. A line drawn through *C* and *P* will be perpendicular to *A B* at the point *P*.

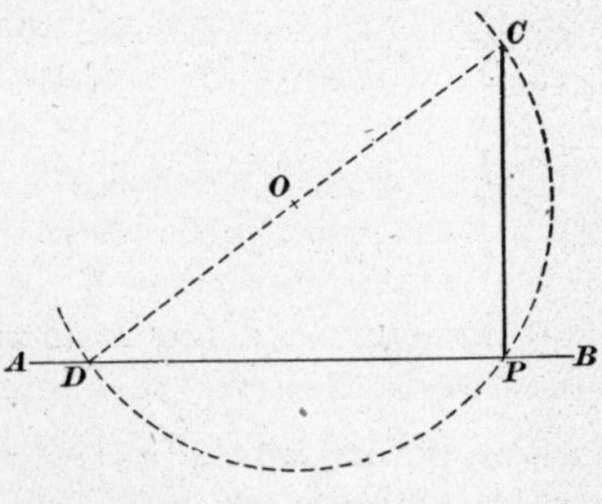

PROBLEM 3.—**To draw a perpendicular to a straight line from a point without it.**

As in Problem 2, there are two cases.

Case I.—*When the point lies nearly over the center of the line.* See Fig. 34; also 3, Case I, of Plate I.

CONSTRUCTION.—Draw AB $3\frac{1}{2}''$ long. Let P be the given

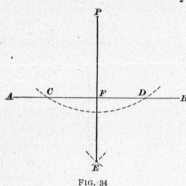

point. With P as a center, and any radius PD greater than the distance from P to AB, describe an arc cutting AB in C and D. With C and D as centers, and any convenient radius, describe short arcs intersecting in E. A line drawn through P and E will be perpendicular to AB at F.

FIG. 34

Case II.—*When the point lies nearly over one end of the line.* See Fig. 35; also 3, Case II, of Plate I.

Draw AB $3\frac{1}{2}''$ long, and let P be the given point. With any point C on the line AB as a center, and the distance CP as a radius, describe an arc PED cutting AB in E. With E as a center, and the distance EP as a radius, describe an arc cutting the arc PED in D. The line joining the points P and D will be perpendicular to AB.

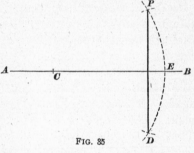

FIG. 35

PROBLEM 4.—**Through a given point, to draw a straight line parallel to a given straight line.**

See Fig. 36; also 4 of Plate I.

CONSTRUCTION.—Let P be the given point, and AB the given straight line $3\frac{1}{2}''$ long. With P as a center, and any convenient radius, describe an arc CD intersecting AB in D. With D as a center, and the same radius, describe the arc PE. With D as a center, and a radius equal to the chord of the arc PE, describe an arc intersecting CD in C. A straight line drawn through P and C will be parallel to AB.

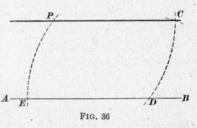

FIG. 36

34. These four problems form Plate I. They should be carefully and accurately drawn in with lead-pencil lines and then inked in. It will be noticed that on Plate I, and Figs. 31 to 36, the given lines are *light*, the required lines *heavy*, and the construction lines, which in a practical working drawing would be left out, are *light dotted*. This system must also be followed in the four plates which are to follow. A single glance enables one to see at once the reason for drawing the figure, and the eye is directed immediately to the required line.

In the first five plates, accuracy and neatness are the main things to be looked out for. The student should be certain that the lines are of *precisely* the length that is specified in the description. When drawing a line through two points, be sure that the line goes through the points; if it does not pass exactly through the points, erase it and draw it over again. If a line is supposed to end at some particular point, make it end there—do not let it extend beyond or fall short. Thus, in Fig. 36, if the line PC does not pass through the points P and C, it is not parallel to AB. By paying careful attention to these points, the student saves himself a great deal of trouble in the future. *Do not hurry your work.*

First ink in all of the light lines and light dotted lines (which have the same thickness); then ink in the heavy required lines after the pen has been readjusted. Now do the lettering (first read carefully the paragraphs under the head "Lettering"), and finally draw the heavy border lines, which should be thicker than any other line on the drawing. The word " Plate " and its number should be printed at the top of the sheet, outside the border lines, and midway of its length, as shown. The student's name, followed by the words " Class " and " No.," and after this his Course letter and *class number* should be printed in the lower right-hand corner below the border line, as shown. Thus, John Smith, Class No. C 4529. The date on which the drawing was completed should be placed in the lower left-hand corner, below the border line. *All of this lettering is to be in capitals $\frac{3}{32}$" high.* Erase the division lines, and clean the drawing by rubbing very gently with the eraser. Care must be exercised when doing this, or the inked lines will also be erased. It is best to use a so-called " Sponge Rubber " for this purpose, as it will not injure the inked lines. *If any part of a line has been erased or weakened, it must be redrawn.* Then write with the lead pencil your name and address in full on the back of your drawing, after which put your drawing in the empty tube which was sent you, and send it to the Schools.

HINTS FOR PLATE I

35. *Do not forget to make a distinction between the width of the given and required lines, nor forget to make the construction lines dotted.*

When drawing dotted lines, take pains to have the dots and spaces uniform in length. Make the dots about $\frac{1}{16}$" long and the spaces only about one-third the length of the dots.

Try to get the work accurate. The constructions must be accurate, and all lines or figures should be drawn of the length or size previously stated. To this end, work carefully and keep the pencil leads very sharp, so that the lines will be fine.

The lettering on the first few plates, as well as on the succeeding plates, is fully as important as the drawing, and should be done in the neatest possible manner. Drawings sent in for correction with the lettering omitted will be returned for completion.

The reference letters like A, B, C, etc., as shown in Fig. 31, are not to be put on the plates.

Do not neglect to trim the plates to the required size. Do not punch large holes in the paper with the dividers or compasses. Remember that the division lines are to be erased—not inked in.

PLATE II

36. Draw the division lines in the same manner as described for Plate I. The following five problems (5 to 9, inclusive) are to be drawn in regular order, as was done in Plate I, with problems from 1 to 4. The letter headings are given in heavy-faced type after the problem number.

PROBLEM 5.—**To bisect a given angle.***

Case I.—*When the sides intersect within the limits of the drawing.* See Fig. 37.

CONSTRUCTION. — Let AOB be the angle to be bisected. Draw the sides OA and OB $3\frac{1}{2}''$ long. With the vertex O as a center, and any convenient radius, describe an arc DE intersecting OA at D and OB at E. With D and E as centers, and a radius greater than the chord of half the arc DE, describe two arcs intersecting at C. The line drawn through C and O will bisect the angle; that is, $AOC = COB$.

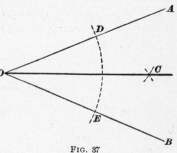

FIG. 37

Case II.—*When the sides do not intersect within the limits of the drawing.* See Fig. 38.

CONSTRUCTION.—Draw two lines, AB and CD, each $3\frac{1}{2}''$ long, and inclined towards each other as shown. With any

----

* Since the letter heading in this problem is very short, it will be better to place it over each of the two cases separately, instead of running it over the division line, as was done with the long headings of the two cases in Plate I. Put Case I and Case II under the heading, as in the previous plate.

point E on CD as a center and any convenient radius, describe arc $FIGH$; with G as a center and same radius, describe arc $HLEF$, intersecting $FIGH$ in H and F. With L as a center and same radius, describe arc KGJ; with I as

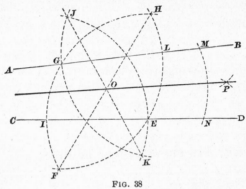

FIG. 38

a center and same radius, describe arc JEK, intersecting KGJ in K and J. Draw HF and JK; they intersect at O, a point on the bisecting line. With O as a center and the same or any convenient radius, describe an arc intersecting AB and CD in M and N. With M and N as centers and any radius greater than one-half MN, describe arcs intersecting at P. A line drawn through O and P is the required bisecting line.

PROBLEM 6.—**To divide a given straight line into any required number of equal parts.**

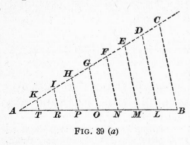

FIG. 39 (a)

See Fig. 39 (a).

CONSTRUCTION. —AB is the given line $3\frac{7}{16}''$ long. It is required to divide it into eight equal parts. Through one extremity A of the line, draw an indefinite straight line AC, making any angle with AB. Set the dividers to any convenient distance, and space off eight equal divisions on AC, as AK, KI, IH, etc. Join C and B by the straight line CB, and through the points D, E, F, G, etc. draw lines DL, EM, etc. parallel to CB, by using the two triangles; these parallels intersect AB in the points L, M, N, etc., which are equally distant apart. The spaces LM, MN, NO, etc. are each equal to $\frac{1}{8}AB$. Proceed in a similar way for any number of equal parts into which AB is to be divided.

Another method is shown in Fig. 39 (*b*). Draw AB as before, and erect the perpendicular BC. Now divide the length of AB by the number denoting the number of equal parts into which AB is to be divided, obtaining, in this case, $3\frac{7}{16}'' \div 8 = \frac{55}{128}''$. As AC is longer than AB, the equal divisions AK, KI, etc. are longer than AT, TR, etc. and may be made any convenient length greater than $AB \div 8$. In this case, $\frac{1}{2}''$ is the most convenient fraction nearest to and greater

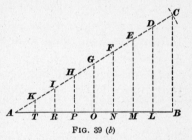

FIG. 39 (*b*)

than $\frac{55}{128}''$; hence, consider AK, KI, etc. to be each $\frac{1}{2}''$ in length, thus making the length of AC $8 \times \frac{1}{2}'' = 4''$. With A as a center and a radius equal to $4''$, describe an arc cutting BC in C, and draw AC. Then with a scale lay off $AK = KI =$ etc. $= \frac{1}{2}''$, and project K, I, H, etc. upon AB, in T, R, P, etc., the required points. The advantage of this method over the other is that the **T** square and triangle can be used throughout, thus making it very much easier to draw the parallels DL, EM, etc.

The student, when drawing this plate, is at liberty to use either of the two methods given in this problem.

PROBLEM 7.—**To draw a straight line through any given point on a given straight line to make any required angle with that line.**

CONSTRUCTION.—In Fig. 40, AB is the given line $3\frac{1}{2}''$ long, P is the given point, and EOF is the given angle. With the vertex O as a center, and any convenient radius, describe an arc EF cutting OE and OF in E and F. With P as a center, and the same radius, describe an arc CD. With D as a center, and a radius equal to the chord of the arc EF, describe an arc cutting CD in C. A line drawn through the points P and C will make an

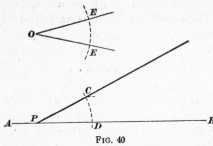

Fig. 40

angle with AB equal to the angle O, or $CPD = EOF$.

PROBLEM 8.—**To draw an equilateral triangle, one side being given.**

CONSTRUCTION.—In Fig. 41, AB is the given side $2\frac{1}{2}''$ long. With AB as a radius, and A and B as centers, describe two arcs intersecting in C. Draw CA and CB, and CAB is an equilateral triangle.

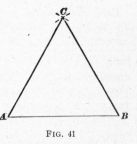

Fig. 41

PROBLEM 9.—**The altitude of an equilateral triangle being given, to draw the triangle.**

CONSTRUCTION.—In Fig. 42, AB is the altitude $2\frac{1}{4}''$ long. Through the extremities of AB draw the parallel lines CD

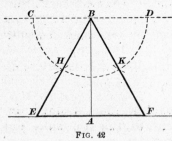

Fig. 42

and EF perpendicular to AB. With B as a center, and any convenient radius, describe the semicircle $CHKD$ intersecting CD in C and D. With C and D as centers, and the same radius, describe arcs cutting the semicircle in H and K. Draw BH and BK, and prolong them to meet EF in E and F. BEF is the required equilateral triangle.

This problem finishes Plate II. The directions for inking in, lettering, etc. are the same as for Plate I.

PLATE III

37. This plate is to be divided up like Plates I and II, and the six following problems are to be drawn in a similar manner:

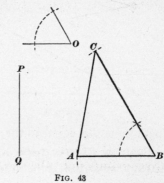

PROBLEM 10. — Two sides and the included angle of a triangle being given, to construct the triangle.

CONSTRUCTION.—In Fig. 43, make the given sides MN $2\frac{1}{2}''$ long and PQ $1\frac{1}{5}''$

FIG. 43

long. Let O be the given angle. Draw AB, and make it equal in length to PQ. Make the angle CBA equal to the given angle O, and make CB equal in length to the line MN. Draw CA, and CAB is the required triangle.

PROBLEM 11.—**To draw a parallelogram when the sides and one of the angles are given.**

CONSTRUCTION.—In Fig. 44, make the given sides MN $2\frac{1}{2}''$ long and PQ $1\frac{4}{5}''$ long. Let O be the given angle.

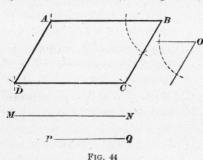

FIG. 44

Draw AB equal to MN, and draw BC, making an angle with AB equal to the given angle O. Make BC equal to PQ. With C as a center, and a radius equal to MN, describe an arc at D. With A as a center, and a radius equal to PQ, describe an arc intersecting the other arc in D. Draw AD and CD, and $ABCD$ is the required parallelogram.

PROBLEM 12.—**An arc and its radius being given, to find the center.**

CONSTRUCTION.—In Fig. 45, $ACDB$ is the arc, and MN,

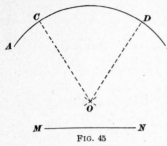

FIG. 45

$1\frac{3}{4}''$ long, is the radius. With MN as a radius, and any point C in the given arc as a center, describe an arc at O. With any other point D in the given arc as a center, and the same radius, describe an arc intersecting the first in O. O is the required center.

PROBLEM 13.—**To pass a circumference through any three points not in the same straight line.**

CONSTRUCTION.—In Fig. 46, A, B, and C are the given points. With A and B as centers, and any convenient radius, describe arcs intersecting each other in K and I. With B and C as centers, and any convenient radius, describe arcs intersecting each other in D and E. Through I and K and through D and E, draw lines intersecting at O. With O as a center, and OA as a radius, describe a circle; it will pass through A, B, and C.

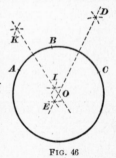

FIG. 46

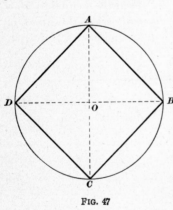

FIG. 47

PROBLEM 14.—**To inscribe a square in a given circle.**

CONSTRUCTION.—In Fig. 47, the circle $ABCD$ is $3\frac{1}{2}''$ in diameter. Draw two diameters, AC and DB, at right angles to each other. Draw the lines AB, BC, CD, and DA, joining the points of intersection of these diameters with the circumference of the circle, and they will be the sides of the square.

PROBLEM 15—**To inscribe a regular hexagon in a given circle.**

CONSTRUCTION.—In Fig. 48, from O as a center, with the dividers set to $1\frac{3}{4}''$, describe the circle $ABCDEF$. Draw the diameter DOA, and from the points D and A, with the dividers set equal to the radius of the circle, describe arcs intersecting the circle at E, C, F, and B. Join these points by straight lines, and they will form the sides of the hexagon. This problem completes Plate III.

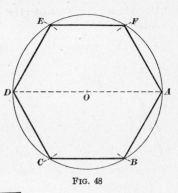

FIG. 48

PLATE IV

38. The first four problems on this plate are more difficult than any on the preceding plates and will require very careful construction. All the sides of each polygon must be of exactly the same length, so that they will space around evenly with the dividers. The figures should not be inked in until the pencil construction is done accurately. The preliminary directions for this plate are the same as for the preceding ones.

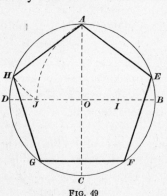

FIG. 49

PROBLEM 16.—**To inscribe a regular pentagon in a given circle.**

CONSTRUCTION.—In Fig. 49, from O as a center, with the dividers set to $1\frac{3}{4}''$, describe the circle $ABCD$. Draw the two diameters AC and DB at right angles to each other. Bisect one of the radii, as OB, at I. With I as a center, and IA as a radius, describe the arc AJ cutting DO at J.

With A as a center, and AJ as a radius, describe an arc JH cutting the circumference at H. The chord AH is one side of the pentagon.

PROBLEM 17.—**To inscribe a regular octagon in a given circle.**

CONSTRUCTION.—In Fig. 50, from O as a center, with the

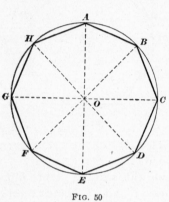

FIG. 50

dividers set to $1\frac{3}{4}''$, describe the circle $ABCDEFGH$. Draw the two diameters AE and GC at right angles to each other. Bisect one of the four equal arcs, as AG at H, and draw the diameter HOD. Bisect another of the equal arcs, as AC at B, and draw the diameter BOF. Straight lines drawn from A to B, from B to C, etc. will form the required octagon.

PROBLEM 18.—**To inscribe a regular polygon of any number of sides in a given circle.**

CONSTRUCTION.—Describe a circle, having O as a center, $3\frac{1}{2}''$ in diameter, Fig. 51, and draw a diameter AOC. With A and C as centers and AC as a radius describe short arcs intersecting at M, and draw MON. Divide AO into as many equal parts as the polygon has sides (in this case eleven), and make OD equal to four of these parts. Draw MDE, and join E and N; NE is one of the sides of the polygon. If the polygon has less than ten sides, find the side of one having twice as many sides, and draw the chord from N to

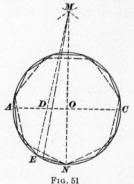

FIG. 51

the end of the second side. The figure also shows (in long dotted lines) the construction of a seven-sided polygon.

PROBLEM 19.—**The side of a regular polygon being given, to construct the polygon.**

CONSTRUCTION.—In Fig. 52, let $A C$ be the given side. If the polygon is to have eight sides, the line $A C$ should be, for this plate, $1\frac{1}{4}''$ long. Produce $A C$ to B. From C as center, with a radius equal to $C A$, describe the semicircle A *1 2 3 4 5 6 7 B*, and divide it into as many equal parts as there are sides in the required polygon (in this case eight). From the point C, and through the second division from B, as *6*, draw the straight line $C 6$. Bisect the lines $A C$

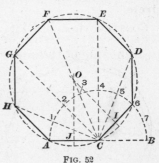

FIG. 52

and $C 6$ by perpendiculars intersecting in O. From O as a center, and with $O C$ as a radius, describe the circle $C A H G F E D 6$. From C, and through the points *1, 2, 3, 4, 5* in the semicircle, draw lines $C H$, $C G$, $C F$, etc., meeting the circumference. Joining the points *6* and D, D and E, E and F, etc., by straight lines, will complete the required polygon.

PROBLEM 20.—**To find an arc of a circle having a known radius, which shall be equal in length to a given straight line.**

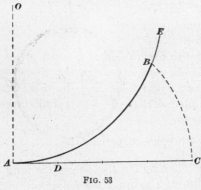

FIG. 53

NOTE.—There is no exact method, but the following approximate method is close enough for all practical purposes, when the required arc does not exceed $\frac{1}{6}$ of the circumference.

CONSTRUCTION.— In Fig. 53, let $A C$ be the given line $3\frac{1}{2}''$ long. At A, erect the perpendicular $A O$, and make it equal in length to the given radius, say $4''$ long.

With OA as a radius, and O as a center, describe the arc ABE. Divide AC into four equal parts, AD being the first of these parts, counting from A. With D as a center, and a radius DC, describe the arc CB intersecting ABE in B. The length of the arc AB very nearly equals the length of the straight line AC.

PROBLEM 21.—**An arc of a circle being given, to find a straight line of the same length.**

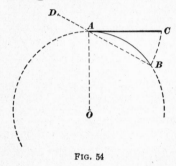

FIG. 54

This is also an approximate method, but close enough for practical purposes, when the arc does not exceed $\frac{1}{6}$ of the circumference.

CONSTRUCTION.—In Fig. 54, let AB be the given arc; find the center O of the arc, and draw the radius OA. For this problem, choose the arc so that the radius will not exceed $1\frac{3}{4}''$. At A, draw AC perpendicular to the radius (and, of course, tangent to the arc). Draw the chord AB, and prolong it to D, so that $AD = \frac{1}{2}$ the chord AB. With D as a center, and a radius DB, describe the arc BC cutting AC in C. AC will be very nearly equal to the arc AB.

PLATE V

39. On this plate there are five problems instead of six. It should be divided into six equal parts or divisions, as the previous ones. The two right-hand end divisions are used to draw in the last figure of Plate V, which is too large to put in one division.

PROBLEM 22.—**To draw an egg-shaped oval.**

CONSTRUCTION.—In Fig. 55, on the diameter AB, which is $2\frac{3}{4}''$ long, describe a circle $ACBG$. Through the center O, draw *O C* perpendicular to *A B*, cutting the circumference *A C B G* in *C*. Draw the straight lines *B C F* and *A C E*. With *B* and *A* as centers, and the diameter *A B* as a radius, describe arcs terminating in *D* and *H*, the points of intersection with *B F* and *A E*. With *C* as a center, and *C D* as a radius, describe the arc *D H*. The curve *A D H B G* is the required oval.

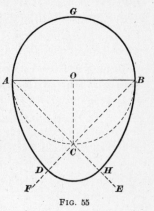

FIG. 55

PROBLEM 23. — **To draw an ellipse, the diameters being given.** The exact method.

CONSTRUCTION.—In Fig. 56, let *B D*, the long diameter, or major axis, which is $3\frac{1}{2}''$ long, and *A C*, the short diameter, or minor axis, which is $2\frac{1}{4}''$ long, intersect at right angles to each other in the center *O*, so that *D O = O B* and *A O = O C*. With *O* as a center, and *O C* as a radius, describe a circle; with the same center, and *O D* as a radius, describe another circle. Divide both circles into the same number of equal parts, as *1–2, 2–3*, etc. This is best done by first dividing the larger circle into the required number of parts,

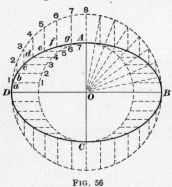

FIG. 56

beginning at the center line *A C*, and then drawing radial lines through the points of division on this circle, to the center *O* of the circles, as shown in the upper right-hand quarter of the figure. The radial lines will divide the smaller circle into the same number of parts that the larger one has been divided into. Through the points of division on the smaller circle, draw horizontal lines, and, through the points of division on the larger circle, draw vertical

lines; the points of intersection of these lines are points on
the ellipse. Thus, the horizontal line $3c$ and the vertical
line $3c$ intersecting at c give the point c of the ellipse.
Trace a curve through the points thus found by placing an
irregular curve on the drawing in such a manner that one
of its bounding lines will pass through three or more points,
judging with the eye whether the curve so traced bulges
out too much or is too flat. Then adjust the curve again,
so that its bounding line will pass through several more
points, and so on, until the curve is completed. Care
should be taken to make all changes in curvature as gradual
as possible, and all curves drawn in this manner should be
drawn in pencil before being inked in. It requires considerable practice to be able to draw a good curved line in
this manner by means of an irregular curve, and the general
appearance of a curve thus drawn depends a great deal upon
the student's taste and the accuracy of his eye.

PROBLEM 24.—To draw an ellipse by circular arcs.

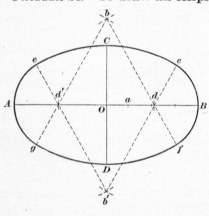

FIG. 57

This is not a true
ellipse, but is very
convenient for many
purposes.

CONSTRUCTION. — In
Fig. 57, use the same
dimensions as before.
On the major axis $A B$,
set off $A a = C D$, the
minor axis, and divide
$a B$ into three equal
parts. With O as a
center, and a radius
equal to the length of
two of these parts, describe arcs cutting $A B$ in d and d'.
Upon $d d'$ as a side, construct two equilateral triangles $d b d'$
and $d b' d'$. With b as a center, and a radius equal to $b D$,
describe the arc $g D f$ intersecting $b d f$ and $b d' g$ in f and g.
With the same radius, and b' as a center, describe the arc $c C e$

intersecting *b' d' c* and *b' d e* in *c* and *e*. With *A* and *B* as centers, and a radius equal to the chord of the arcs *A c* or *B e*, describe arcs cutting *A B* very near to *d'* and *d*. From the points of intersection of these arcs with *A B* as centers, and the same radius, describe the arcs *c A g* and *e B f*.

PROBLEM 25.—**To draw a parabola, the axis and longest double ordinate being given.**

EXPLANATION.—The curve shown in Fig. 58 is called a **parabola.** This curve and the ellipse are the bounding

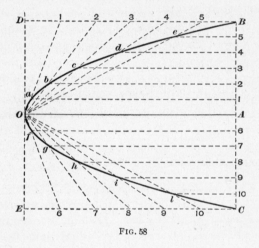

FIG. 58

lines of certain sections of a cone. The line *O A*, which bisects the area included between the curve and the line *B C*, is called the **axis.** Any line, *B A* or *A C*, drawn perpendicular to *O A*, and whose length is included between *O A* and the curve, is called an **ordinate.** Any line, as *B C*, both of whose extremities rest on the curve, and is perpendicular to the axis, is called a **double ordinate.** The point *O* is called the **vertex.**

CONSTRUCTION.—Make the axis *O A* equal to 3½″, and the longest double ordinate *B C* equal to 3″. *B A*, of course, equals *A C*. Draw *D E* through the other extremity of the axis and perpendicular to it; also draw BD and CE parallel to OA and intersecting $D\dot{E}$ in D and E. Divide DB and AB into the same number of equal parts, as shown (in this case six); through the vertex O, draw $O\,1$, $O\,2$, etc. to the points of division on DB, and through the corresponding points 1, 2, etc., on AB, draw lines parallel to the axis. The points of intersection of these lines, a, b, c, etc., are points on the curve, through which it may be traced. In a similar manner, draw the lower half $Ofghil C$ of the curve.

PROBLEM 26.—**To draw a helix, the pitch and the diameter being given.** ,

EXPLANATION.—The helix is a curve formed by a point moving around the cylinder and at the same time advancing along its length a certain distance; this forms the winding curved line shown in Fig. 59. The center line $A\,O$, drawn through the cylinder, is called the **axis** of the helix, and any line perpendicular to the axis and terminated by the helix is of the same length, being equal to the radius of the cylinder. The distance $B\,12$ that the point advances lengthwise during one revolution is called the **pitch.**

CONSTRUCTION.—As mentioned before, this figure occupies two spaces of the plate. The diameter of the cylinder is $3\frac{1}{2}''$, the pitch is $2''$, and a turn and a half of the helix is to be shown. The rectangle $FBED$ is a side view of the cylinder, and the circle $1'$, $2'$, $3'$, $4'$, etc. is a bottom view. It will be noticed that one-half of a turn of the helix is shown dotted; this is because that part of it is on the other side of the cylinder, and cannot be seen. Lines that are hidden are drawn dotted. Draw the axis $O\,A$ in the center of the space. Draw FD $3\frac{1}{2}''$ long and $4''$ from the top border line; on it construct a rectangle whose height $FB = 3''$. Take the center O of the circle $2\frac{3}{4}''$ below the point H on the axis $A\,O$, and describe a circle having a diameter of $3\frac{1}{2}''$, equal to the diameter of the cylinder. Lay off the pitch from B to 12 equal to $2''$, and divide it into a convenient number of equal parts (in this case 12), and divide the circle into the same number of equal parts, beginning at one extremity of the diameter *12' O 6'*, drawn parallel to *B E*. At the point *1'* on the circle divisions, erect *1'–1'* perpendicular to *B E*; through the point *1* of the pitch divisions, draw *1–1'* parallel to *B E*, intersecting the perpendicular in *1'*, which is a point on the helix. Through the point *2'*, erect a perpendicular *2'–2'*, intersecting *2–2'* in *2'*, which is another point on the helix.

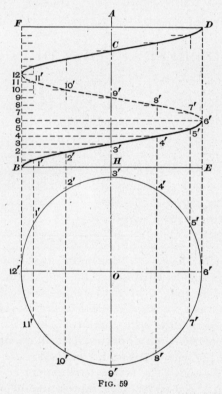

Fig. 59

So proceed until the point *6* is reached; from here on, until the point *12* of the helix is reached, the curve will be dotted. It will be noticed that the points of division *7'*, *8'*, *9'*, *10'*, and *11'* on the circle are directly opposite the points *5'*, *4'*, *3'*, *2'*, and *1'*; hence, it was not necessary to draw the lower half of the circle, since the point *5'* could have been **the** starting point, and the operation could have been conducted backwards to find the points on the dotted upper half of the helix. The other full-curved line of the helix can be drawn in exactly the same manner as the first half.

This ends the subject of practical geometry. Mechanical drawing, or the representation of objects on plane surfaces, will now be commenced.

THE REPRESENTATION OF OBJECTS

40. There are five kinds of lines used in mechanical drawing, thus:

The light full line. ⎯⎯⎯⎯⎯⎯⎯⎯⎯⎯⎯⎯⎯

The dotted line. ------------------------------

The broken-and-dotted line. ⎯ ⋅ ⎯ ⋅ ⎯ ⋅ ⎯

The broken line. ⎯ ⎯ ⎯ ⎯ ⎯ ⎯

The heavy full line. ⎯⎯⎯⎯⎯⎯⎯⎯⎯⎯⎯

The light full line is used the most; it is used for drawing the outlines of figures, and all other parts that can be seen by the eye.

The dotted line, consisting of a series of very short dashes, is used in showing the position and shape of that part of the object represented by the drawing which is concealed from the eye in the view shown; for example, a hollow prism closed on all sides. The hollow part cannot be seen; hence its size, shape, and position are represented by dotted lines.

The broken-and-dotted line, consisting of a long dash, and two dots or very short dashes repeated regularly, is used to indicate the center lines of the figure or parts of the figure, and also to indicate where a section has been taken when a sectional view is shown. This line is sometimes used for construction lines in geometrical figures.

The broken line, consisting of a series of long dashes, is used in putting in the dimensions, and serves to prevent the dimension lines from being mistaken for lines of the drawing.

The heavy full lines are made not less than twice as thick as the light full lines, and are used for shade lines.

Further explanations in regard to these lines will be given when the necessity for using them arises.

41. The illustrations in this and the following paragraphs should be carefully studied, but the student is not required to send in drawings from same. In Fig. 60 is shown a perspective view of a frustum of a pyramid having a rectangular base and a hole passing through the center of the frustum. This figure represents the frustum as it actually appears when the eye of the observer is in a certain position. The angles at A, B, C, and D are right angles, the hole is round, and the sides $A B$ and $D C$ are of equal lengths; so also are $A D$ and $B C$; but, if they were measured on the

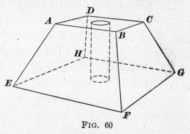

FIG. 60

drawing, it would be found that their lengths are all different. The same difficulty would be met with in trying to measure the angles and edges of the sides $A B F E, B F G C$, etc. The real length of any line can be found only by a person perfectly familiar with perspective drawing, and then only with great difficulty. Consequently, this method of representing objects is of no use to a patternmaker, carpenter, machinist, or engineer, except to show what the object looks like. In order to represent the object in such a manner that any line or angle can be measured directly, what is termed **projection drawing,** or *orthographic projection,* is universally employed. In the perspective drawing shown in Fig. 60, three sides of the frustum are shown, and the other three are hidden; in a projection drawing, but one side is usually shown, the other five being hidden.

A line or surface is *projected* upon a plane, by drawing perpendicular lines from points on the line or surface to the plane, and joining them.

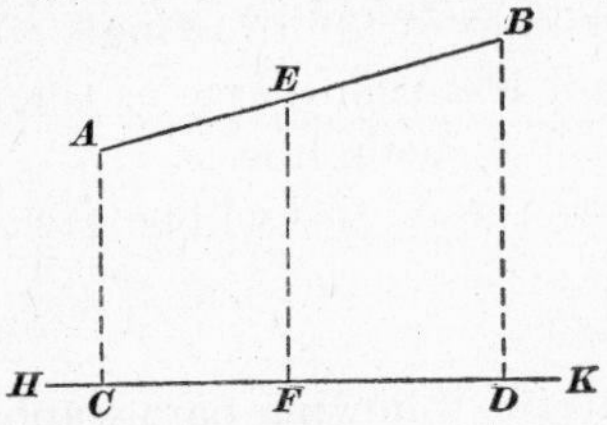

Thus, if perpendiculars be drawn from the extremities of a line, as AB, to another line HK, as shown in Fig. 61, that portion of HK included between the feet of these perpendiculars is called the **projection** of AB upon HK. Thus, CD is the projection of AB upon HK, the point C is the projection of the point A upon HK, and the point D is the projection of the point B upon HK.

FIG. 61

The projection of any point of AB, as E, can be found by drawing a perpendicular from E to HK, and the point where this perpendicular intersects HK is its projection. In this case, the point F is the projection of the point E upon HK.

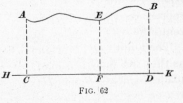

FIG. 62

It makes no difference whether the line is straight or curved—the method of finding the projection is exactly the same. See Fig. 62.

In a similar way, a surface is projected upon a flat surface.

Thus, it is desired to project the irregular surface $abdc$, Fig. 63, upon the flat surface $ABDC$. Draw the lines aa', bb' perpendicular to the flat surface; join the points a' and b', where these perpendiculars intersect the flat surface $ABDC$, by a straight line $a'b'$, and $a'b'$ is the projection of the line ab upon $ABDC$.

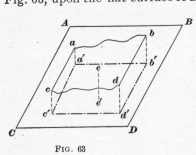

FIG. 63

In the same way, $a'c'$ is found to be the projection of ac; $c'd'$, the projection of cd; and $d'b'$, the projection of db. Hence, the projection of the irregular surface *a b d c* upon the flat surface *A B D C* is the quadrilateral *a′ b′ d′ c′*.

The projection of any point, as *e*, is found as before, by drawing a perpendicular from the point *e* to the surface; thus, *e′* is the projection of the point *e* upon the plane *A B D C.*

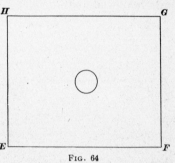

FIG. 64

Suppose that the frustum, Fig. 60, were placed on a plane surface (a surface perfectly flat, like a surface plate), and the outline of the bottom were traced by passing a pencil along its edges, including the round hole, the result would look like Fig. 64, in which the rectangle *E F G H* represents the bottom of the frustum and the circle represents the hole.

The angles and lengths of the sides are exactly the same as they are on the frustum itself; a similar drawing could be made to represent the top, but it is unnecessary, for the reason that the top can be projected on Fig. 64, and both objects accomplished in one drawing. Fig. 65 illustrates the meaning of the last statement. Here *A′ B′* is the projection of the edge *A B*, Fig. 60; *B′ C′*, of *B C*, etc.

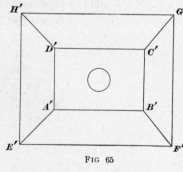

FIG 65

A′ E′ is the projection of the edge *A E*; *B′ F′*, of *B F*, etc. This drawing shows the figure as it would look if the eye were directly over it. A drawing which represents the object as if it were resting on a horizontal plane, and the observer looking at it from above, is called a **top view**, or **plan.** The line of vision is thus perpendicular to the faces *A B C D* and *E F G H* of the frustum. The lines *A B,*

BC, etc., EF, FG, etc., and the diameter of the hole, can be measured directly. The drawing is not yet complete, since it does not show whether the ends and sides are rounding, hollowed out, or flat. For this purpose, two more

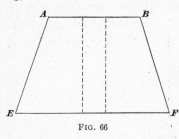

Fig. 66

views are necessary—*a vertical projection*, or *front view*, commonly called a **front elevation,** and a *side projection*, or **side view.** A front view (elevation) is drawn by imagining the eye to be so situated that the observer looks directly at the front of the object; in other words, the line of vision is parallel to the faces of the frustum. The side looked at is then drawn as if it were projected on a vertical plane at right angles to the horizontal plane, the vertical plane being also parallel to the edges EF and HG of the frustum shown in Fig. 60. The drawing would then look like Fig. 66. Here the trapezoid $ABFE$ represents the side $ABFE$ of the frustum; the altitude of the trapezoid being the same as the altitude of the frustum, it can be measured directly. The hole cannot be seen when the observer looks at the frustum in this position; hence, it is indicated by dotted lines. The projections of the lines AB and DC (also, of EF and HG, of AE and DH, and of BF and CG) coincide.

To draw the side view (sometimes called a **side elevation**), imagine the frustum to be revolved around on its axis 90° to the left, and then draw it in precisely the same manner as the front elevation, by projecting the different lines upon a plane at right angles to the horizontal plane, and perpendicular to the edges EF and HG, that is, parallel to BC and FG. The side elevation would then be drawn as shown in Fig. 67. In this view the lines AD

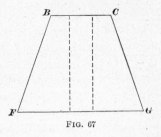

Fig. 67

and BC (also, EH and FG, DH and CG, and AE and BF) coincide.

42. In order to show clearly the different views, and to guard against one view being mistaken for another, they are always arranged on the drawing in a certain fixed and invariable manner. Fig. 68 shows this method of arrangement.

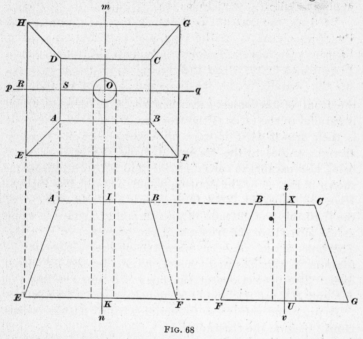

FIG. 68

The plan is drawn first, then the two elevations. It is usually immaterial which of these views is drawn first, but the general arrangement is as shown. Any departure from this method of arrangement should be distinctly specified on the drawing in writing, unless the purpose of the draftsman is so clearly evident that no explanation is needed. The broken and dotted lines are the **center lines**; they serve to show the connection existing between the different views of the object, and to indicate axes of cylindrical surfaces of any kind. It will be noticed that, in the plan view, the two center lines cross each other at right angles, and that their point of intersection O is the center of the circle which represents the hole. Whenever a circle is drawn, two center lines should also be drawn through its center at right angles to each other; this enables any one looking at a drawing to instantly locate the center of any circle. This remark also applies to ellipses, semicircles etc.

To draw the frustum as shown in the last figure, either the front elevation or the plan is drawn first—whichever happens to be more convenient. Suppose the front elevation to be drawn first. Draw the vertical center line $m\,n$; measure the altitude of the frustum, and lay it off on this line, locating the points I and K; through these points, draw the lines $A\,B$ and $E\,F$ perpendicular to $m\,n$; make $A\,I = I\,B = \frac{1}{2}\,A\,B$, measured on the frustum; also $E\,K = K\,F = \frac{1}{2}\,E\,F$, measured on the frustum, and draw $A\,E$ and $B\,F$. Lay off the radius of the circular hole on both sides of the center line $m\,n$, and draw the dotted lines parallel to $m\,n$ through the extremities of these radii to represent the hole. The front elevation is now complete. To draw the plan, decide where the center is to be located on $m\,n$, and draw the horizontal center line $p\,q$. With the point of intersection O of the two center lines as a center, and with a radius equal to the radius of the hole, describe a circle. Through the points A, B, E, and F, draw indefinite straight lines parallel to $m\,n$. On both sides of the center line $p\,q$, lay off on these lines $D\,S$ and $S\,A$, equal to $\frac{1}{2}\,D\,A$, and $H\,R$ and $R\,E$, equal to $\frac{1}{2}\,H\,E$, both $D\,A$ and $H\,E$ being measured on the frustum. Through the points H, E, D, and A, draw the lines $H\,G$, $E\,F$, $D\,C$, and $A\,B$, and join the points H and D, E and A, F and B, and G and C by straight lines, as shown. The figure thus drawn will be the plan.

To draw the side elevation, prolong the lines $A\,B$ and $E\,F$, and draw the center line $t\,v$. Lay off, on each side of $t\,v$, $F\,U$ and $U\,G$ equal to $\frac{1}{2}\,F\,G$, measured on the frustum, and $B\,X$ and $X\,C$ equal to $\frac{1}{2}\,B\,C$, measured on the frustum. Join B and F, and C and G, by the straight lines

BF and CG, and draw the hole dotted as in the front elevation. The drawing is now complete.

The student should have by this time a good idea of how simple objects may be represented by the different views of a drawing, and can now begin on the next plate.

DRAWING PLATE, TITLE: PROJECTIONS—I

43. In making actual drawings of objects when the size of the plate is limited, it is usually impossible to divide it up into a certain number of parts, as in the case of the preceding plates, for the various figures differ widely in their sizes. These drawings should be so made that no part shall come nearer than $\frac{3}{4}''$ to the border line, and the figures should be so arranged as to present a pleasing appearance to the eye, and not be scattered aimlessly all over the drawing.

Fig. 1 represents a **rectangular prism** $2''$ long, $1\frac{1}{2}''$ wide, and $\frac{3}{4}''$ thick. The prism is represented as if it were standing on one of its small ends, with the broad side towards the observer. The elevation $ABDC$ is drawn first; in this case, it will be a rectangle $2'' \times 1\frac{1}{2}''$. The top view, or plan, $FEBA$ is next drawn; this is a rectangle $1\frac{1}{2}'' \times \frac{3}{4}''$, the side AB being the projection of the front of the prism, and the side FE of its back. Lastly, the side elevation is drawn; this is another rectangle $BEHD$, $2'' \times \frac{3}{4}''$, the side BD representing the projection of the front of the prism, and the side BE corresponding to the right-hand end BE of the plan.

Fig. 2 is a **wedge** standing on one of its triangular ends. It is the rectangle shown in Fig. 1, cut diagonally through the corner from E to A on the plan. It will be noticed that the two elevations are exactly the same as in Fig. 1, the plan showing the difference between the two figures.

Fig. 3 is another wedge, standing on one of its rectangular sides, formed by cutting through the prism, in Fig. 1, from A to D. The plan and side elevation are the same as in Fig. 1. Here, the front elevation shows the difference between Figs. 1 and 3. The point D of the elevation is projected on the plan in the point D, and the point opposite D, perpendicular to the plane of the paper, is the point H, shown in all of the side elevations.

Fig. 4 is also a wedge; it is formed by cutting through the prism in Fig. 1 from B to H. The front elevation and plan are the same as shown in Fig. 1, the side elevation being different. The point H in the side elevation opposite D is here projected in the point H of the plan; the point opposite C in the front elevation, and opposite H in the side elevation, is projected in the point K of the plan, the line $K H$ being opposite $C D$ in the plane of the base.

Fig. 5 shows a **cylinder** $1\frac{1}{4}''$ in diameter and $2''$ long. The side elevation is not given, since all elevations of a cylinder whose bases are perpendicular to its axis are the same. Either view may be drawn first, according to convenience.

Fig. 6 shows a **hexagonal prism** $2''$ long; the distance between any two parallel sides is $1\frac{1}{4}''$. In this case, the plan (a regular hexagon) must be drawn first. It is desired also that two of the parallel sides shall be horizontal. To draw the plan in this position, with the dimensions given, choose the center O of the hexagon; draw two center lines at right angles to each other, as $m n$ and $p q$. With O as a center, and a radius equal to one-half of the distance between two parallel sides ($1\frac{1}{4}'' \times \frac{1}{2} = \frac{5}{8}''$), describe a circle. Now, use the **T** square to draw two horizontal lines through the points of intersection of this circle with the center line $m n$. By means of the **T** square and 60° triangle, draw $A B$ and $C D$ through O, in such a manner that the angles $A O q$ and $C O p$ each equal 60°; this is done by keeping the longer of the two short sides of the triangle vertical, and passing the pencil along the hypotenuse. Through E and H, the points of intersection of $A B$ with the two parallel lines, draw $E K$ and $H G$ parallel to $C D$; and through F and I, the points of intersection of $C D$ with the two parallels, draw $F G$ and $K I$ parallel to $A B$. This completes the hexagon, and also the plan of the prism. To draw the front elevation, measure

off, on the center line $m\,n$, the distance $J\,L$ equal to $2''$, and
through the points J and L draw the two horizontal lines $S\,e$
and $R\,f$.   Project the points $K,\ I,\ H,$ and G upon $S\,e$, as
shown by the dotted lines; and through the points of intersection of these dotted lines with $S\,e$, draw the vertical
lines $S\,R,\ a\,b,\ c\,d,$ and $e\,f$, thus completing the front elevation.   To draw the side elevation, extend the lines $S\,e$
and $R\,f$, and draw the center line $t\,v.$ Make $U\,W$ equal
to $1\frac{1}{4}''$, which is equal to the distance between the parallel
sides, and draw $U\,X$ and $W\,Y$; also, $M\,Z$, the point M corresponding to the point K of the plan.

Fig. 7 represents a **hexagonal pyramid**; the distance
between two parallel sides of the base is $1\frac{1}{4}''$, and the altitude
is $2''$.   As in Fig. 6, the plan must be drawn first.   Then, to
draw the front elevation, lay off $O\,I$ on the center line $m\,n$
equal to the altitude, and through I draw the base line $A'D'$.
Project the points $D,\ E,$ etc. of the plan upon $A'D'$, as
shown by the dotted lines, and join them with the point O
by the straight lines $A'O,\ F'O,\ E'\dot{O},$ and $D'O$; these lines
are the vertical projections of the edges of the pyramid; the
horizontal projections of the edges are $F\,O,\ E\,O,\ D\,O,$ etc.
The side elevation can be easily drawn, and does not require
a special description, the length of the base $B\,F$ being equal
to the distance between the parallel sides, or $1\frac{1}{4}''$.

Fig. 8 shows a **rivet** $\frac{7}{8}''$ in diameter, having a button
head $1\frac{1}{2}''$ in diameter.   The side elevation is not given,
since it is exactly the same as the front elevation.   Either of
the two views may be drawn first, according to convenience.
Suppose that the elevation is first drawn.   Draw the center
line $m\,n$, and the line $A\,B$ for the base of the head.   On the
center line lay off from the line $A\,B$, or the base of the head,
a point O, at a distance of $\frac{17}{32}''$, the height of the head.
With the compasses set to a radius of $\frac{51}{64}''$, and from a point
on the center line $m\,n$, describe an arc $A\,O\,B$, taking care
to pass this arc through the point O.   Lay off from, and on
both sides of, the center line $m\,n$ a distance of $\frac{7}{16}''$, or $\frac{1}{2}$ of
the diameter of the rivet, and draw $E\,G$ and $F\,H$.   Draw
the other center line $p\,q$ of the plan, and with O as a center,

and a radius equal to the radius of the button head, describe a circle. With the same center, and a radius equal to $\frac{7}{16}''$, describe the dotted circle, the horizontal projection of the rivet. The irregular line GH indicates that only a part of the rivet is shown. This is done so as not to take up too much space on the drawing.

Fig. 9 shows an ordinary **square-headed bolt** $\frac{7}{8}''$ in diameter, having a head $1\frac{3}{8}''$ square and $1\frac{3}{16}''$ thick. Draw the center lines mn and pq. Construct the rectangle $ABDC$, $1\frac{3}{8}'' \times 1\frac{3}{16}''$, the elevation of the head. Locate the points E and F at a distance of $\frac{7}{16}''$ from each side of the center line, and draw EG and FH. With the compasses set to a radius of $1\frac{3}{8}''$ and from a point on the center line mn, describe the arc representing the chamfering of the head. Draw the plan of the head $LKBA$ (a square whose edge measures $1\frac{3}{8}''$), and the dotted circle $\frac{7}{8}''$ in diameter, the projection of the body of the bolt, which cannot be seen in this view.

Fig. 10 shows a **distance piece** used to separate two other parts, and to keep them a certain distance apart. The arrangement of the views of this figure is somewhat different from the preceding ones, in order to make room for it on the drawing. Draw the center line nm, and construct the figure according to the dimensions marked on the plate. Use a radius of $\frac{1}{8}''$ for the fillets at A, B, C, and D, and an equal radius to round the corners at E, F, G, and H.

Fig. 11 shows a **square cast-iron washer.** Instead of making an elevation and plan as usual, a section is taken through pq; that is, the washer is imagined to be cut on the line pq, with all that part of the figure to the left of pq removed, and an elevation drawn of the remaining part. In order to distinguish a sectional drawing without any possibility of mistake, the so-called section lines are employed. These are usually drawn by laying a 45° triangle against the edge of the T square, and drawing a series of parallel lines as nearly equally distant apart as can be judged by the eye. For cast iron, these lines are full, thin lines, all of the same thickness, and must not be drawn too near together. The method of sectioning for other materials will be given later on. It is not usual to draw the section lines in pencil, but to wait until the outlines of the drawing have been inked in, and then section directly with the drawing pen. The shortest distance apart of the section lines should rarely be *less* than $\frac{1}{16}''$, unless the drawing is of such small dimensions as to cause a sectioning of this width to look coarse. This is the case with Figs. 11 and 12 of this plate. In these two figures make the section lines a full $\frac{1}{32}''$ apart. Only that part of the figure is sectioned which is touched by the cutting plane, the rest of the figure being drawn as if it were projected upon the cutting plane. The corners of this figure should be rounded with a radius of $\frac{1}{16}''$; the other dimensions can be obtained from the plate.

Fig. 12 is a **cast-iron cylindrical ring.** It is shown in plan and section. The dimensions given suffice for the drawing of the figure without further explanations. The inner circle of plan is the projection of the innermost points of the ring which form a circle whose diameter is $A\,B$.

44. When inking in a drawing, it is generally best to draw the circles and other curved lines first, and the straight lines afterwards. This enables the draftsman to easily blend into one line the straight lines meeting the curves, so that their points of meeting cannot be detected; it enables the tangent lines to be drawn with better success, and also shortens the time of inking in a drawing. It will be noticed that some of the straight lines are heavy and some light, and that parts of the full-line circles are heavy and the rest of the circle light. These are the shade lines; they are described later on. The student may make all of the full lines except the border lines of this plate, and the three following plates, of the same thickness, if he so desires. The dotted lines used to indicate those parts of the figures that are hidden must be of the same thickness as full lines, while the construction lines and center lines should be very thin.

45. Dimensions.—The dimension lines and figures on this and succeeding plates are to be inked in by the student.

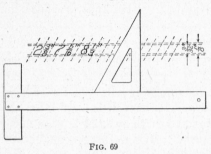

FIG. 69

Make the dimension figures $\frac{3}{32}''$ high, and of the same style as those shown in Art. **20.** Fractions should be $\frac{1}{8}''$ high over all. If there is not room for figures of this size, great care should be taken to make them *clear*.

Until after the student has obtained sufficient practice in lettering, he should draw guide lines in pencil for the dimension figures, as in Fig. 69, unless he can make them look well without. All the figures should have the same slant of 60°, and, when printing fractional dimensions, the *whole* fraction should have the same slant as the figures; that is, the denominator should be under the numerator in a *slanting* direction, and not straight below it. Make the dividing line between the numerator and denominator horizontal, not slanting.

Dimension and extension lines must be light, broken lines of the same thickness as the center and construction lines. Care should be exercised to make the arrowheads as neatly as possible and of a uniform size. They are made with a Gillott's No. 303 pen, and their points must touch the exten-

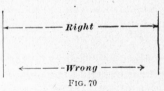

FIG. 70

sion lines, as illustrated in Fig. 70. Do not make arrowheads too flaring.

When putting in the dimensions, care should be taken to give *all* that would be needed to make the piece which the drawing represents, but do not repeat the same dimension on different views. Thus, in Fig. 1 of this plate, the length is given in the front elevation as 2″, and it is obviously unnecessary to give the same dimension in the side elevation.

Again, the dimension lines should be put where they would be most likely to be looked for. In Fig. 10 of this plate, the diameter of the central part of the distance piece is marked $1\frac{1}{4}''$ in the elevation; it could have been marked on the side elevation, as the diameter of the dotted circle, but a person wishing to find the size of this part of the piece would naturally look for it in the front elevation. This is also true of the diameter of the flange. The diameter of the hole could be on the plan or elevation, but it is put on the plan because it is denoted there by a full line, while in the elevation the hole is dotted. Never cross one dimension line by another, if it can well be avoided. Thus, in Figs. 2 and 4 of this plate, the bounding lines of the triangular views are extended by fine broken lines, in order that the dimension lines ($\frac{3}{4}''$) may not cross the lines marking the length and width of the wedge.

The student should ink in all the figures used for dimensions shown on this and succeeding plates, on his drawing, but should omit the letters used to describe the different objects. The titles should be made in block letters as shown on sample copies. The date, name, course letter, and class number are to be put on as in the preceding plates.

DRAWING PLATE, TITLE: PROJECTIONS—II

46. The figures on the last plate were drawn under the supposition that the center lines, and at least one flat side, were parallel to the plane of the paper—the center lines were also either vertical or horizontal. This is always possible in detail drawings, where each piece is drawn separately by itself, but in the case of machines, where the parts are placed at different angles, they cannot always be drawn in this manner. The figures on this plate are so drawn that they show objects similar to those in the last plate, but at different angles. The student should exercise particular care to understand this plate and the two succeeding ones; if he thoroughly masters them, he should experience no great difficulty in the plates that follow.

Fig. 1 shows a **rectangular prism** $2\frac{3}{4}''$ long, $2''$ wide, and $1''$ thick, standing in a perpendicular position on one of its small ends in such a manner that the broad sides make an angle of 30° with a horizontal line. Draw the plan first. To do this, construct the rectangle $A B C D$ $2'' \times 1''$, with the parallel edges $A B$ and $D C$ making an angle of 30° with the horizontal ; this may be done by holding the head of the T square against the left-hand end of the board, and using the 60° triangle. To construct the front elevation, draw a horizontal line $A'C'$ and project A upon this line, thus obtaining the point A'. Draw $A'E$ perpendicular to $A'C'$, and make it equal in length to $2\frac{3}{4}''$, the length of the prism. Through E draw $E G$. Project the points B and C upon $A'C'$, and draw $B'F$ and $C'G$. The back edge $D'H$ of the prism is not seen, and, hence, its position is indicated by the dotted line $D'H$.

The side elevation can be drawn in a similar manner by projecting the points $A B C D$ upon a vertical line, as IL. Produce $A'C'$ and $E G$, and make $B'D'$ equal to IL. Now use the spacing dividers, and set off $B'C'$ equal to IC, and $B'A'$ equal to IK. Through B', C', A', and D', draw the vertical lines $B'F$, $C'G$, $A'E$, and $D'H$, drawing $A'E$ dotted, because, when looking at the prism in the direction of the arrow, the edge $A'E$ is not seen.

Fig. 2 is the same **prism** shown in Fig. 1, but in a different position. The two broad sides are parallel to the plane of the paper, and the prism is tipped in such a manner that the base makes an angle of 160° with the horizontal. The elevation must be drawn first. To do this, draw a horizontal line; then, by using the protractor, draw the line $E F$, making an angle of 160° with the horizontal, reckoning from right around to the left, opposite to the motion of the hands of a clock. Make $E F$ equal in length to $2''$, and on it construct the rectangle $E F B A$, $2\frac{3}{4}'' \times 2''$; it will be the vertical projection or front elevation of the prism. The method of drawing the plan and side elevation is apparent without further explanation.

Fig. 3 is the same prism shown in Figs. 1 and 2, but with the narrow sides parallel to the plane of the paper, and tipped until the base makes an angle of $17\frac{1}{2}°$ with the horizontal. The sizes are the same as in the two preceding figures, and it should be drawn without further explanation, the front elevation being drawn first.

Fig. 4 shows a hexagonal prism having two of its parallel sides parallel to the plane of the paper, and its axis vertical; instead of a side elevation at right angles to the horizontal, a side elevation is desired, as if the vertical prism were looked at in the direction of the arrow, or at an angle of 30° with the horizontal. Draw the plan first and then the front elevation from the dimensions given. To draw the other view, first draw the center line $m\,n$, and then, by use of the **T** square and 30° triangle, draw the lines $A\,B$, $C\,D$, $E\,F$, and $G\,H$, from the points A, C, E, and G, as shown. Also draw in a similar manner the other four dotted lines at the base of the prism; then draw the line $I\,B$ at a right angle to the lines $A\,B$, $C\,D$, etc. At the point I, draw the line $I\,J$ parallel to the center line $m\,n$, and, with I as a center, and the points B, D, F, H, K, L, etc. as radii describe arcs, as shown, cutting the vertical line $I\,J$ at the points J, M, N, O, P, Q, etc. Through the points J, M, N, O, P, Q, etc. draw horizontal lines as shown. On each side of the vertical center line $m\,n$, lay off a distance of $\frac{3}{4}''$, or one-half the distance between the parallel sides of the prism, which is $1\frac{1}{2}''$, as shown in the plan, and draw the lines $R\,S$ and $T\,U$. This view is then completed by drawing the lines $V\,R$, $V\,T$, $W\,X$, and $Y\,X$, as shown. The lines at the base are drawn in a similar manner.

Fig. 5 represents a hexagonal pyramid whose axis is parallel to the plane of the paper, the base making an angle of 30° with the horizontal. It is desired to find the vertical projection of the side elevation. Having drawn the plan $A\,B\,C\,D\,E\,F$ and the side elevation $O'A'B'C'D'$, as snown from the dimensions marked on the drawing, choose the position of the vertical center line $t\,v$; project O' and O''' upon it in the points O'' and O^{IV}, and, through O^{IV} and O''', draw a fourth center line $r\,s$. On this, lay off $O^{IV} G'$ and $O^{IV} H'$ equal to $O\,G$ and $O\,H$, and construct the projection $A'' B'' C'' D'' E'' F'$, as indicated by the broken and dotted lines. Join $O'' E''$, $O'' F'$, etc. by straight lines, and it will be the required projection. The figure thus drawn represents the pyramid as it would appear placed so that its base made an angle of 30° with the horizon, the line of vision being horizontal to the observer looking at it from the left side.

Fig. 6 shows a **cylinder** whose axis is parallel to the plane of the paper and makes an angle of 77° with the horizontal. The vertical side projection is required. Draw the plan and front projection as shown from the dimensions given. Draw the center line $t\,v$ vertical, and project the center O' upon it in O''; also, A' in A'', and H' in H''. To find the remaining points on the projected circle, divide the diameter $A\,H$ of the plan into a convenient number of equal parts, in this case 7, as $A\,1$, 1–2, 2–3, etc. Through the points thus laid off, draw the lines 1–$1''$, 2–$2''$, 3–$3''$, etc., parallel to the center line $m\,n$. Through the points A', $1''$, $2''$, $3''$, etc., draw the horizontal lines as shown by the dotted lines. From and on each side of the vertical center line $t\,v$, lay off distances on each side of the horizontal lines just drawn equal to the length of that part of the lines 1–$1''$, 2–$2''$, 3–$3''$, etc. included between the center line $p\,q$ and the semicircle $A\,C\,H$; thus, on the horizontal line drawn through the point O', the distances $O''C''$ and $O''D''$ are each equal to $O\,C$ in the plan. The distances 1^{IV}–$1'''$ and 1^{IV}–1^{V} are each equal to the distance from 1 to the point of intersection of the semicircle on the line 1–$1''$. The remaining distances are laid off in a similar manner. A curve traced through the points thus found will be the required projection of the upper base of the cylinder. The projection of the lower base is found in exactly the same way. Drawing $C''E'$ and $D''F'$ completes the required projection.

DRAWING PLATE, TITLE: CONIC SECTIONS.

47. This plate shows the different forms of the curves formed by the intersection of a cone or cylinder by a plane. If the plane of intersection is perpendicular to the axis of the cone or cylinder, the curve of the intersection will be a circle; but if it is inclined to the axis, it will be an ellipse in the case of a cylinder, and an ellipse, hyperbola, or parabola in the case of a cone, according to the angle of inclination.

Fig. 1 is a **cone cut by a plane** which does not intersect the base of the cone. *When the cutting plane does not intersect the base*, or the new base of the cone when the cone is extended, the curve of intersection is an **ellipse.**

Draw the plan and front elevation of a right cone whose altitude is $3\frac{3}{8}$ inches and whose base is 3 inches in diameter. Cut this cone by a plane $a\,b$, making an angle of 52° with the base. See figure.

Divide the circle which represents the base of the cone in the plan into any number of parts, in this case 24, and, through the points of division A, E, H, etc., draw the radii $O\,A$, $O\,E$, $O\,H$, etc. to the center O. Draw also from these points straight lines $A\,A'$, $E\,E'$, $H\,H'$, $B\,B'$, etc., parallel to the axis of the cone $O'n$, and cutting the base $A'B'$ in the points E', H', etc. From these points, draw lines to the apex O' of the cone, and cutting the base $A'B'$ in points E', H', etc. From these points, draw lines to the apex O' of the cone, as $E'O'$, $H'O'$, etc., cutting the plane $a\,b$ in the points D', F, etc. From these points D', F, etc., draw straight lines $F'FF''$, $D'DD''$, etc., parallel to the axis $O'n$ of the cone, and intersecting the radii $O\,A$, $O\,E$, $O\,H$, $O\,B$, etc., in the points C, D, F, K, F'', D'', etc., and through these points of intersection draw the ellipse by aid of an irregular curve.

Fig. 2 is a cone of the same size as in the preceding problem; but the cutting plane $a\,b$ is, in this case, parallel to one of the elements* of the cone, and intersects the base. The

---

*Any straight line drawn on the surface of a cone and passing through the apex (as $O'H'$, Fig. 1, or $O'A'$, Fig. 2, etc.) is called an **element.**

curve formed by the intersection of a cone by a plane parallel to one of its elements is called a **parabola.** The plan and front elevations of the cone and curve of intersection are found in a manner similar to the method used in the last problem. To find the side elevation, proceed as follows: Draw the side elevation $O''A''B''$ of the cone with the center line $t v$ as its axis. Draw the projection lines $F'F'''F^{IV}$, $D'D'''D^{IV}$, etc., and make $K'F'''$ and $K'F^{IV}$ equal to KF and KF''; make $I'D'''$ and $I'D^{IV}$ equal to ID and ID'', etc., and trace a curve through the points thus found. The result will be the side elevation of the cone when cut by a plane parallel to one of its elements and having the upper part removed. The side elevation of Fig. 1 may be drawn in a similar manner.

Fig. 3 is a cone having the same dimensions as the two preceding problems, but cut by a plane $a b$ parallel to the axis of the cone and perpendicular to the vertical plane of projection. When the cutting plane intersects the base of a cone and is not parallel to any element (that is, if the acute angle included between the cutting plane and the base is greater than the angle $O'A'B'$ included between any one element and the base), the curve of intersection is called a **hyperbola.**

The plan and front elevation are constructed as before, the horizontal projection of the curve for this particular case, where the cutting plane is parallel to the axis of the cone, is also a straight line. The side elevation is found as in the last problem, by drawing the lines of projection $F'F'''F^{IV}$, $D'D'''D^{IV}$, etc., and making $I'D'''$ and $I'D^{IV}$ equal to ID and ID'', $K'F'''$ and $K'F^{IV}$, equal to IF and IF'', etc. The curve drawn through the points thus found will be the required hyperbola.

Fig. 4 shows the **intersection of a cylinder,** $3\frac{3}{8}''$ long and $2''$ in diameter, by a plane $a b$, making an angle of $57°$ with the base. The plan and elevation may be drawn as shown, the horizontal projection of the curve being a circle, having the same diameter as the base. To construct the side elevation of the curve, divide the circle representing the base of the cylinder in the plan into any number of parts, in this case 24, and through the points of division A, B, C, etc. draw the radii OA, OB, OC, etc. to the center O.   Draw also from these points straight lines AA, LBB', KCC', IDD', etc. parallel to the axis mn of the cylinder, and cutting the base in the elevation.   From the points A, B', C', D', etc. draw lines $D'E'$, $C'F$, $B'G'$, etc. at right angles to the axis mn.   Make $I'E$ and $I'E'$ each equal to ID; $K'F$ and $K'F'$ each equal to KC; $L'G$ and $L'G'$ each equal to LB, etc.   The curve drawn through these points will be the side projection, or side elevation, of the curve of intersection.

DRAWING PLATE, TITLE: INTERSECTIONS AND DEVELOPMENTS

48.   On this plate some dimensions are given in decimal fractions instead of common fractions.   Such decimal dimensions should be laid off with a decimal scale, if the student has one.   A decimal scale is a scale with inches divided into tenths, hundredths, etc.   If the student has no decimal scale (and such a scale is not essential), he should take the nearest value of the decimal fraction in thirty-seconds of an inch.

To change a decimal fraction to a common fraction, having a desired denominator, multiply the decimal by the desired denominator of the common fraction, and express the result as a whole number, which whole number will be the numerator of the fraction.

Thus, to express $.765''$ in fourths, we have $.765 \times 4 = 3.06$ fourths $=$ say, $\frac{3}{4}''$.   To express $.765''$ in sixteenths, we have $.765 \times 16 = 12.24$ sixteenths $=$ say, $\frac{12}{16}''$.   To express $.765''$ in thirty-seconds, we have $.765 \times 32 = 24.48$ thirty-seconds $=$ say, $\frac{24}{32}''$.

The length of the circumference of a circle $=$ the diameter $\times 3.1416$; hence,

The length of circumference of a circle whose diameter is
$$1\tfrac{3}{8}'' = 3.1416 \times 1\tfrac{3}{8}'' = 4.32'' = 4\tfrac{5}{16}''.$$

The length of circumference of a circle whose diameter is
$$1\tfrac{1}{2}'' = 3.1416 \times 1\tfrac{1}{2}'' = 4.71'' = 4\tfrac{23}{32}''.$$

The length of circumference of a circle whose diameter is
$$1\tfrac{1}{4}'' = 3.1416 \times 1\tfrac{1}{4}'' = 3.93'' = 3\tfrac{15}{16}''.$$
The length of circumference of a circle whose diameter is
$$1\tfrac{9}{16}'' = 3.1416 \times 1\tfrac{9}{16}'' = 4.9''.$$
$$4.9'' \div 2 = 2.45'' = 2\tfrac{7}{16}'' \text{ (see Fig. 10)}.$$

49. This plate deals with the intersection of surfaces and their development. Fig. 1 shows the intersection of **two unequal cylindrical surfaces** whose axes $p\,q$ and $m\,n$ intersect at right angles. Their dimensions are given in the figure. For the sake of convenience, a bottom view is given, instead of a top view, as usual. First draw the front elevation, omitting, of course, the curve of intersection $E\,Q\,G\,D\,C\,B\,A$, which must be found. Then draw the side elevation and the bottom view, as shown. Divide the circle which represents the side projection of the cylindrical surface $F\,E\,A\,1$ into any convenient number of parts, in this case 12, and draw the projection lines $7\,E,\,6\,Q,\,5\,G,\,4\,D,\,3\,C,\,2\,B$, and $1\,A$ parallel to the axis $p\,q$. Also draw the projection lines 4–$4'$, 3–$3'$, 2–$2'$, 1–$1'$, etc. parallel to the axis $t\,v$. Choose a convenient point O, and through it draw two lines $O\,I$ and $O\,K$ parallel to the axes $p\,q$ and $m\,n$ of the cylinders. Continue the lines 4–$4'$, 3–$3'$, etc. downwards, until they cut $O\,I$ in 8, 7, 6, 5, etc. Now make $O\,8' = O\,8$, $O\,7' = O\,7$, etc.; this may be most conveniently done by taking O as a center, and describing arcs of circles with radii equal to $O\,8$, $O\,7$, $O\,6$, etc., cutting $O\,K$ in $8'$, $7'$, $6'$, etc. Through $8'$, $7'$, $6'$, etc., draw the lines $8'D'$, $7'C'$, $6'B'$, etc. parallel to the center line $r\,s$. Through the points D', C', B', and A', draw the lines $D'D$, $C'G$, and $B'Q$, parallel to the center line $m\,n$, and intersecting the lines $4\,D$, $5\,G$, $6\,Q$, $3\,C$, and $2\,B$ in the points D, G, Q, etc. The curve traced through these points will be the front elevation of the curve of intersection of the two cylindrical surfaces.

Fig. 2 shows the intersection of **two equal cylindrical surfaces** at right angles to each other, as in the case of a pipe elbow. When two cylinders having *equal diameters intersect, and their axes also intersect*, the front elevation of the curve of intersection is always a straight line, no matter what angle the two axes make with each other.

Fig. 3 shows a symmetrical **three-jointed elbow** formed by the intersection of three cylindrical surfaces. The diameter of each of the three surfaces is $1\frac{1}{2}''$. The center lines of the surfaces $RAGS$ and $MNPH$ are to be at right angles to each other; then, in order that the arrangement shall be symmetrical, the center line of the third surface $AMHG$ must make an angle of $45°$ with the center lines of the other two.

To construct the elevation as shown in the figure, draw the two center lines mn and pq at right angles to each other; they intersect at 6. Lay off $6I = 1\frac{1}{2}''$ and draw an indefinite line RS through I perpendicular to mn. Make IR equal to $IS = 1\frac{1}{2} \times \frac{1}{2} = \frac{3}{4}''$, and draw RA and SG parallel to mn. Draw OK parallel to mn and $1\frac{1}{2}''$ below it. Through the point O, where RS and OK intersect, draw OT passing through 6, and bisect the angle ROT by the line OA, which intersects RA and SG in A and G. Lay off $6J = 2\frac{1}{4}''$ and draw PJN perpendicular to pq. Make $JP = JN = 1\frac{1}{2} \times \frac{1}{2} = \frac{3}{4}''$, and draw PH and NM parallel to pq. Draw OM so as to bisect the angle TOK; OM intersects PH and NM in H and M. Finally, draw AM and GH.

Fig. 4 shows the intersection of **two unequal cylindrical surfaces** whose axes intersect at an angle of $65°$ instead of $90°$, as in Fig. 1. The method of finding the curve of intersection is in all respects similar to that used in Fig. 1, and, as the corresponding points have béen given the same letters or figures, the directions given for Fig. 1 can be applied to Fig. 4 also.

Fig. 5 shows a **cylindrical piece of iron** $2\frac{13}{16}''$ in diameter that has been gradually turned down to $1\frac{5}{16}''$ diameter, and then having the larger part flattened on two sides. The large and small parts of the piece are connected by a graceful curve. The problem is to find the curve of intersection $A\,1\,2\,3\,B$ formed by the flattening. Draw the plan and front elevation from the dimensions given; also draw the curve $C\,6'\,5'\,4'$, and its equal on the opposite side, so that they look to the eye about as seen in the drawing. In order that all the work sent to us may be alike, the radius of this curve and the position of the center have been given on the drawing. To locate the center, draw an indefinite horizontal straight line $1'' + 1\frac{1}{16}'' = 2\frac{1}{16}''$ above the base of the piece; and with C and D as centers, and a radius of $1\frac{1}{8}''$, describe short arcs cutting the line just drawn. The points of intersection will be the required centers. With O as a center, and radii of convenient lengths, as $O\,4$, $O\,5$, $O\,6$, etc., describe arcs cutting $A'B'$ in $3'$, $2'$, $1'$, etc. Through the points 4, 5, 6, etc. draw the lines 4–$4'$, 5–$5'$, 6–$6'$, etc., parallel to the center line $m\,n$, and intersecting the curve $C\,4'$ in $4'$, $5'$, $6'$, C, etc. Through the points A', $1'$, $2'$, etc. draw lines $A'A$, $1'$–1, $2'$–2, etc., parallel to $m\,n$, intersecting horizontal lines drawn through C, $6'$, $5'$, $4'$, etc., in A, 1, 2, 3, etc. The points A, 1, 2, 3, etc. are points on the required curve, and through them the curve may be drawn.

Fig. 6 is the **cylindrical surface** of one section of the elbow $1\,7\,A\,G$ of Fig. 2 rolled out into a flat plate; hence, if a flat plate were cut into the same shape and size as Fig. 6 and bent into a cylinder so that the ends $1\,G'$ and $1'G''$ touch each other, the vertical projection or front elevation would be the same as shown by $1\,7\,A\,G$ in Fig. 2. If a second plate were cut out in the same manner and bent into a circle, the two pieces on being brought together, as shown in Fig. 2, would touch at every point. The problem is to find the shape of the curve $G'A'G''$. The length of the line 1–$1'$ is evidently equal to the length of the circumference of a circle whose diameter is $1\frac{3}{8}''$, or $4.32''$, very nearly. Produce the line 1–7, Fig. 2, and make 1–$1'$ equal in length to $4.32''$. Divide the circle $1\,2\,3\dots.12$ into a convenient number of equal parts, in this case 12, and erect the perpendiculars $1\,G$, $2\,F$, $3\,E$, etc., cutting the line of intersection $G\,A$ of the cylindrical surfaces in G, F, E, etc. Divide the line 1–$1'$ into the same number of equal parts that the circle was divided into, thus making the length 1–2 equal length of arc 1–2; 2–3, length of arc 2–3, etc. Through 1,

2, *3*, etc., draw the perpendiculars *1 G'*, *2 F'*, *3 E'*, etc. and
project the points *G*, *F*, *E*, etc. upon these perpendiculars,
as shown, thus locating the points *G'*, *F'*, *E'*, *D'*, *C'*, *B'*, *A'*
of the left-hand half of the required curve. The points on
the right-hand half are found in the same manner, as shown,
and the required curve can be drawn through these points.

50. A drawing like Fig. 6 is called the **development**
of the cylindrical surface *1 7 A G*.

Fig. 7 is the **development of the cylindrical surface**
A G H M of Fig. 3. Make *1–1'* = $1\frac{1}{2}$ × 3.1416 = 4.71″,
nearly, and divide it into 12 equal parts to correspond with
the 12 equal parts into which the dotted circle is divided.
Project the points *6*, *5*, etc. of the dotted circle upon *O A* as
shown, thus locating the points *B*, *C*, etc. Through *B*, *C*,
etc., draw *B 6*, *C 5*, etc., perpendicular to *O T*. Make *1 G'*
= *1 G'''* = *1 G*, *2 F'* = *2 F'''* = *2 F*, *3 E'* = *3 E'''* = *3 E*, etc.
Through *G'*, *F'*, *E'*, etc., trace the curve *G' F' E'* . . . . *G''*, and,
through *G'''*, *F'''*, *E'''*, etc., trace the curve *G''' F''' E'''* . . . .
*G*ᴵⱽ. Drawing *G' G'''* and *G'' G*ᴵⱽ completes the figure.

Fig 8 is the development of the cylindrical surface *1 F E A*,
Fig. 1. The method used here is in all respects similar to
the two preceding problems. In this case, the distances
1 A, *7 E*, and *1' A'* are all equal to *1 A* or *E F*, in Fig. 1;
and *2 B*, *6 Q*, *8 Q'*, and *12 B'* are all equal to *2 B* or *6 Q*, in
Fig. 1. The development of *L M P N* is not given, for want
of room, but the method will be explained in Fig. 10.

Fig. 9 is the development of the cylindrical surface
1 F E A, Fig. 4. The student should have no difficulty in
drawing this, after having studied the preceding problems.

Fig. 10 is the development of the cylindrical surface
L M P N, Fig. 4. Owing to the want of room, only that
half of the development is shown which contains the part to
be cut out. The length of a circle $1\frac{9}{16}$″ in diameter is 4.9″,
nearly; half of this is 2.45″. Hence, the line *Y' Y''*,
Fig. 10, which equals the length of the semicircle *Y' A' Y''*,
Fig. 4, is 2.45″ long. The distance *X' Y'* = *X'' Y''* equals
the length of the cylinder, *L N* or *M P*. Lay off *X' S* equal

to the length of the arc $Y'D'$; SR equal to the arc $D'C'$; RN equal to the arc $C'B'$; NM equal to the arc $B'A'$, etc. Find the lengths of these arcs by means of the method given in connection with Fig. 54. Draw through these points the perpendiculars SS', RR', etc. With the spacing dividers, set off SD_1 equal to SD in Fig. 4; RG_1 equal to RG; NQ_1 equal to NQ; and ME_1 equal to ME. Also, $R'C_1$ equal to $R'C$; $N'B_1$ equal to $N'B$; and $M'A_1$ equal to PA. In exactly the same manner, find the points on the right-hand half of the curve. If a plate were cut of the same size and shape as shown in Fig. 10, and rolled into a semicylindrical surface, the diameter of which is $1\frac{9}{16}''$, it would exactly fit the plate cut like Fig. 9 rolled into a cylindrical surface, the diameter of which is $1\frac{1}{4}''$, the two being placed together as shown in Fig. 4.

Fig. 11 shows a **conical surface cut by a plane,** and Fig. 12 shows its **development.** Draw the elevation and horizontal projection of the base as shown in Fig. 11. Divide the projected circle (base of cone) into a convenient number of equal parts, in this case 12, and project the points *1*, *2*, *3*, etc. on the base *1'-7'*, thus locating the points *1'*, *2'*, *3'*, etc. Join these points with the apex O of the cone, by the lines $O1'$, $O2'$, $O3'$, etc., cutting the plane in A, B, C, etc. Now, choose a convenient point O, Fig. 12, and with this as a center, and a radius equal to $O1'$, or $O7'$, Fig. 11, the slant height of the cone, describe an arc *1-1'* of a circle. Make the *length of this arc* equal to the length of the circumference of a circle having the same diameter as the base of the cone. This may be conveniently done as follows: length of arc = 2 × 3.1416 = 6.28'', nearly. Draw a straight line 6.28'' long and divide it into, say, 4 equal parts. Describe an arc having a radius equal to $O1'$, the slant height of the cone, and find the length of a part of this arc equal to 6.28 ÷ 4 = 1.57'' by means of the method described in connection with Fig. 53. With the dividers set for the chord of the arc just found, space off the chord four times on the longer arc *1 2 3 ....1'*, Fig. 12. Divide the arc into the same number of equal parts that the circle *1 2 3 . . . . 12* has been divided into, that is, 12 parts. Join the points of division *1, 2, 3*, etc. with the center O by the lines $O\,1,\,O\,2,\,O\,3$, etc., as shown. Project the points B, C, D, etc., Fig. 11, upon $O\,1'$, in B_1, C_1, D_1, etc., as shown, and lay off $O\,A$ equal to $O\,A'$ equal to $O\,A_1$ Fig. 11; $O\,B$ equal to $O\,B'$ equal to $O B_1$; $O\,C$ equal to $O\,C'$ equal to $O\,C_1$, etc., and through these points draw the curve. A plate cut of the same size and shape as shown by $A\,G\,A'\,1'\,7\,1$ can be bent into the conical surface shown by the elevation $A\,G\,7'\,1'$.

Particular attention must be given to the method explained above for laying out the curve of the development in Fig. 12. It would be entirely wrong to take the measurements from the lines $O\,F$, $O\,E$, $O\,D$, $O\,C$, etc., Fig. 11. The reason for this is that these lines, being on the surface of the cone, are inclined towards the observer, and so do not appear in their true lengths. The line $O\,D$, for example, if measured on the surface of the cone itself, would evidently be of the same length as the line $O D_1$; but in the figure it is much shorter. The line $O D_1$, however, appears in its true length in the figure, because it is not inclined to the observer in the position shown. The actual distance of point D from the apex O, therefore, is $O D_1$, which is the distance to be laid off for point D in the development. The same holds true for the other points.

SHADE LINES

51. The use of the heavy shade line will now be explained. In Fig. 71, by means of the shade lines, the draftsman knows, without looking at any other view of the object, that the rectangles *1* and *4* represent square holes, and *2* and *3*, square bosses. When he looks at the other view, it is to find the depth of the holes and the height of the bosses. This explains the use of the shade lines, viz.: to show, from that view of the drawing which is being examined, whether the part looked at is above or below the plane of the surface; that is, for example, whether the rectangles *1*, *2*, *3*, and *4* are the tops of bosses or bottoms of holes, and, consequently, whether they extend

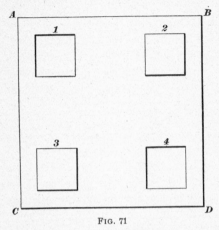

FIG. 71

above or below the surface of *ABDC*. In order that the shading may be uniform on all drawings, the light is assumed to come in one invariable direction, in such a manner as to be parallel to the plane of the paper, to make an angle of 45° with all horizontal and vertical lines of the drawing, and to come from the upper left-hand corner of the drawing. Each view of the object represented is shaded independently of any of the others; and, when shading, the object is always supposed to stand in such a position that the drawing will represent a top view. Any surface that can be touched by drawing a series of parallel straight lines, making an angle of 45° with the horizontal and vertical lines of the drawing, is called a **light surface;** a surface that cannot be touched by lines having this angle is called a **dark surface.** All of the edges caused by the intersection of a light and dark surface, or two dark surfaces, are usually shaded; that is, the edges thus formed are drawn in heavy lines. Exceptions to this rule are sometimes made by experienced draftsmen, when a rigid adherence to it will produce a bad effect or will render the drawing ambiguous.

Fig. 72 shows a plan of a series of triangular wedges radiating from the common center *O*. The top is, of course, a light surface, and, in order to determine whether the perpendicular surfaces are light or not, the 45° triangle may be used. Take the wedge *R O A*. A line drawn at an angle of

45°, the direction of the arrows, would strike the side of which OA is the edge; hence, this side is a light surface, and the top being also a light surface, the line OA must be light. OR, on the contrary, is a heavy line, since the light cannot strike the side of which OR is the edge without passing through the wedge. Hence, this is a dark surface, and its intersection OR with the light surface OAR requires a shaded line. For the same reason, AR is also shaded. The same reasoning as

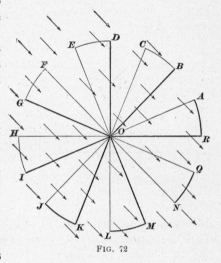

FIG. 72

the above applies to the lines OB, OD, OG, OI, OK, and OM; also, to QN, ML, and KJ. CB is not shaded, because the light strikes the surface of which CB is the edge, as shown by the arrow, making CB the intersection of two light surfaces. ON makes an angle of exactly 45° with the horizontal, and is treated as if it were the edge of a light surface; this is done in every case in which the line considered makes an angle of 45° with the horizontal.

In shading holes, or any parts of the drawing denoting depressions below the surface under consideration, a slightly different assumption is made. Fig. 73 shows the plan of a square block with a hexagonal hole in the center. If the light passed over the surface $ABCD$, parallel to the plane of the paper as previously assumed, all the inside surfaces would be dark, and the entire outline of the hexagon $EFGHIK$ would be shaded. In order to prevent this and make the work similar to that which has preceded, the rays of light are assumed to make an angle of 45° with the plane of the paper when shading holes and depressions.　Hence, the light will strike the surfaces whose edges are GH, HI, and IK, as shown by the arrows, leav-

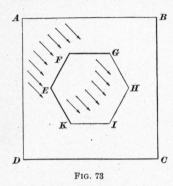

FIG. 73

ing the surfaces whose edges are KE, EF, and FG dark as before.　Therefore, these latter edges will be shaded, and the edges GH, HI, and IK will be light.　See also Fig. 71.

The conventional method of shading circles which represent the projections of cylinders, or circular holes, is as follows: AB, Fig. 74, is the projection or end view of a cylinder having for a base the circular area AB.　Draw the arrows EA and FB, making angles of 45° with the horizontal diameter, and tangent to the circle at A and B.　That half of the circle in front of these two points of tangency is to be shaded,

and, in order to make the drawing look well, the center point for the compasses is shifted along the line CH parallel to EA and FB in the direction of the arrow an amount equal to the thickness of the desired line.　With the same radius that was used to describe the original circle, describe part of another circle, being careful not to run over the first circle, and stop-

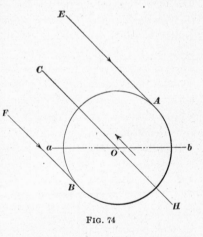

FIG. 74

ping when the two lines coincide.　The directions for shading a hole are precisely the same as for the projection of a cylinder base, except that the half BCA of the circle in Fig. 75 is to be shaded, the center being shifted as before, but in the opposite direction, as shown by the arrow.

Vertical projections of cylinders are shaded as shown in the front elevation of Fig. 5, Drawing Plate, title: Projections—I.

After studying the foregoing concerning shade lines, the student should be able to see the reason for the using or omitting of any shade lines on the drawings in the following plates. In the case of an object like the hexagonal prism in Fig. 6, Drawing Plate, title: Projections—I, no part of the upper base or line Se is shaded, although, strictly speaking, the part $c\,e$ of the line should be shaded; but, as this would make part of the straight line $S\,e$ heavy and the greater part light, the whole line is drawn light. This is one of the exceptions previously mentioned.

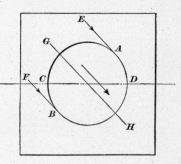

FIG. 75

MECHANICAL DRAWING

INTRODUCTION

DIVISIONS OF THE SUBJECT

1. While every drawing executed by means of the T square, triangles, and other drawing instruments, is a *mechanical drawing*, this term is usually restricted to drawings representing machines, machine parts, and objects used in the mechanic arts. In recognition of this restricted meaning of mechanical drawing, the term "geometrical drawing" was used in the preceding paper to signify that the subjects treated dealt with those general geometrical principles that form the foundation of all instrumental drawing.

A **mechanical drawing** is the language employed by the designer of machinery to convey his ideas to others; as, for instance, to the workman who is to construct the part or machine represented.

2. A workman that constructs a machine or machine part from drawings is said to "work to drawings," and requires not only a true representation of the object to be made, but all its dimensions as well. The drawing must also give other instructions, such as the material to be used, method of manufacture, etc. A mechanical drawing of this kind is called a *working drawing*.

§ 14

3. While the systems used in the drawing offices of the leading manufacturing companies for producing drawings vary in many important details, it should be noted that good drawings made in one office can be read in others, and that the parts represented can be made in other shops, even when office and shop practice differ to a marked degree. In general all mechanical drawings are made as plain as possible, shading and other aids to the eye being omitted except on complicated drawings, when shading is occasionally resorted to in order to bring out the important features of the design.   The shading of surfaces, lines, and holes is becoming less and less common, but when used, the instructions given in *Geometrical Drawing* will be followed.

It is not good practice to spend time on elaborate titles or figures.   Plain letters, easily read, serve all purposes and do not waste the time of the draftsman.

The methods here described are those which have been found to be the most representative and complete, and the student can easily adapt himself to any local regulation, if the principles here explained do not agree in every particular with the practice in the office in which he first starts as draftsman.

WORKING DRAWINGS

KINDS OF WORKING DRAWINGS

4. **Working drawings** are divided into two general classes, namely: *assembly*, or *general*, *drawings* and *detail drawings*.

Assembly, or **general, drawings** show the workman the relation between, and the places or positions occupied by the component parts of a structure, machine, device, fixture, implement, etc.   If any dimensions are given, they are usually only the leading ones.

5. **Detail drawings** show the exact shape and size of each integral part.   For this purpose they are supplied with

all the dimensions required by the workman and any additional explanatory notes that the draftsman may consider
necessary.

Detail drawings may be made so complete that they will
answer for the patternmaker, blacksmith, and machinist,
and they are usually so made in the smaller shops.   In the
large shops, however, separate drawings are often made for
these men; the detail drawing for the use of the patternmaker then contains only the dimensions and notes needed
by him to make the pattern; that for the blacksmith contains only the dimensions needed for making the forging;
and, finally, that for the machinist contains only the dimensions needed by him.

6. Attention is called to the fact that practice varies in
regard to the dimensions given on detail drawings, at least
as far as drawings for the patternmaker and blacksmith are
concerned.   In some places, the dimensions given represent
the size the object is to be when finished; hence, the blacksmith or patternmaker must make necessary finishing allowances himself.   In other places the finishing allowance is
made by the draftsman; the dimensions given are then those
of the pattern or forging.   If in doubt about the practice
followed in a particular drawing office, find out by inquiry
what system is used.

In the drawings which follow, the finished dimensions
only are given, the necessary allowances being made by the
patternmaker or blacksmith.

SCALES

7. It is seldom convenient to make the drawing of a part
full, or life, size, it being more often necessary to show the
part as reduced in size.   Thus, supposing it is desired to
make a drawing $\frac{1}{4}$ size, then $12''$ on the object will be represented by $3''$ on the drawing, hence if $3''$ is laid off and
divided into 12 equal parts, each of these parts will represent $1''$ on the object.   If these parts are subdivided into 2,

FIG. 1

4, or 8 parts, each will represent $\frac{1}{2}''$, $\frac{1}{4}''$, or $\frac{1}{8}''$ on the object.   A scale of this kind is called a $\frac{1}{4}$ **scale,** or a **scale of 3″ to the foot.**   A $\frac{1}{8}$ **scale,** or a **scale of $1\frac{1}{2}''$ to the foot,** is constructed in the same way, except that $1\frac{1}{2}''$ would be laid off instead of 3″.

In some cases, the scale is increased as in small machines, such as instruments, etc.

8. The dimensions given on a drawing are always followed and it is seldom necessary to state the scale to which drawings are made, although this may be done if it in any way adds to the clearness of the drawing. It is common practice to have parts on the same detailed sheet drawn to different scales, the more complicated parts being drawn as near full size as possible, and the less complicated parts being drawn to a much reduced scale.

9. Fig. 1 shows a scale which is convenient for the student, inasmuch as it combines eleven systems of subdivision and may be used for all the work ordinarily done in a drafting room.   This scale is triangular in section and 12 inches in length, and on each of its edges there is laid off a scale, as shown at A, B, and G.   The scale at G is " full size "; that is, this edge of the scale is divided into inches and fractions of an inch down to sixteenths, and is used for drawings in which an object is represented in its natural size.   On its opposite side, at B, is shown the quarter-size scale of 3″ = 1 ft.   The first 3-inch (actual size) division, from B to C, is subdivided into 12 parts representing inches, and each inch is then divided into proportional fractions of an inch, generally eighths. From C to D, D to E, and E to F, the scale is marked in its main divisions of 1 foot each, each foot being $3''$ long, actual size. From A to B the scale is independently divided into spaces of $1\frac{1}{2}''$ (actual size) to form an eighth-size scale, or $1\frac{1}{2}'' = 1$ ft., the divisions of the latter occurring on and between the marks for the $3''$ $= 1$ ft. scale.

The other sides and edges of the instrument are divided into scales of $1''$ and $\frac{1}{2}''$, $\frac{3}{4}''$ and $\frac{3}{8}''$, $\frac{1}{4}''$ and $\frac{1}{8}''$, and $\frac{3}{16}''$ and $\frac{3}{32}''$ to the foot. Different makers do not always arrange their scales in the same manner. Thus, instead of having a full-size scale and scales of $3'' = 1$ ft. and $1\frac{1}{2}'' = 1$ ft. on one side, as shown in Fig. 1, some makers have the full-size scale and $\frac{3}{16}'' = 1$ ft. and $\frac{3}{32}'' = 1$ ft. on one side. It will be observed that the numbering of the feet on these scales does not start at the end of the instrument, but at the first main division from the end. Thus, on the quarter-size scale the zero mark is placed at C and the first foot is measured to D. This is done so that the feet and inches may be laid off independently and with one reading of the scale.

The figures indicating the number of feet on this scale are placed along the inside edge at D, E, and F, the numbers running in a direction away from the part containing the inches. The numbers indicating inches run in an opposite direction from those defining the feet.

10. To lay off 2 ft. $3\frac{3}{4}''$ on a scale of $3'' = 1$ ft., and from a given point, place the scale on the point so that the 2-foot mark will be directly over it; then from the zero mark C lay off $3\frac{3}{4}''$, as shown, locating a second point. The length of the distance thus laid off between the two points represents 2 ft. $3\frac{3}{4}''$. The scale of $1\frac{1}{2}'' = 1$ ft. is used in a similar manner to lay off the same distance. The figures indicating feet on this scale are placed nearer the edge, in order to prevent confusion in reading.

To draw to half size, or to a scale of $6'' = 1$ ft., use the full-size scale, and remember that every $\frac{1}{2}''$ on that scale corresponds to 1″ on the object; that is, that every dimension is only one-half of the real length. To lay off $5\frac{7}{8}″$, lay off 5 half inches and $\frac{7}{16}″$ over; the result is a line $5\frac{7}{8}″$ long to a scale of 6″ = 1 ft.

11. It may happen that a draftsman is obliged to make a scale, when the size of his plate is limited and a general drawing of some object is desired. In such a case, one scale may be too large to enable the drawing to be made on a sheet of the required size; another scale may make it too small to show up well. For example, a $\frac{1}{8}$ scale may be too large and a $\frac{1}{16}$ scale too small; a $\frac{1}{12}$ scale may be just right. If the draftsman has no $\frac{1}{12}$ scale (that is, a scale of 1 inch to the foot), he may make one by taking a piece of heavy drawing paper and cutting out a strip about the size of an ordinary scale and laying off the inch divisions on it. Each division or part will represent 1 foot on the object. Divide one of the end parts into 12 equal parts and each will represent 1 inch on the object. Lines indicating half and quarter inches may be drawn if considered necessary.

Fig. 2 shows part of a scale made in this manner, giving

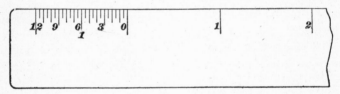

FIG. 2

feet, inches, and half-inches—the quarters, eighths, etc. of an inch being judged by the eye.

To make a $\frac{1}{5}$ scale, lay off 12″ and divide this distance into 5 equal parts, using one of the methods described in *Geometrical Drawing*. Using the same method, divide one of the end divisions into 12 equal parts, to represent inches, and then divide each of these parts into halves, quarters, eighths, etc.

DUTIES OF DRAFTSMEN

12. A brief description of the duties of the draftsman, according to his rank and experience in the modern drafting room, is given herewith. There are usually three, and sometimes four, grades of men:

1. The *designer*, who, as his name indicates, designs the apparatus.

2. The *leading*, or *head*, *draftsman*, who takes the ideas of the designer and works them up into practical form. Very often the designer does his own laying-out work, and in such case, fills both the position of leading draftsman and designer.

3. The *detailer*, who works either directly or indirectly for the leading draftsman, takes his assembly drawings and makes up the details, calling for proper material, parts, and quantities. His work approaches more and more nearly to that of the leading draftsman, as he gains in skill and familiarity with the machine designed.

4. The *tracer*, who takes the pencil detail drawings, and makes tracings for reproduction, his work in turn approaches more and more nearly the work of the detail draftsman as he gains in skill and experience. It is probable that the young man who starts work without previous practical experience will start work as a tracer. If he does this work neatly and intelligently, he can count upon promotion to the more responsible position of detail draftsman, if opportunity offers, from which position he can then advance himself higher and higher.

13. The necessity of carefully following all instructions in making tracings cannot be too forcibly presented. Slovenly work will at once create a bad impression, while painstaking work, and carefully made and presentable tracings, will immediately place the tracer in favorable standing with his employers At the start it is better to work slowly until the subject presented is well in hand and perfectly understood. While speed is important, accuracy must come first.

DRAWING PLATES

GENERAL INSTRUCTIONS

14. The general instructions which follow, apply to all the mechanical-drawing plates treated in this Section.

From the start, the student should remember that it is essential to do neat and accurate work; that all lines, figures, and letters must be clear cut and distinct; that there must be no doubt as to the meaning of limits or dimensions; that mistakes made on drawings are often more serious than errors in the shop, for they may not be located until the various parts of the machine are to be assembled. He must also keep in mind the necessity of making drawings concise, but not needlessly complicated; that dimensions are not to be duplicated; that when working drawings once leave his hands marked "complete" it should not be necessary to refer to him for further particulars.

15. Size of Plates.—The plates are to be of the same size as those drawn in connection with *Geometrical Drawing*, $14'' \times 18''$, with border lines drawn $\frac{1}{2}''$ from edge, making working limits of drawing $13'' \times 17''$.

16. Title and Number of Drawing.—The title or name of drawing is to be placed in the lower right-hand corner of sheet, and a space of $1\frac{1}{2}'' \times 4''$ is to be reserved for this title; the height will vary, but the length will always be $4''$. In addition to the title there will be given in this space the number of the drawing, the draftsman's name, and the date when the drawing was finished. If desired, the date can also be given when drawing was started.

17. Fractions.—Fractions are to be written with dividing line horizontal, thus: $\frac{3}{4}''$, $\frac{7}{16}''$; never thus: $5/16''$, with dividing line inclined.

18. Abbreviations. — Abbreviations are only used on drawings when lack of space prevents use of complete word, although there are a few abbreviations which can be used without hesitation, having been practically fixed by long practice, thus: D. or "Diam." for diameter; R. or "Rad." for radius; "Thds." for threads; f. for finish.

19. Definitions. — The word **drill** placed near a dimension or hole is always taken to mean that a hole is put through the object by drilling.

Ream or **reamed** placed near a hole means that the hole is finished by reaming.

The word **tap** following a dimension and a number always means that the hole is to be finished by tapping with a tap of the dimensions given; that is, "$\frac{1}{2}$–13 tap" would mean that the hole is to be tapped with a $\frac{1}{2}''$ tap, 13 threads to the inch.

The word **cored** implies that finish is unnecessary, the hole being produced by a core, which is placed in the mold when the casting is made. Cores are arranged for by the patternmaker.

The terms **shrinking fit, driving fit, forced fit,** and **turning fit,** always imply that the workman is to make allowance for the kind of fit called for, all holes being made to nominal dimensions, and the allowance necessary made on the part which goes into the hole.

F all over means machine or part is to be finished all over.

When wishing to convey special information, write your note in plain English so that it cannot be misunderstood.

20. Dimensions. — All dimensions above 24" are to be given in feet and inches, the inches being designated by accent (") mark, and feet by abbreviation ft., thus 6 ft. $4\frac{1}{2}''$; never use accent mark for feet, as there is then danger of confusion.

When micrometer or gauge measurements are required, all dimensions are given to three decimal places; thus,

1.000" would indicate one inch measured with gauge or micrometer; 6.250" would indicate 6¼", and 0.250" would indicate ¼" measured in the same way. Note that a zero should always be placed ahead of the decimal point when dimensions are less than one inch; this avoids all confusion as to value of decimal.

Where possible all dimensions should be given so as to read from bottom and right-hand side of drawing.

Intermediate dimensions always start from some finished surface, or center line, this giving a base from which work can be checked.

PENCIL DRAWINGS AND TRACINGS

21. The method of making working drawings differs from the method which has been followed in *Geometrical Drawing*, the pencil drawing not being inked in. In modern shop practice, original drawings are not sent to the shop, but reproductions, called **tracings,** are made on **tracing cloth,** which is a cloth made semi-transparent by sizing, and then blueprints are made from the tracings. A description of the blueprint process will be given farther on. Since the tracing can be made to serve as an original drawing, it is not necessary to ink in the pencil drawing, although it may be retained as a record.

Following the above general shop practice, the drawings made in connection with the study of this subject will first be made in pencil and afterwards traced. The methods to be followed in making the pencil drawing will be those which have been used in penciling the plates in *Geometrical Drawing*.

22. For the pencil drawing a good grade of Manila paper upon which lines can be easily drawn and erased is sufficient. The tracing cloth is then placed over the paper drawing and the lines inked in on the cloth. All ink lines on tracings must be uniformly black without regard to the width of these lines. In general, the lines will be made about 50 per cent. heavier than they would have been if inked in on the original paper drawing.

At first it will be found very difficult to get lines that are distinct and uniformly black, but by strictly following directions, it will become quite as easy to make a good tracing as it is to ink in the drawing on drawing paper.

The plates to be drawn in connection with this subject all have numbers, which begin with 1001. They are to be drawn in the order of their numbers.

PLATE 1001, TITLE:

PRACTICE SHEET

23. Plate 1001 is intended for a practice sheet in tracing and is introduced to give the student an opportunity to familiarize himself with the methods of making lines on tracing cloth, and will not serve in any way as a working drawing. We would suggest that after having carefully penciled the drawing on Manila paper, it be traced several times before submitting the tracing to the Schools for criticism.

In order to distinguish readily between references to figure numbers on the drawing plates and to those in the text, the former will be printed in heavy-face type and the latter in ordinary type.

24. Suggestions for Making the Pencil Drawing. Figs. **1, 2,** and **3** are squares $5\frac{1}{16}''$ on a side, and the lines drawn in them are $\frac{3}{16}''$ apart, some being full lines, some dotted, and some heavy lines; the positions of all parallel lines are to be fixed by scale measurements, care being used to place them symmetrically. All lines should be a trifle heavier than is shown on the engraved plate, as the engraving is somewhat smaller than the tracing. In locating the squares let their top sides be $\frac{3}{4}''$ below the upper border line, leaving a space of $\frac{5}{16}''$ between first and third squares and their adjacent border lines and a space of $\frac{19}{32}''$ between each of the squares.

Fig. 4 is a series of 10 concentric circles, $\frac{1}{4}''$ apart, of lines varying in thickness, the outside circle being 5″ in diameter. When drawing these circles—and at all times when several arcs are described from the same center—be careful to keep the leg of the compass that contains the needle point perpendicular to the plane of the paper and press the compasses as lightly as possible against the paper; otherwise, a hole will be made in the paper at the center from which the arcs are struck, which will wear larger all the time. It will then be difficult to ensure accuracy, and the hole will present an unsightly appearance. This caution is particularly necessary when inking in a tracing, as the hole enlarges much more rapidly than on paper and will be reproduced in all blueprints taken from the tracing.

Fig. 5 is a combination of semicircles enclosed in an outer circle 5″ in diameter.* Place the horizontal diameters of these circles $3\frac{1}{4}''$ above the lower border line and their vertical diameters $2\frac{13}{16}''$ and $8\frac{1}{2}''$ from the left-hand border line.

In order to draw this latter figure, first draw the horizontal and vertical diameters, as shown, which are 5″ long. Divide the horizontal diameter into 8 equal parts, then draw the outer circle. Bisect each of these main divisions and with the points of bisection as centers draw the semicircles as shown, first describing the two smallest semicircles —one above and one below the horizontal diameter—then the two next larger; and so on, until the figure is completed.

In drawing this figure the student should take very great care to make the semicircles meet accurately, as this is the object of this exercise.

25. Fig. 6 represents an ellipse whose major axis is 5″ and minor axis is $2\frac{1}{2}''$, located respectively 4″ above the lower border line and $2\frac{7}{8}''$ from right-hand border line. The ellipse may be constructed in one of the ways described in

---

* The distances for locating the various views on this or any of the succeeding plates are always to be measured with a full-size scale.

Geometrical Drawing, or by the following approximate method, which is rapid and is accurate enough for practical purposes:

Draw the two axes a, a' and b, b', Fig. 3, and join a and b by the line ab; lay off bc equal to $oa - ob$ and bisect ac by the perpendicular de, which intersects bb' produced in e and oa in g. Lay off $oe' = oe$, and $og' = og$, and draw $e'f$, $e'f'$, and ed'. With e and e' as centers, and $eb = e'b'$ as a radius, describe the arcs dbd' and $fb'f'$; and with g and g' as centers, and $ga = g'a'$ as a radius, describe the arcs daf and $d'a'f'$.

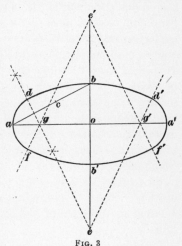

Fig. 3

The points e and e' may lie within or without the ellipse, according to the difference between the axes.

26. In the lower right-hand corner of the sheet is a space reserved for the title with lines drawn as shown. Make this space $1\frac{1}{2}''$ high and $4''$ long and subdivide it by a line $\frac{1}{2}''$ above and parallel with the lower border line. In the lower space draw a vertical line $1\frac{3}{4}''$ from the right-hand border line. The title and number should be centrally located in their respective spaces, and the letters and figures should be $\frac{1}{4}''$ high. Fill in the title with the type of letters indicated.

The tracing can now be begun.

27. Tracing the Drawing.—The two sides of the tracing cloth are known as the glazed side and the dull side. Place the tracing cloth over the carefully prepared pencil drawing, glazed side up, putting extra thumbtacks in each corner, and smoothing out all wrinkles. Either side of the tracing cloth may be used for inking in. The glazed side takes ink much better than the dull side, the finished drawing looks better and will not soil as easily, and it is also easier to erase a line that has been drawn on this side. Pencil lines can be more satisfactorily drawn on the dull side, and if it is desired to photograph the drawing, it is better to draw on this side. The draftsman uses either side, according to the work he is doing and to suit his individual taste, or to follow the practice of the drafting room in which he is employed.

Care must be taken to remove all dirt and grease, otherwise the ink will not flow well from the pen. This is done by taking a knife or file and scraping or filing chalk upon the tracing cloth; then with a soft rag (cotton-flannel, or chamois) rub it over the tracing cloth, being sure to rub chalk over every part. The chalk powder must be fine and must be rubbed off gently after being spread on the surface. The use of the powdered chalk makes it possible to ink the drawing satisfactorily and prevents the ink running, as it sometimes does when chalk is not used.

28. Now take the **T** square and with the right-line pen draw all the horizontal lines, starting at the top and working down, drawing the light lines first, and gradually spreading the pen until the heavier lines are taken care of.

Next, draw the vertical lines, then the inclined lines, then the circles, and finally the ellipse, which will be drawn by the method just described.

29. Before fixing the width of the line, draw your pen on the edge of tracing cloth outside the bounding lines on which the tracing is cut or else on a separate piece of tracing cloth; until your pen works freely and smoothly, and produces lines of the right weight, do not attempt to draw any lines on the tracing cloth. You need not expect to make a good tracing at the first trial, but will be surprised at the rapid improvement after one or two practice sheets have been drawn.

When the lines are all drawn, put in the title and the designation of figures. In tracing, remember that ink dries slowly and care must be taken to avoid smearing.

The letters in the title will be made freehand, the shape and size of letters being limited by guide lines which you will draw in the proper positions. All working lines used on the drawing are omitted on the tracing cloth, center lines only being retained.

Before mailing your tracings to the schools write on the dull side with a lead pencil your address and class letter and number.

———

PLATE 1002, TITLE:

DRAWING-ROOM STANDARDS

30. This Plate is intended as another practice sheet in tracing, and at the same time serves as an introduction into the regular routine of drawing-room work.

Considerable stress was laid in *Geometrical Drawing* on the necessity of learning how to letter neatly; all that has been said there is endorsed here, and any proficiency the student has acquired in lettering will stand him in good stead.

In making working drawings, however, time should not be uselessly spent in making elaborate titles; freehand lettering is, therefore, used almost exclusively. Sometimes— for instance in making assembly drawings which are not sent to the shop and where the drawing is made for display or other purposes—lettering is done with the T square and triangle. But even then the rather elaborate block letter described in *Geometrical Drawing* is seldom used; a simpler alphabet, as that shown as Type I on drawing Plate 1002, is used instead. Two types of freehand lettering were shown in *Geometrical Drawing*, only the second of which is recommended for use on working drawings, as it is the simpler of the two. It is repeated as Types II, III, and IV on Plate 1002, differ only in size.

31. It is important that all sheets of drawing for the same shop have uniform lettering, and that the various types of lettering are used always for one and the same purpose. In this work the following plan will be adopted:

Letters shown under head of Type II are the style of letters which will be used in the **main title** of all the drawing sheets which follow. These letters are $\frac{1}{4}''$ in height and are spaced as shown.

Capitals shown under head of Type III will be used for all **capitals** except the main title.

Type IV will be used for all **lower-case letters in body of drawing,** and in **bill of materials,** and the figures in all **dimensions.**

Types III and IV are made freehand, but it is advisable at all times to draw guide lines on the pencil drawing before the work is started, these guide lines not appearing on the tracing, of course.

It is recommended that the lettering be done on the pencil drawing as well. It will serve to nicely locate the words, etc., and when lettering the tracing, any misplacement can then be remedied. Any good, sharp, steel writing pen, not too hard, may be used in lettering, but a so-called *crow quill pen*, especially adapted for this work, is recommended.

DEFINITIONS OF LINES

32. Surface Lines.—**Surface lines** refer to those lines which limit or bound the delineation of a part and should be of the same weight all about the figure.

33. Dimension Lines. — **Dimension lines** are lines drawn to show limits to which dimensions apply and are ended with an arrowhead, put in freehand, the arrowheads should always touch the lines which limit the dimension,

thus: $\longmapsto 2\frac{1}{2}'' \longrightarrow$ Never thus: $\longleftarrow 2\frac{1}{2}'' \longrightarrow$ A short

dimension may be indicated thus: $\rightarrow \frac{3}{32}'' \leftarrow$ Placing arrowheads outside of limiting lines.

Do not put dimension lines in or over delineation of parts, or place figures where they cannot be easily read.

34. Center Lines.—Center lines are usually drawn at the working center of the object shown, and are extremely important as indicating the point from which work is to be laid out. Dimensions are frequently given from the center lines and they serve as a guide for all dimensions even when not used to limit them. In making working drawings it is important that one of the center lines should be first located, as this will immediately fix the starting point of drawing. This working point is not necessarily the geometrical center of the figure, but is fixed by some important point about which the delineation begins and which is relatively important in the complete object.

This line is also used to indicate where a section has been or is to be taken. If, however, a partial section is indicated, the remainder of the view being in elevation or plan, the full (surface) line is used, except where there is an opening appearing in both parts of the view; in this case, the dash and dot would be used where the line crosses the opening, and the full line where it crosses the solid portion.

35. Hidden Surface Lines. — Hidden surface lines are lines drawn to show the surfaces of hidden parts, and it will be noticed that the part hidden in one view is sometimes drawn full in the other views, indicating that from one position the part cannot be seen, while from the other position it is in view.

36. As was stated in Art. **22,** all lines on tracings should be fully 50 per cent. heavier than the lines used on the plates drawn in connection with *Geometrical Drawing.* The only case in which a fine line should be used is when locating points by intersecting lines, and even then they are not actually needed, since the points can be located by fine pencil lines, and being once located the lines passing through the points may be as heavy as desired. Fine lines on tracings render it very difficult to obtain a good blue-print.

It will be noticed that the broken and dotted line, here used for center lines and to indicate where a section is to be or has been taken, consists of a repetition of long dashes, each followed by *one* dot. In *Geometrical Drawing* two dots were used. Both forms of this line are widely used, but the student is recommended to use the one here shown, as it is simpler. When working in a drafting room, however, he must conform to the standards in force there.

SECTIONS AND SECTION LINING

37. In order to show the interior of hollow objects, they are often drawn in section, and the kind of material is then usually indicated by certain combinations of lines. Unfortunately, there is no universally adopted standard; thus, a certain combination of lines may indicate that the material is cast iron if drawn in one office; in another office this same combination may have been adopted to represent brass; and so on. As far as working drawings are concerned, there is usually no difficulty experienced on account of this diversity of practice, since as a general rule the material is, and should always be, distinctly specified on the drawing in order to prevent any mistake on the part of the workman.

38. The most commonly used combinations of lines for different materials are shown in Plate 1002, under heading Standard Cross-Sections. Steel of all kinds is indicated as shown at *A*; *B* shows the sectioning employed for wrought iron. Cast iron is usually sectioned as shown at *C*, and this type of cross-sectioning will be used for *all* materials unless it is deemed advisable on complicated drawings to designate kind of material by character of cross-section, in which case the standard sections here shown will be used. Brass and other similar copper alloys are sectioned in the manner shown at D. For lead, Babbitt, and similar soft metal, the sectioning shown at E is extensively used. Wood, when cut across the grain, is usually sectioned as shown in the upper half of F, and when cut along the grain, as shown in the lower half. Wood is also frequently indicated on a drawing by section lines, even when it is not a section. Glass and stone, when in section, are often indicated in the manner shown by the upper half of G; when not in section, they are frequently drawn as shown in the lower half. Concrete may be indicated as at H; I gives a common representation of leather. Rubber and wood fiber are sectioned as shown at J; firebrick, as shown at K; and water, as shown at L.

The squares inside which the various kind of cross-sections are to be drawn should be $1\frac{1}{2}''$ square; a space of $1''$ should be left between each square in a horizontal row and of $\frac{3}{4}''$ between those in a vertical row. The square C should be $2\frac{1}{4}''$ below upper border line and $1''$ from right-hand border line.

All section lines are spaced without the use of a scale or special instrument, the eye being the only guide in placing them evenly, and the student will follow this plan in drawing the sections shown. With practice, great skill can be acquired in spacing the lines evenly, and the work can be done very rapidly.

39. Sections of material that appear too thin on a drawing to be conveniently sectioned, or when it is desired to make the section very prominent, are often blackened in, as shown in Fig. 4. In order to separate different pieces, a white line is then usually

FIG. 4

left between them. Black sections are most frequently employed for sectional views of structures composed of plates and rolled sections, such as I beams, angle irons, bulb angles, rails, Z bars.

39—8

40. On many sectional views, it will be noticed that the section lines do not run in the same direction. This invari-

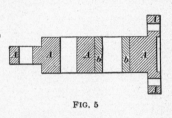

FIG. 5

ably means that there is more than one piece in the section given. Thus, referring to Fig. 5, it will be seen that the section lining shown at b, b is at a right angle to the other section lining. It is the general rule among draftsmen that all parts of the same piece shown in section must be section-lined in the same direction, irrespective of the continuity of the section. Thus, referring again to Fig. 5, the fact that all section lining marked A is in the same direction immediately establishes the fact that this part of the view is a section of the same piece. Likewise, since the sectioning shown at b and b runs in the same direction, it follows that b and b are sectional views of one piece, which is separate from A.

The above rule governing the direction of section lines is always adhered to when possible; when any departure is necessary, care is taken to prevent ambiguity. Where only the sectional view is given, it is often very difficult to understand the drawing, and sometimes a violation of the above rule will cause an erroneous conclusion to be drawn. Referring to (a), Fig. 6, cover up the front view shown at (b). Then, since the section of a and a', and also that shown at b and b', are respectively in the same direction, any one would be perfectly justified in assuming that a and a' was a sectional view of a rod fitted with a solid bushing $b\,b'$. Furthermore, since c, c and c', c are sectioned the same way, the conclusion that they were the jaws of a forked rod would be justifiable. Referring now to view (b), it is seen that b and b' are separate brass boxes; the part a' is seen to be separate from the cap a, and the note "*Rods Removed*" indicates that c is separate from c'. The way the sectional view should have been section-lined to correspond to the front view shown at (b) is given in Fig. 6 (c).

41. When a cutting plane passes through the axis of a shaft, bolt, rod, or any other solid piece having a curved surface and located in the plane on which the section is taken, it is the gen-

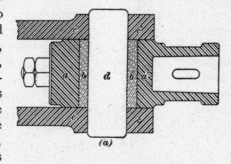

(a)

eral practice not to show such solid pieces in section, but in full. Thus, in Fig. 6 the sectional view (*a*) is taken on the plane represented by the line *x y*, in view (*b*), which passes through the axis of the pin *d*. This pin is shown in full, however, in views (*a*) and (*c*). The

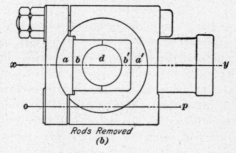

Rods Removed
(b)

practice here shown is rarely departed from by experienced draftsmen, since it makes a drawing easier to read and also saves considerable time in making the drawing.

42. Fig. 6 also shows another feature that is frequently met with in shop drawings. Referring to the

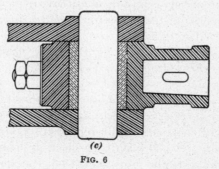

(c)

FIG. 6

illustration, it is seen that no bolt is shown in the lower half of the object in so far as the front view (*b*) is concerned. A center line *o p* is drawn in, however, which indicates to the workman—who reasons from the symmetry of the object in respect to the center line xy—that the lower half of the object is to be supplied with a bolt placed in the plane given by the center line op. In case of symmetrical work, draftsmen will frequently complete only one half of the view and merely indicate the other half by a few lines or not at all, trusting to the judgment of the workman for a correct reading of the drawing. In the best practice, a note is made on the drawing calling attention to the fact that the indicated portion of the view is a duplicate of the completed portion.

PLATE 1003, TITLE:

DETAILS

43. The majority of the succeeding text illustrations are supposed to represent the preliminary pencil drawings to be made by the student and from which he is to make the final tracings. In these pencil drawings little use is made of dotted lines, as the main purpose of such drawings is that of indicating the *location* of the various lines; the distinction between full and dotted lines and such that are to be omitted altogether being made during the process of tracing. In the pencil drawing distinction is made to some extent between those lines that are merely construction lines and those that constitute the real outlines of a view, in so far that at first all lines that are not sure to be one of the outlines are drawn faintly. After the length and location of the outlines have been definitely determined they are strengthened and in this manner distinguished from mere construction lines or such that are to be shown as dotted lines. The first eight figures of this Plate show the conventional methods of representing screws; they are drawn full size. The actual projection of a screw thread will be similar to the projection of a helix; but in order to save the time required to locate the points and trace in the curves, the following methods are universally used, except, perhaps, in the case of screws of very large diameter and pitch.

44. To locate the upper row of views on this Plate, draw a horizontal line $1\frac{1}{8}''$ below the upper border line and locate the top sides of the views along this line. Draw another horizontal line $4\frac{15}{16}''$ below the same border lines to limit the lengths of these views. Leave a space of $\frac{3}{4}''$ between Fig. 1 and the left-hand border line and the same space between each of the views in that row. Fig. 1 represents a single square-threaded screw $1\frac{1}{2}''$ in diameter and $\frac{3}{8}''$ pitch. To draw the screw follow the directions given herewith in connection with Fig. 7. First draw the center line mn and a line ab at right angles to it. Make the distance ab equal to the diameter of the screw, or $1\frac{1}{2}''$, and through the points a and b draw lines ad and be parallel to the center line mn. Also lay off on the line ab distances af and bg

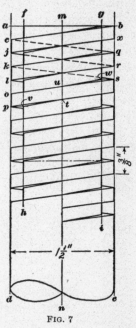

FIG. 7

equal to one-half of the pitch ($\frac{3}{8}'' \times \frac{1}{2} = \frac{3}{16}''$), and through the points f and g draw lines fh and gi parallel to the center line mn. These lines show the depth of the thread. On the line ad lay off the width of the groove and of the thread, ac, cj, jk, etc., each equal to one-half of the pitch, or $\frac{3}{8}'' \times \frac{1}{2} = \frac{3}{16}''$. Draw the line bc, and through the points j, k, l, o, etc. draw lines parallel to bc intersecting line be at points x, q, r, s, etc. Draw faint pencil lines joining the points c and q, j and r, k and s, etc., to represent the back edges of the threads and make the parts that are seen full lines. Draw faint horizontal lines from points j, l, p, etc., to the line fh and from the points of intersection draw lines to the center points of the lower side of the threads, such as vt, these lines representing the visible bottom lines of the threads. Likewise draw horizontal lines from the points q, s, etc., to the line $g\,i$ and from the points of inter-section draw the lines $u\,w$, etc.   The method of drawing the remainder of the screw should be apparent.

In some drawing offices this conventional method of rep-resenting screw threads is further simplified by omitting the lines indicating the back edges of the threads as well as those that represent the bottom lines. The threads will then be indicated by a series of parallelograms, such as $c\,b\,x\,j$, $k\,q\,r\,l$, etc.   The screw *17* in Fig. 43 has been drawn in this manner.

It will be noticed that the width of the thread and of the groove, measured parallel to the center line $m\,n$, and the

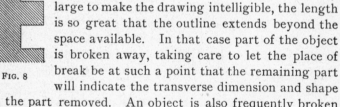

FIG. 8

depth of the thread are all exactly the same; that is, they are each equal to one-half of the pitch. If a section were taken through the center line $m\,n$, the thread and groove would look like, Fig. 8, a series of squares; hence the term *square thread*.

When a long and comparatively slender object is to be drawn, such as these screws, it often happens that when drawn to a scale sufficiently large to make the drawing intelligible, the length is so great that the outline extends beyond the space available.   In that case part of the object is broken away, taking care to let the place of break be at such a point that the remaining part will indicate the transverse dimension and shape of the part removed.   An object is also frequently broken off when it is unnecessary to show it complete, as in the case of Fig. 1, where it is simply a question of showing the con-struction of the threaded part and where the other part may be a straight rod of any desired length.

The fact that part of an object is broken away is indicated by a so-called **break**.   Breaks may be indicated in various ways; most commonly the break is given an outline that will reveal the shape of the object. The conventional method of indicating the break on a round rod is that shown at the lower end of Fig. 1.

An example of a break where the central part of an object is removed is shown in Fig. **9**. Here the removed

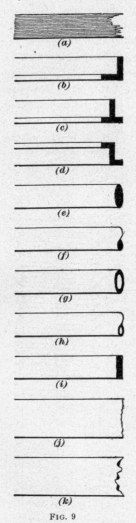

part is simply part of a straight rod, and therefore it need not be drawn, especially when it is a question of saving space. The remaining parts are pushed together and the true length of the screw indicated by the adjacent dimension, here 20″. Conventional methods of indicating breaks are shown in Fig. 9. Wood is usually shown broken in the manner illustrated at (a), angle irons as at (b), **T** irons as at (c), **Z** bars as at (d). Cylindrical objects are occasionally broken as shown at (e), but most frequently in the manner shown at (f). Pipes and similar hollow cylindrical objects may be broken as shown at (g); but more frequently the break is made as shown at (h). Rectangular objects may be broken in the manner shown at (i); plates and objects other than those included between views (a) and (i) are often shown broken off by drawing a wavy freehand line as in (j) and (k). As a rule the break is indicated by section lines, as in Fig. **1**. On small objects, or in views drawn on a small scale, it is sufficient to show the break in black, as in Fig. 9.

FIG. 9

45. Fig. **2** shows a **double square-threaded screw** $1\frac{1}{2}''$ in diameter and with $\frac{3}{4}''$ pitch. The reason for using a double thread is that if the single square thread were used, the depth would be so great as to weaken the bolt or rod on which it was cut and render it unsafe for the purpose for which it was intended. To prevent this, either the diameter of the rod must be increased or the thread must be cut of the same depth and thickness as a thread of half the pitch, or, in this case, as if the pitch were $\frac{3}{4}'' \times \frac{1}{2} = \frac{3}{8}''$, as in the preceding problem; another thread of the same size and pitch ($\frac{3}{4}''$) must be cut half way between these first threads, thus giving a double thread. The pitch, or distance that the screw would advance in one turn, would be $\frac{3}{4}''$, the same as if it were a single-threaded screw of $\frac{3}{4}''$ pitch, while the depth of the thread is only half as great. To draw it, proceed exactly as in the last figure, and follow the direc-

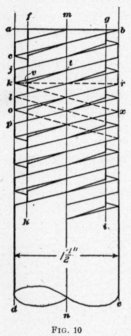

FIG. 10

tions given herewith in connection with Fig. 10. To get the direction of the line bc, Fig. 10, which in this figure represents the projection of the bottom edge of the top of the thread, lay off ac equal to one-half the pitch, or $\frac{3}{4}'' \times \frac{1}{2} = \frac{3}{8}''$, and draw the line bc. The width of the threads and grooves, and also the depth of the threads, is one-fourth of the pitch, or $\frac{3}{4}'' \times \frac{1}{4} = \frac{3}{16}''$.

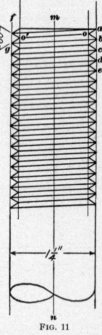

FIG. 11

Through the points k, l, o, etc., draw faint pencil lines kx, etc. to represent the back edges of the threads, and make the parts that are seen full lines. Through the point k

draw a faint pencil line *k r* at right angles to the center line *m n*, intersecting the line *f h* in *v*, and draw the line *t v*, which represents the bottom of the thread. The remainder of the screw should be drawn without trouble.

46. Fig. 3 and Fig. 11 show a **single V-threaded screw** $1\frac{1}{4}''$ in diameter and having 7 threads to the inch; that is, the pitch is $\frac{1}{7}''$. Draw a cylinder $1\frac{1}{4}''$ in diameter, having *m n* for the center line. Lay off *a b*, *b c*, *c d*, etc. each equal to the pitch, or $\frac{1}{7}''$. Do the same on the left-hand side. With the aid of the **T** square and 60° triangle make the angles *a o b*, *f o' g*, etc., 60°. The rest of the thread can be drawn by referring to the figure.

47. Fig. 4 represents a screw exactly like the preceding one, except that the thread is left-handed instead of right-

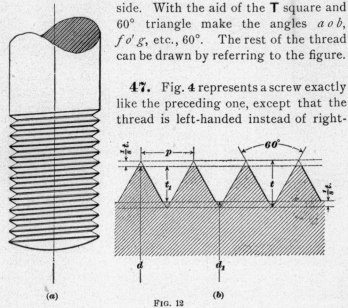

FIG. 12

handed. To ascertain whether a thread is left-handed or right-handed, hold the screw in such a position that its axis is horizontal. If the thread is right-handed, as it usually is, the angle that the edge of the thread makes with the horizontal on the right-hand side is obtuse; if left-handed, it makes an acute angle with the horizontal on the right-hand side. No further instruction should be necessary for drawing the thread.

The **Seller's triangular** or **V thread,** commonly called the **American thread,** or **United States Standard,** which is used in the United States, is shown in Fig. 12 (*a*). Fig. 12 (*b*) is an enlarged section of the thread.   The *angle* between the sides of the thread is 60°.   The distance *p* indicates the pitch of the screw.   As shown in the figure, a section of a single thread is an equilateral triangle, the altitude of which is *t*; to form the United States Standard thread one-eighth the altitude of the triangle is cut off from the apex, and the angle at the root is filled in to a like depth.   Hence the *real depth* of the thread t_1 is three-quarters the altitude of the triangle, that is, $t_1 = \frac{3}{4}t$.

48.   Fig. 5 represents a **double V-threaded screw** $1\frac{1}{4}''$ in diameter.   It has $3\frac{1}{2}$ threads per inch; that is, the pitch is $1'' \div 3\frac{1}{2} = \frac{2}{7}''$.   The remarks made in connection with Figs. 2 and 3 apply here.

49.   Fig. 6 and Fig. 13 represent a section of a **brass nipple.**   When the diameter of a nipple is given, the inside diameter is always meant, unless otherwise stated.   The actual diameter of a nipple or pipe is very rarely given, but must be taken from printed tables.   The *nominal diameter* of the nipple shown in the figure is 1'', but the actual inside diameter is 1.05''; from the table, the outside diameter is found to be 1.32'', making the thickness .135''.   Owing to the thinness of the shell, pipe threads are finer than the threads on the same sized rods.   The coarsest pipe thread is 8 threads per inch.   The number of threads per inch on the nipple shown is $11\frac{1}{2}$.   The thread is tapered 1 in 16; that is, the diameter of the threaded part is increased by $\frac{1}{16}''$ for each inch in length, to make a tight fit, and the length of the threaded part on each end is $0.51'' + 0.52'' = 1.03''$, of which length the distance between *a* and *b*, Fig. 13, represents the perfect thread, while from *b* to *c* the thread is imperfect. On account of the small size of the thread and the crowded condition of the lines, Fig. 13 is drawn on a larger scale and only one end of the nipple is shown, the construction of the other end being identical.   To draw the nipple proceed as

follows: Draw a cylinder 1.32″ in diameter and with *m n* as
a center line; lay off the inside diameter.equal to.1.05″ and
draw *de* and *fg*. When decimal parts of an inch are
required, lay off the dimension in the nearest 64ths of an
inch by consulting Table V at end of this paper. Draw
a horizontal line, through point *a*, across the cylinder, and
lay off the points *h*, *k* (indicating the minimum outside
diameter of the threaded part) 1.28″ apart. Draw a second

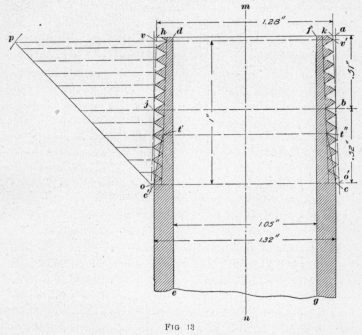

Fig 13

horizontal through *b*, intersecting the other side of the cylinder at *j*, and a third horizontal through *c* intersecting the
other side at *c′*. Join the points *h, j* and *k, b* by straight lines
and produce them until they intersect the line *c c′* at *o* and *o′*.
These lines indicate the position of the tops of the threads.

Draw a horizontal line 1″ above *c c′*, intersecting the
lines *h o* and *k o′* at points *v, v′*. Prolong the line *v v′* indefinitely toward the left, then divide the distance *vo* into
11½ parts by means of the method given in *Geometrical*

Drawing, as follows: Apply the compasses to the scale and open them until they span 23 divisions (in this case sixteenths), and then with this length as a radius and with the center at *o*, strike an arc intersecting the line *v v'* at *p*. Connect *o* and *p* by a straight line and, starting at *o*, mark off eleven-eighths by means of a scale and a sharp-pointed pencil. From these points, with the aid of the **T** square, draw horizontal lines to the lines *h o* and *k o'*, the intersection with the former line locating the tops of the threads and with the latter the bottom of the threads. By means of the **T** square and the 60° triangle draw a couple of threads, beginning at *v* and also a few threads at *k*, remembering that the divisions on *k o'* are to be advanced half a thread, as shown; that is, the top of one thread and the bottom of the preceding thread on the other side will both be on one horizontal line. Through the bottoms of the threads thus found, draw lines parallel with *h o* and *k o'*; these lines will indicate the bottom of all the threads. Complete the threads along *h o* and *k o'* as if they were perfect, and continue the threads above *v v'* to the upper end of the nipple.

Counting from *o*, draw a horizontal line through the top point of the fourth thread and extend said line until it intersects the bottom lines of threads at *t'* and *t''*. Join the points *t'*, *c'* and *t'' c* by straight lines, which lines will indicate the bottoms of the imperfect threads. It will be noticed that from points *b* and *j* downwards the tops of the threads, as drawn, extend beyond the sides of the cylinder and consequently these parts will also be imperfect. When inking in the drawing only those parts of the threads should be shown that lie *inside* the outer edges of the cylinder and *outside* the lines *t' c'* and *t'' c*. As the size of the threads, when drawn on the plate, are very small, it is not expected that the student will be able to draw them correctly in their minute details, but it is necessary that the total number of threads shall be correct. Table IV, giving the dimensions of standard threads for gas and water pipes, is found at the end of this paper.

50. Fig. **7** shows another method of representing a V-threaded screw. This method has the advantage of making a neat-looking drawing and of being very rapid in delineation. The pitch is laid off as in the three preceding figures. The heavy lines represent the bottom of the thread and their lengths are determined by constructing an equilateral triangle on the pitch distance, as shown in Fig. 14, and limiting the line to distances between two corresponding vertexes of the triangle. The diameter of the screw is 1″ and the number of threads per inch is 8.

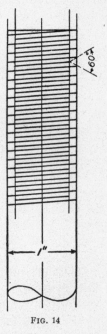

51. Fig. **8** represents the screw shown in Fig. **7,** but with the heavy lines replaced by light ones. This method has many advantages in making tracings, as it makes the resetting of the pen unnecessary, and the ink does not take so long to dry. Fig. **7** will be used for ordinary work; Fig. **8,** when there are a number of details of the same sort, making complete representation inadvisable.

FIG. 14

When screws are represented, as shown in Figs. **7** and **8,** it is not customary to lay off exact distances to represent the tops and bottoms of threads. The distances between the lines are made even and of any length that presents a good appearance. This adds, of course, to the rapidity with which a drawing can be made.

The right-hand V thread is considered as a standard and is always furnished unless some other is specifically called for. When left-hand, double, or multiple threads are wanted, it is customary to place a note near the part detailed calling attention to the fact.

52. When a screw thread is hidden by part of the object and it is deemed necessary to show its location, dotted lines are drawn in one of the three ways illustrated in Fig. 15. Of these methods, (*a*) is the most complete, but (*b*) is the form generally used and is clear. Fig. 15 (*c*) should not be used unless supplemented by a note, "$\frac{3}{4}''$ stud " or " $1\frac{1}{8}''$ bolt," etc.

53. Draw a horizontal line $6\frac{1}{4}''$ below the top border line and locate the tops of Figs. **9, 11, 13, 15, 17**, and **19** along this line. Lay off on it a point $1\frac{1}{4}''$ from the left-hand

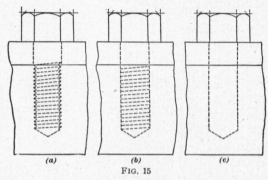

(a)   (b)   (c)

FIG. 15

border line, and through this point draw the center line of Figs. **9** and **10**. From this point, also, lay off other points $1\frac{29}{32}''$ apart, through which draw the center lines for Figs. **11** to **22** inclusive, excepting Figs. **23** and **24**, which are drawn separately.

Figs. **9** and **10** of the plate represent the ordinary and conventional method of representing a hexagon bolt and nut. The example selected is a bolt $1''$ in diameter and $20''$ long, with the thread portion cut 8 threads to an inch, head $1\frac{5}{8}''$ across flats; the curve at the lower end of the bolt is drawn with a radius equal to diameter of bolt. By $1\frac{5}{8}''$ across flats is meant $1\frac{5}{8}''$ between parallel sides, that is, twice *o k*, Fig. 16.

That the student may fully understand the method of laying out the nut and the head of the bolt, the method which is to be followed will be described in detail. It is not common practice to show more than one view of either a bolt or nut, the shape being determined by the delineation.

To lay out the nut, first draw two horizontal lines ac and bd across center line mn (see Fig. 16) 1″ apart, this being the diameter of the bolt, and the proper thickness of the nut corresponding. The head of the bolt is somewhat thinner, being, as shown, $1\frac{3}{16}″$ thick. In order to determine the proper point at which the lines ab, cd, ef, and gh are drawn, draw a semicircle $1\frac{5}{8}″$ in diameter (the width of the nut across flats) with the intersection o of the lines ac and mn as the center; draw a tangent ij to this circle, perpendicular to the center line. Draw two other tangents to the circle, using the 60° triangle. The intersecting points i and j of the tangents will locate the lines ef and gh, e being the projection of i and g the projection of j on ac; the intersection of the tangents with the perpendicular ac will locate the lines ab and cd.

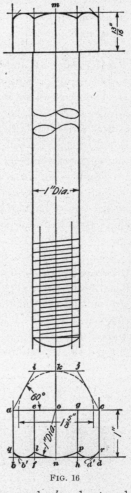

FIG. 16

To construct the curves which form the top of the nut draw a circular arc from o as a center, with a radius equal to the diameter of the bolt (in this case 1″), tangent to the perpendicular bd, which limits the thickness of the nut, until it intersects ef in l, and gh in p; find by trial a radius such that arcs can be struck from l to q, and from p to r, and be tangent to bd; the centers for these arcs must lie on lines parallel to the center line mn and half way between aq and el and gp and cr. Draw curves for the head of the bolt in same manner.

Instead of indicating the corners bd, Fig. 16, as parts of a spherical surface, they are often drawn as being parts of

a conical surface, the side of which forms an angle of 45°
with its axis.   Lines $q\,b'$ and $r\,d'$ are then drawn tangential
to the curves $q\,l$ and $r\,p$.   Fig. 23 is also drawn in this manner.   Where it is the purpose of representing a nut or head
in a conventional manner, it is a saving of time to omit
these additional lines.

54.   Figs. **11** and **12** show the conventional method of
representing a square-head bolt and nut.   Their curves
are constructed in much the same manner as those of the
hexagonal-head bolt, except that they are drawn with a
radius twice the thickness of the bolt.   Dimensions correspond to those given in Fig. **9**, except length, which is 6″;
the width of the head is $1\frac{5}{8}$″ across flats.

Complete information as to the construction of standard
bolt heads, nuts, screw heads, etc., is given in Fig. 64.
Any dimensions not given in the instructions referring to
Plate 1003 will be found there.

55.   Fig. **13** is a hexagonal-head capscrew; the head of
the capscrew is smaller than a corresponding hexagonal-
head bolt, being $1\frac{1}{4}$″ across flats.   The dimensions given
will be followed, and are standard dimensions for a bolt of
this size.   Curve of head is drawn by taking radius 2 times
diameter of bolt.

Fig. **14** represents a $\frac{1}{2}$″ 13-thread setscrew, $1\frac{3}{8}$″ long.
Head is $\frac{1}{2}$″ across flats, and the two curves on same are struck

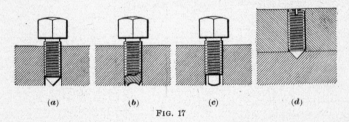

(a)   (b)   (c)   (d)

FIG. 17

with a radius equal to twice the diameter of screw.   Draw
the curves at neck of screw with a radius of $\frac{1}{8}$″.   The information needed for drawing the lower end is given in Fig. 64.

The form of setscrew shown in Fig. **14** is the one most in use. Some other forms are represented in Fig. **17**, in which (*a*) is called a **cone-point setscrew**, (*b*) a **cupped setscrew**, (*c*) a **round, pivot-point setscrew**, and (*d*) a **headless, cone-point setscrew**.

Figs. **9, 10, 11, 12,** and **13** are drawn to $\frac{1}{2}$ scale or 6″ = 1 ft., while Figs. **14, 15, 16, 17, 18, 19, 20,** and **22** are drawn full size.

56.   Fig. **15** represents a round-head, $\frac{14}{24}$ machine screw, $1\frac{3}{4}''$ long; 14 is the gauge of the body of the screw; 24 gives the number of threads per inch. The screw is drawn by drawing a center line and laying off the parts as shown. No. 14 gauge practically corresponds to $\frac{1}{4}''$, and measurements may be made with this as a basis; thickness of the head is $\frac{3}{16}''$; width of head is $\frac{7}{16}''$.

The outline of the head should be a compound curve, but on account of the small size of the view it is difficult to show it in this form; it will suffice if in its place a circular arc is drawn with a radius of $\frac{7}{32}''$.

57.   Fig. **16** is a fillister-head machine screw of the same dimensions as that shown in Fig. **15**. The head is $\frac{3}{16}''$ thick below the round and $\frac{23}{64}''$ in diameter. The radius of the round top is equal to the diameter of head.

58.   Fig. **17** is a machine screw of corresponding length and diameter, except that it has a flat head; thickness of head is $\frac{9}{64}''$; diameter of head, $\frac{15}{32}''$.

It will be noticed that the dimensions for length of screws are given under the head in Figs. **15** and **16,** and including head in Fig. **17**.

59.   Fig. **18** represents a cotter pin 1″ long and $\frac{1}{8}''$ in diameter. This pin is split and is put through the ends of bolts or studs to prevent nuts or washers working off. Make the eye $\frac{1}{4}''$ in diameter.

60.   Figs. **19** and **20** are conventional methods of representing round-head and flat-head wood screws. Dimensions previously given apply to these screws, except the gauge of body is No. 12, which approximately corresponds to $\frac{7}{32}''$. Diameters of heads of Figs. **19** and **20** are approximately $\frac{7}{16}''$ and $\frac{3}{8}''$, respectively. Make the straight parts of the screws $\frac{5}{8}''$ long, and the rounded points $\frac{1}{16}''$ thick.

61. Fig. **21** shows a $2''$ eyebolt, $4\frac{1}{2}$ threads to the inch, with a $3''$ hole in the eye and corresponding dimensions outside. This part is drawn to $\frac{1}{4}$ scale, or $3'' = 1$ ft.

62. Fig. **22** shows the representation of $\frac{1}{4}''$ lag bolt, $1\frac{5}{8}''$ long. Lag bolts have square heads. The head is $\frac{3}{8}''$ across flats and the curve drawn with a radius of $\frac{1}{2}''$. The body of bolt is drawn similar to Fig. **19**.

63. Figs **23** and **24** give conventional methods of representing keys drawn to $\frac{1}{2}$ scale or $6'' = 1$ ft.; they are plainly dimensioned and will need no detailed description of method of drawing them. These figures also indicate a convention quite frequently employed to show a section in a view other than the one the section should appear in, the little squares showing the depth of the keys and the shape of a cross-section.

64. Parts represented in Figs. **9** to **24** are standard parts which are seldom, if ever, drawn on detailed drawings. They are called for, however, in the title, and they are frequently shown in assembly drawings, in which case they will be drawn as represented, and with the principal dimensions only, if any, given.

Additional information on the construction of standard nuts and bolts, machine and wood screws, together with the standard gauges for Morse drills, and steam, gas, and water pipes are found at the end of this paper under Useful Tables.

INSTRUCTIONS AND DEFINITIONS

65. Before starting work on the next plate, further instructions and definitions are necessary.

Part Numbers.—When a detailed working drawing is completed, letters or numbers are placed near the parts delineated so that they may be easily identified, and this practice will be followed on all future plates, a number being placed near the part and enclosed by a circle $\frac{3}{8}''$ in

diameter, thus ①

Part numbers start at 1.   Be careful to place them at a point where they will not interfere with dimensions, center lines, or surface lines.   These part numbers will be referred to in the material list, as explained later.

66.   Pattern Numbers.—All machine details which are made from castings must first have a pattern, and it is common practice to have the draftsman call for these patterns, giving them the proper number by which they can be known and referred to.   The first time a part which requires a pattern is shown on a drawing, it will have a pattern number assigned to it, which will be the number of the drawing with a letter annexed, thus: Part 1, Plate 1004, is made of cast brass and its pattern number will be 1004–A.   This number serves as an immediate means of identification and gives any person who handles the pattern the number of drawing upon which all dimensions can be found.   This pattern number is called for in the material list of which an explanation follows.

67.   Material List. — All detailed working drawings have a list of materials placed at some convenient part of the drawing, which is a list of parts shown on the drawing, the number of parts necessary to complete the apparatus shown, the material from which they are made, and a note calling for patterns when they are necessary.   This material list is best placed above—and is practically an extension of—the title. The list is divided into six columns which, taken together, are 4″ wide, the same width as the main title previously described. Starting at the left-hand side, column 1 is made $\frac{1}{4}$″ wide and is the quantity column, showing the number of parts required in order to complete the part detailed; column 2 is made $1\frac{5}{8}$″ wide, and gives the common shop name of the part; column 3 is $\frac{1}{4}$″ wide, and shows the part number; column 4 is made 1″ wide, and shows the material from which the part is to be made; column 5 is made $\frac{5}{8}$″ wide, and is reserved for the word "pattern" when one is necessary; column 6 is made $\frac{1}{4}$″ wide, and contains the letter by which the pattern will be known when called for, it being preceded by the number of the drawing. It frequently happens that patterns made for one machine can be used to produce castings for another machine under construction. In such cases the pattern would be designated in the material list by the number and letter first assigned to it. It is not at all necessary to put a heading over these columns, as the use which is made of them soon fixes their object in the mind of the draftsman.

The material list is divided into sections by horizontal lines $\frac{3}{16}$″ apart. Standard details, such as machine screws, bolts, nuts, washers, keys, and similar parts, have part numbers assigned to them, but are seldom detailed on the drawing, the material list giving all the information that is necessary in order to supply them to the person who is to assemble the part.

The material list is best arranged in such a way that the lowest number is put at the bottom of the list. The reason for this is to permit the adding of another detail, if such should become necessary, or, in other words, placing the parts in this order in the title permits the extension upwards of the space occupied by the latter as desired, some titles being short (vertically) and others long, according as the machine drawn is more or less complicated.

68. Position of Views.—The main view or elevation once having been located, the right-hand view of object will

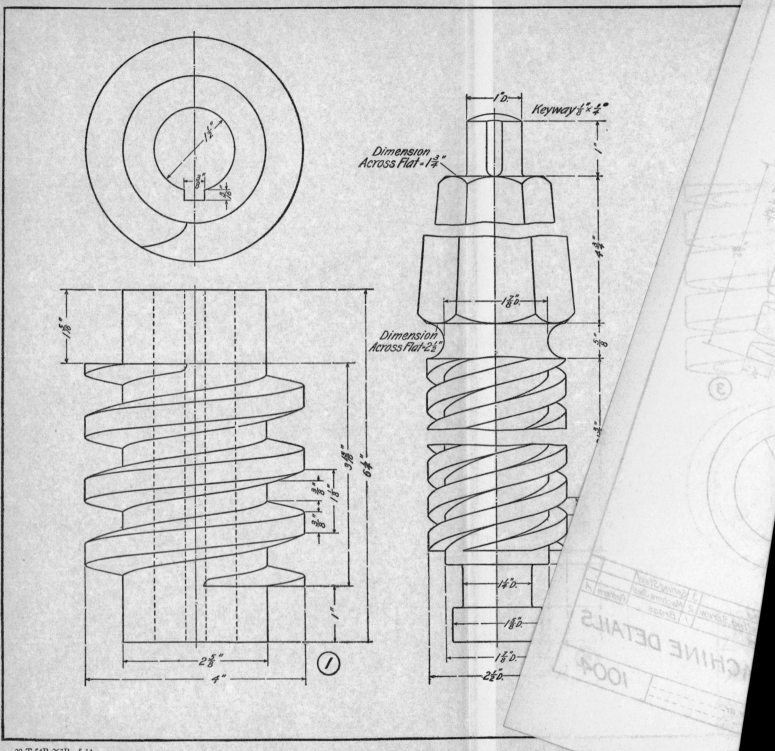

be shown at the right of the elevation, the top view at the top, bottom view at the bottom, etc. This method of location of views is technically known as *third-angle projection* and is more generally used than *first-angle projection*, which differs from it by having the right-hand view of the object placed on the left-hand side of the main plan, the bottom at the top, etc. An explanation as to the use of the first-angle and third-angle projection, is given fully in *Practical Projection*. Either plan may be used, but each drawing office has a standard practice which must be followed. In the plates which follow, third-angle projection is adopted as standard.

PLATE 1004, TITLE:

MACHINE DETAILS

69. This Plate is intended to give the student practice in drawing helical curves. In the previous plates screw threads have been represented by straight lines, and this conventional plan is followed whenever possible to save time. When, however, the dimensions of a threaded piece are large, especially when the pitch of the thread is steep and the scale used is large, the true projection of the screw thread is often drawn; this the draftsman should do with as little loss of time as possible. The necessary directions are given below for each of the three parts represented on this plate.

It is often difficult for a beginner to form a clear idea of the appearance of an object from a mechanical drawing, and there is, therefore, shown in Figs. 18, 19, and 20 half-tone reproductions of photographs of the parts represented by the drawing. The attention of the student is particularly called to the method of drawing the adjusting screw, **2,** it being broken at two points, in order to permit it to be drawn within the limits of the drawing.

70. Draw border lines and lines for the title as shown, allowing space above the title for the material list of the

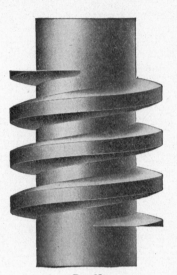

FIG. 18

FIG. 20

FIG. 19

three parts which are to be described and drawn. Do not letter the title until the drawing is completed. All the parts shown on this plate are to be drawn full size.

Part **1** is a single-threaded worm with a $1\frac{1}{2}''$ hole through it; its over-all length is $6\frac{1}{4}''$; the hub diameter is $2\frac{5}{8}''$, which is also the diameter of the worm at the bottom of the thread. The length of the threaded portion is $3\frac{15}{16}''$, the hub being $1''$ long at one end and $1\frac{5}{16}''$ long at the other end. The worm has a diameter of $4''$ over the outside of the threads.

The method of drawing the worm is as follows, referring to Fig. 21. Draw a center line $m\,n$, $3\frac{1}{2}''$ from the left-hand border line. Parallel to this line draw two other lines $p\,q$ and $r\,s$, each $2\frac{5}{8}'' \div 2 = 1\frac{5}{16}''$ from it; these lines determine the bottom of the thread, and also the diameter of the hub. Then draw two lines $t\,u$ and $v\,w$ parallel to the center line, and $4'' \div 2 = 2''$ from it; they determine the top of the thread.

Locate two points a and a' on the center line $6\frac{1}{4}''$ apart, a being $1\frac{3}{4}''$ from the lower border line. Through both of these points draw with the **T** square a perpendicular to the center line, thus defining the length of the hub. Locate two other points b' and b on the center line, one $1\frac{5}{16}''$ below a' and the other $1''$ above a. Through these points draw perpendiculars to $m\,n$; these lines are to limit the length of the threaded portion of the worm.

71. Now proceed to construct the thread. This will necessitate a number of construction lines being drawn that are not, however, to appear on the final tracing; they are made on the pencil drawing only. The pitch, that is, the distance between the top of one turn of the thread and the corresponding point on the next turn, is $1\frac{1}{8}''$, and since the length of the threaded portion of the worm is $3\frac{15}{16}''$, there will be $3\frac{15}{16}'' \div 1\frac{1}{8}'' = 3\frac{1}{2}$ turns of the thread; hence, the number of equal spaces representing the tops and bottoms of the thread is $3\frac{1}{2} \times 2 = 7$; therefore, divide the line $b\,b'$ into seven equal parts $b\,I$, $I\,II$, etc. The thread itself is to have approximately the shape of a **V** thread, except that

instead of making the angle x 60°, this angle is determined
from the pitch of the thread and the amount of flattening at
the top and bottom.   Referring to the Plate, the dimen-

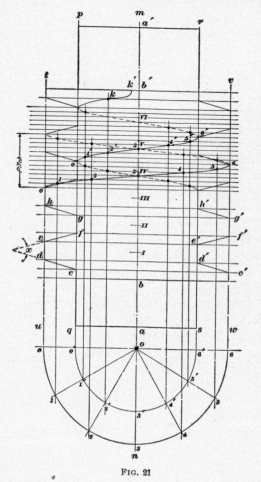

Fig. 21

sions show that the flattening at the top, and also at the
bottom, is $\frac{3}{8}''$; that is, de and fg, Fig. 21, are each equal
to $\frac{3}{8}''$.   Hence, on each side of the division points b, I, II,
III, etc., just obtained, lay off $\frac{3}{8}'' \div 2 = \frac{3}{16}''$, and draw cc',

dd', ee', ff', gg', etc., perpendicular to mn, which, intersecting with the lines tu, pq, rs, and vw locate the points defining the tops and bottoms of the thread. Draw the straight lines cd, ef, etc., and $c'd'$, $e'f'$, etc., as shown. Note herewith that the top of the thread on one side corresponds to the bottom of the thread on the other side of the center line.

72. To construct the curves defining the helixes, locate some point o on the center line, and with o as a center, draw two semicircles whose diameters are equal to the top and bottom diameters of the threads; that is, $4''$ and $2\frac{5}{8}''$, respectively. Divide the semicircles into any convenient number of equal parts. This is done by first dividing the exterior semicircle into the required number of parts, as 0, 1, 2, 3, 4, 5, and 6, then drawing radii to each point from o; this divides the interior semicircle into the same number of equal parts at the points $0'$, $1'$, $2'$, $3'$, $4'$, $5'$, and $6'$. The division of the circles is most quickly effected by the use of the 60° triangle. If, as in this particular case, six divisions are chosen for reasons now to be explained, the pitch must be divided into twice the number of equal parts that the semicircles have been divided into, that is, into 12 parts, in order to also delineate the rear part of the thread. As the pitch is $1\frac{1}{8}'' = \frac{18}{16}''$, these divisions are $\frac{18}{16}'' \div 12 = \frac{3}{32}''$ apart. The lines cc', dd', ee', ff', etc. are either $\frac{3}{16}''$ or $\frac{3}{8}''$ apart, and those that are $\frac{3}{8}''$ apart already have the distance between them halved by the points I, II, III, etc.; hence, these divisions can be utilized at once, and it is only necessary to halve them again to get the required 12 divisions. Draw perpendiculars to mn through the division points. From points 1, 2, 3, 4, 5, and $1'$, $2'$, $3'$, $4'$, $5'$, of the semicircles, draw lines to intersect the aforesaid perpendiculars. The intersections are points of the helixes, those made with lines 1–1, 2–2, 3–3, 4–4, 5–5, belonging to the top of the thread, those made with lines $1'$–$1'$, $2'$–$2'$, $3'$–$3'$, $4'$–$4'$, $5'$–$5'$, belonging to the bottom of the thread, as shown in Fig. 21. Through the points which have thus been located, draw a curve, as shown, using for this purpose the irregular curve. The remaining outlines of the thread can be drawn in the same manner; but an easier and quicker method is to cut a curve, of the same shape as those already drawn, out of bristol board or cardboard and use it as a templet. It will be noticed that the part of the curves between points *2* and *4*, and *2'* and *4'*, respectively, is very flat; it is so nearly a straight line that it may be so considered and drawn, so that the irregular curve will have to be used only to delineate the parts *0–1–2*, *0'–1'–2'*, *4–5–6*, and *4'–5'–6'* of the helix. The student will do well to draw the straight portions of the helixes first, and to employ in doing so his two triangles in the manner shown in *Geometrical Drawing*, the lines being parallel, and then to join on the curved portions.

Draw two other lines (see Plate) parallel to the center line and $1\frac{1}{2}'' \div 2 = \frac{3}{4}''$ from it; these lines will be dotted and determine the location of the hole through the hub.

73. The top view of the worm is shown above the figure just constructed, and consists mainly of circles, the center one showing the hole, the next one the diameter of the hub, and the outer one the outside diameter of the screw. This view is located with its center on the extended center line of the lower view, letting the center of the concentric circles be $2\frac{1}{4}''$ below the upper border line. When the thread is cut in the lathe it runs out, on both ends naturally, into thin edges which are afterwards rounded off more bluntly. This is shown conventionally by the curves in the plan and elevation; see $k\,k'$, Fig. 21.

A keyway $\frac{3}{16}''$ deep and $\frac{3}{8}''$ wide is cut through the central part of the worm in order to keep it from turning on the shaft on which it will be placed. This keyway is plainly shown in the plan, and is indicated in the elevation by dotted lines.

74. Part **2** on Plate 1004 is a triple-threaded, adjusting screw with a tapered hexagonal head, and is drawn full size.

It is also shown broken at two points, since if shown in its full length, a smaller scale would be necessary.

Draw a center line parallel to and 9″ from the left-hand border line. The method of constructing the screw is the same as that shown in connection with the worm, except that the thread is square instead of V - shaped. The pitch or distance between corresponding points of the same thread is $1\frac{7}{8}''$; the depth of the thread is $\frac{5}{16}''$, and the width of the thread at base and root is $\frac{5}{16}''$. Three separate curves are constructed, there being three separate threads. (If the screw had been a double or a quadruple one the number of divisions chosen for the semicircles would properly have been 8, for

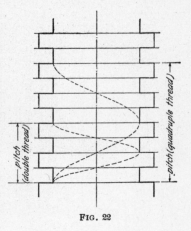

FIG. 22

in laying out the tops and bottoms of the threads one would have obtained already 4 or 8, respectively, of the required divisions of the pitch, as shown in the accompanying sketch, Fig. 22, where the dotted lines indicate the paths of the two threads.) A templet can be made as before, after one of the threads has been fully constructed.

In order to properly construct the tapered hexagonal head, it should be noticed (see Plate 1004) that the dimension given is $1\frac{3}{4}''$ across flats at a point 1″ from the end of the adjusting screw, the rounded top portion not being considered in dimensioning. Locate the point c on the center line, Fig. 23, 3″ below the upper border line, and draw through it a perpendicular $a\,b$. With the point c as a center, draw a semicircle $1\frac{3}{4}''$ in diameter, this being the dimension across flats, and using the 60° triangle and T square, draw tangents to the semicircle to locate points $a, b, x,$ and y; through the points x and y draw lines parallel to center line and intersecting $a\,b$. These points determine the points in which the lines defining the edges of hexagonal head intersect $a\,b$.

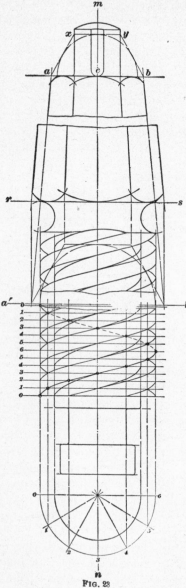

FIG. 23

To determine the proper taper, draw a line $a'\,b'$, Fig. 23, $4\frac{3}{4}''$ (see Plate) from and parallel to $a\,b$, and proceed as before, in the present instance drawing a semicircle on the line $a'\,b'$, with a diameter of $2\frac{1}{2}''$, that being the distance across the lower sides of the flats. Find the points of intersection in the same manner as the points of intersection at top are determined, and corresponding to a, x, y, and b. The tapered portion being so long that it cannot be conveniently shown upon the drawing, it is broken; consequently, the lines that have been penciled will not be fully drawn, the top portion only of the tapered lines being drawn.

In order to draw the lower portion, locate the line $r\,s$ perpendicular to the center line and at some convenient point, for instance $2\frac{5}{8}''$ below $a\,b$. Project the points already located for the lower portion of the hexagonal portion of the adjusting screw; then draw lines through these points parallel to the tapering lines already determined for the top portion.

The methods of constructing curves at the head and base of this hexagonal portion of this screw will be the same as those used in the preceding plate in laying out the hexagonal bolts and nuts.

75. Part **3** on Plate 1004 is a helical spring, drawn full size. It is made of $\frac{1}{2}''$ square steel wound around a $2''$ mandrel in such a manner that $\frac{1}{4}''$ space remains between the turns for the play of the spring. The curves formed by the edges of the twisted steel bar are helixes, as in a screw thread, and have a pitch equal to the height of the bar plus the clearance, or $\frac{1}{2}'' + \frac{1}{4}'' = \frac{3}{4}''$. To draw the spring proceed in a manner similar to that employed in drawing the worm, laying out, Fig. 24, the top and bottom lines, $g\,h$, $k\,l$, $o\,p$, etc. of the coil, the distance $h\,l$ being $\frac{1}{2}''$, $l\,p$ being $\frac{1}{4}''$, $p\,r$ being $\frac{1}{2}''$, etc., and then constructing the helixes. The latter are very flat, and it will be sufficient to determine just one point of the curves on each side near the extreme right and left, the rest being indicated by straight lines.

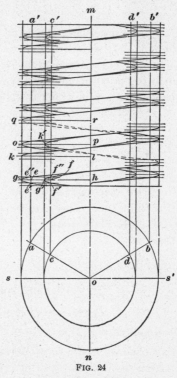

FIG. 24

To determine these points, draw in the plan, the center of which is located $4\frac{7}{16}''$ above the lower border line, two radii $o\,a$ and $\varrho\,b$, Fig. 24, with a

30° triangle, and draw parallels $a\,a'$, $c\,c'$, $d\,d'$, and $b\,b'$ to the center line $m\,n$ from the intersections of the radii with the circles. Since the angles $a\,o\,s$ and $b\,o\,s'$ are $30° = \frac{30}{360} = \frac{1}{12}$ of a circle, the pitch would be divided into 12 equal parts, were the helixes drawn exactly correct. Hence, on each side of the top and bottom lines of the coil lay off points e', e'', f', f'', etc., the distances $e\,e'$, $e\,e''$, etc., being $\frac{1}{12}$ of the pitch, or in this case, $\frac{3}{4}'' \div 12 = \frac{1}{16}''$. Draw the curves $e'\,g\,e''$, $f'g'f''$, etc. freehand, making them look well and uniform in outline. Do the same on the right-hand extremities of the helixes and connect the proper curves by straight lines, as shown.

76. This Plate serves to give practice in representing helixes. It would not be bad practice, however, to represent the curves wholly by straight lines, especially if the drawing must be quickly made, and particularly in the case of parts **1** and **3,** in which the curves are very flat. In the case of part **2,** the substitution of straight lines for the curves would look somewhat awkward on account of the large pitch.

In a hurried drawing, one would then perhaps draw this part to a smaller scale, when the substitution of straight lines for the curves would be less objectionable; or the thread may be represented in the conventional form shown in Fig. **1,** Plate 1003, and a note added calling for a triple thread.

PLATE 1005, TITLE:

HAND WHEEL AND PULLEY

77. The objects to be drawn on this Plate are shown in half-tone reproductions of photographs, Figs. 25 and 26. Attention is called to the relative size of the hand wheel, part **1** on Plate 1005, and the pulley, part **2.** The latter, it will be noted, is much larger than the former, but appears smaller in the drawing, being drawn to $\frac{1}{4}$ scale, while the hand wheel is drawn full size. This plate affords an illus-

tration of a very common practice of showing standard parts on a very much reduced scale, while those less commonly used are drawn full size or as nearly so as may be possible.

It will also be noticed that a third part called for in the title is not shown on the drawing; this is a set-

FIG. 25

screw $\frac{5}{8}''$ in diameter, 11 threads to the inch, a common and commercial article, which is fully understood from

FIG. 26

the description in the bill of material given thus :
" $\frac{5}{8}''$–11 setscrew."

78. On this Plate finish marks are introduced, being
indicated by the letter f, showing that the surfaces are to be
machine finished where the marks appear.

Where it is desired to show a finish for a portion of a
surface only, as on the rim of the hand wheel, the finished
portion is limited by lines between which the finish line is
drawn, as shown on the right of the lower figure representing a sectional view of the hand wheel.

79. It is also frequently desirable or necessary to show
some portion of an object more in detail than is necessary
on the rest of the figure; this is illustrated in the cross-
section of the pulley at the point GH and drawn full
size below. A section of this sort when not shown as
a regular part of a drawing, may be put at any convenient
place on the sheet, near to main views of the part drawn,
if possible.

80. On the plan (top view) of parts **1** and **2,** cross-
sections of the arms are indicated at points near the hub and
rim in the hand wheel and midway between hub and rim in
the pulley; these sections show that the arms are oval
in shape, the thicknesses being given in the lower views—
$\frac{3}{8}''$ in the hand wheel and $\frac{5}{8}''$ in the pulley.

To draw the Plate proceed as follows: Starting with
part **1,** draw a horizontal center line mn, Fig. 27, $5''$ from
the upper border line, and a vertical center line pq, $4\frac{1}{2}''$ from
the left-hand border line. With the point o of the intersection of these two center lines as a center, draw a circle
$1\frac{5}{8}''$ in diameter, showing the end view of the hub; next
draw a circle $1\frac{3}{4}''$ in diameter; this indicates the enlarged
portion of the hub where the arms join it. Next draw a
square $\frac{5}{8}''$ on each side, whose center corresponds with the
center of the hub; this indicates the end view of the hole
that is put through the hub. Draw the external outline

of the hand wheel, which is a circle $7\frac{1}{4}''$ in diameter, and then the internal outline, a circle $5\frac{1}{4}''$ in diameter.   Then

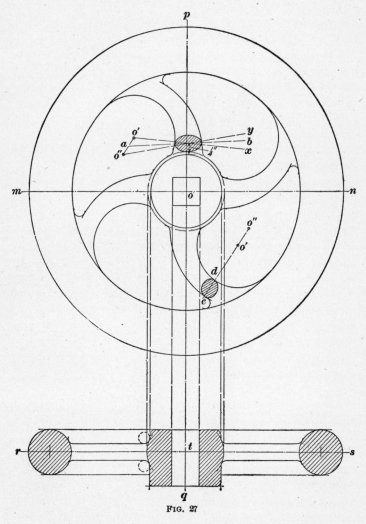

FIG. 27

draw the arms, which are made up of circular arcs whose centers are located by giving their distances from the center lines. Leave the plan for the present and proceed to draw the lower view, which is a section taken on the center line *m n*.

The lower view is what is called a *conventional section*, and the sectioning indicates that the material is cast iron; this is verified by reference to the bill of materials. The rim is cut on the horizontal center line, and so is the square hole in the hub, but the hub itself is represented as being cut on a line passing between and free of the arms. This is done to avoid drawing the curves that would result in cutting the arms by a true central section, which would entail useless labor. Moreover, the conventional section allows the round outline of the hub to be shown at its enlarged central portion between the arms.

Draw a horizontal center line *r s*, Fig. 27, $2\frac{3}{8}''$ from the bottom border line. On this center line lay off to the right and left of the point of intersection *t* with the vertical center line *p q*, $7\frac{1}{4}'' \div 2 - 1'' \div 2 = 3\frac{1}{8}''$, locating the centers of the circles representing the sections of the rim. Draw horizontal lines tangent to the $1''$ circles; lay off from the upper line $1\frac{1}{4}''$ downwards, the length of the hub, and draw the bottom line of the hub. From the upper figure or plan carry down vertical projection lines representing the square hole; also draw similar lines tangent to the circles representing the hub. Next lay off $\frac{3}{8}'' \div 2 = \frac{3}{16}''$ each side of the center line *r s*, and draw the horizontal lines, limiting the thickness of the arms.

81. Round Corners and Fillets.—The figures are now completed except the sections of the arms in the plan, or upper figure, the curves representing the enlarged portion of hub in the lower figure, and the various small circular arcs rounding off the corners. The latter will be drawn first, using the radii given on the Plate. Sharp corners are always avoided in machinery, especially in castings, unless called for by special reasons. Corners are, therefore, rounded off. In the case of concave corners the patternmaker often resorts to the use of some plastic material, such as putty, strips of leather, or even lead to fill in

the corner so as to round it.   From this practice the rounding out of a concave corner is called a **fillet**, and this term
has come to be applied to the little circular arc used by
the draftsman to represent it.

82.   Next draw the rounded outlines of the enlarged portion of the hub.   Through the points of intersection with
the horizontal center line *r s*, and the tangents to the circles
in the plan defining the hub, draw circular arcs tangent to
the fillets, circles joining the arm to the hub, as shown in
Fig. 27.   The drawing of these circular arcs will require a
little trying before the proper radius is found; the centers
lie on *r s*, of course.

Lastly, draw the cross-sections of the arms in the upper
figure.   As said above, the arms are elliptical or oval in
section.   They are so, however, only the greater part of
their length; at their ends they are smoothly joined to the
rim and hub respectively, the ovals thus gradually flaring
out to run over into the surfaces of the rim and hub.   This
joining need not be shown further than indicated by the
fillets; the patternmaker will know how to proceed.   The
cross-sections are taken in the portion of the arm where they
are sure to be truly oval.

The section in the lower part of the figure is taken
on a line *c d* (see Fig. 27) passing through the centers *o'*
and *o''* of both circles outlining the shape of the arms.
The cutting plane is thus perpendicular to both these
curved outlines.   The other section in the upper part of
the figure near the hub is taken $\frac{1}{4}''$ from the hub (where
it is sure to be truly oval).   This section cannot be perpendicular to both outlining circles, as the cutting-plane line
cannot be made to pass through both centers.   Therefore,
a cutting plane *a b* is chosen midway between a plane *o' x*
passing through center *o'* and a plane *o'' y* passing through
the center *o''*.

83.   It will be noticed that for some circles the radii are
given, and for others the diameter.   No general rule can be

made to apply to the choice of dimensions of this sort
except the general one that dimensions that will be of service to the machinist will be given in diameters, and those
that will be of service to the patternmaker should be given
as a radius; machinists use calipers to determine correct
diameters, while the patternmaker lays out his work from a

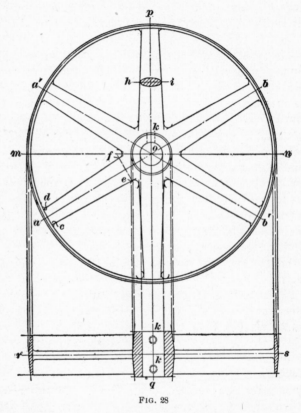

Fig. 28

radius dimension.   It will be noticed also that the dimension
for the bore of the pulley is written in a manner different
from the others; that is, it is not indicated by means of
a line with arrowheads on both ends.   The word *bore*
indicates that the pulley pattern provides for a hole
much smaller, so that it can be bored out for smaller

shafts, if so desired. The dimension given ($1\frac{3}{4}''$) is for the machinist.

84. Part **2** is very similar in shape to part **1,** except that it is much larger, that the rim is flat—because it is intended to carry a driving belt—and that the arms have straight outlines. Being much like the hand wheel otherwise, the pulley is drawn in much the same manner. The scale used is $3'' = 1$ ft.

Locate the horizontal center lines $m\,n$ and $r\,s$ (see Fig. 28) $3\frac{3}{8}''$ and $7\frac{1}{4}''$, respectively, from the upper border line, and the vertical center line $p\,q$ $4\frac{3}{8}''$ from the right-hand border line. Draw circles about o representing the outside and inside of the rim and hub. The outside of the rim will be represented by two circles, an outer one $20''$ in diameter giving the outline of rim at the center, and an inner one with a radius $\frac{1}{8}''$ smaller giving the outline at the edge. Making the rim higher in the center is for the purpose of keeping the belt from slipping off. The amount of rise in the center, that is, the difference between the radius at the edge and that at the middle, or what is the same thing, the difference between the thickness of the rim at those two points is called the *crown* of the rim, which is seen from the small section at the right-hand lower corner of the drawing to be $\frac{5}{16}'' - \frac{3}{16}''$ $= \frac{1}{8}''$. The inside of the rim is perfectly straight and appears therefore in the plan as a single circle drawn with a radius $\frac{5}{16}''$ smaller than that of the outermost circle. The outside of the hub is also represented by two circles, $3''$ and $3\frac{1}{4}''$ in diameter. The diameter of the bore is $1\frac{3}{4}''$.

Now draw the arms. Lay out the center lines $a\,b$, $a'\,b'$ of the four arms not vertical, by means of the 60° triangle. They are tapered, and the small end of each at the rim is $1\frac{3}{8}''$ across on tangent to the inside circle of the rim; the large end is $2''$ across at a point $2\frac{3}{8}''$ from the center. By these dimensions the taper of the arms is established. Hence, draw a perpendicular to the center line of an arm, tangent to the inside circle of the rim and lay off on it points c and d $1\frac{3}{8}'' \div 2 = \frac{11}{16}''$ from the center line on each

side. Draw another perpendicular $2\frac{3}{8}''$ from the center and lay off on it points e and f $1''$ from the center line. Draw the lines ce and df. The limiting lines of the arms are joined at the inner ends by circles of $\frac{5}{16}''$ radius, lines of adjacent arms being tangent to them. The outer ends of the arms are joined to the rim by fillets of $\frac{5}{16}''$ radius. Draw in all these fillets. Draw the oval section of the arm at hi, Fig. 28, midway between center of pulley and rim.

Next draw the lower figure, a sectional elevation, by projecting from the plan the various diameters of rim, hub and hole, and then laying out the width of the rim, the length of the hub, and the thickness of arms, exactly as was done in the case of the hand wheel.

Note again that only the hub and rim are shown in cross-section on lower view, as it is common practice not to show the arms or any part of them in cross-section, even though a cutting plane be passed through them. Notice also that although the web formed around the hub by joining the arms by fillets is intersected by the cutting plane, it is not shown in the section, the outer lines of the hub being drawn straight across.

There should be no difficulty in drawing the large detail section GH of the rim.

The holes k, k indicate the positions of the two $\frac{5}{8}''$ set-screws mentioned in the bill of materials, which fasten the pulley to the shaft. The full circles indicating these holes are surrounded by circles in dotted lines, this being the conventional method to indicate that the holes are tapped.

When finishing the title and bill of materials, note that part **3** is called for, but is not shown on the drawing, it being a standard piece.

Part **1** requires a pattern to be made. Hence, the pattern is designated by the number of the drawing, and being the first on the list in the bill of materials is marked *1005–A*. This fact is indicated in the bill of materials by the word *Pattern*, and being the first on the list it is marked *A*.

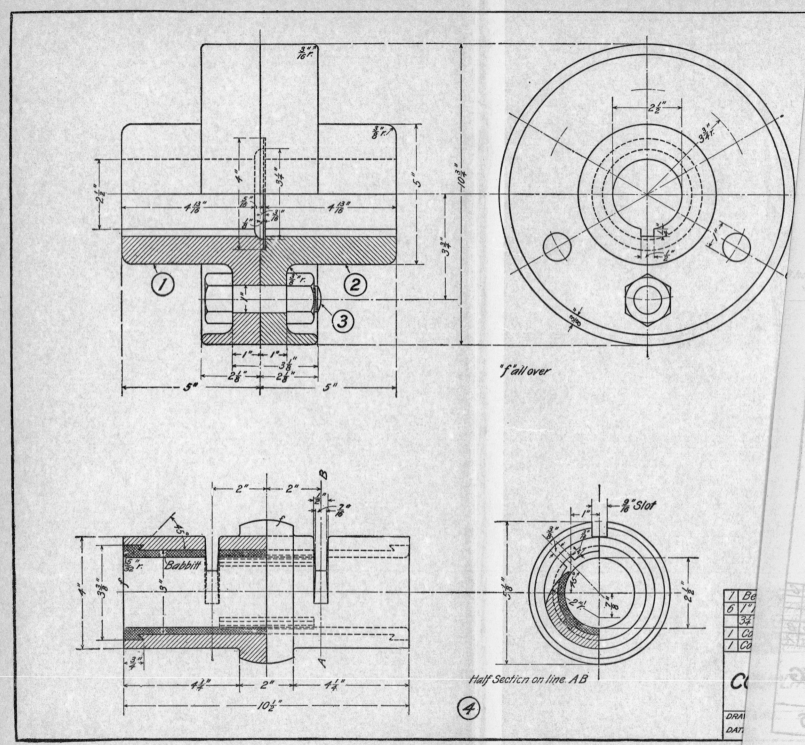

"f" all over

Half Section on line AB

④

The pattern itself is designated by the number of the drawing and the letter given it, hence it is marked *1005–A*.

Part **2** can be cast from another pattern drawn from specifications furnished on drawing numbered 999 and marked *Pattern E* in the bill of materials. Therefore, in the space left for the word " pattern " in the bill of materials and on the same line as the piece referred to, insert *999–E*, thus indicating that a new pattern is not required.

PLATE 1006, TITLE:

COUPLING AND BEARING

85. The upper figure shows an elevation and side view of a flange coupling used to connect two lengths of shafting. For example, suppose that in a shop or factory there are many machines to be driven from an engine. A belt is carried from the driving pulley of the engine to a pulley on a shaft overhead, which in turn is supported in bearings. This shaft is strung along the whole length of the shop over all the machines to be driven, and pulleys are carried on it from which belts transmit motion to the various machines. It is evident that such a long shaft cannot be made in a single piece and, therefore, it is put up in certain lengths that are connected by couplings. Such a coupling invariably consists of three principal parts, one that is securely fastened to the end of one shaft, a second that is similarly fastened to the end of the other shaft to be connected to the first, and a third part consisting of means to firmly fasten the first two parts together.

In the flange coupling drawn on Plate 1006 these three principal parts are the flange numbered **1,** the flange numbered **2,** and the bolts, of which there are six, numbered **3.** The flanges are fastened to the shafts by keys, which prevent them turning thereon, and the bolts in turn fasten the two flanges together, so that the whole structure becomes a solid piece. The coupling is intended for two $2\frac{1}{2}''$ shafts, and both flanges are, therefore, bored out to that size.

The lower part of the elevation shows the coupling in cross-section with a bolt in position. The upper part shows the external view of the coupling, the dotted lines indicating the position of the raised boss on part **1** which fits into the recess in part **2**, recess and boss insuring true alinement when the two parts which have been previously keyed to the shaft are bolted together.

The two parts of the coupling are first bored and then faced up on the abutting surfaces; they are then clamped together, and the keyway is cut. In the side view it will be noticed that but one bolt is shown, and but two bolt holes in addition, a note being added stating that there are six holes equally spaced; this is common practice on a working drawing, repeated parts being indicated only and not drawn

FIG. 29

in full. An idea of the appearance of the coupling when finished will be got from the half-tone view in Fig. 29.

86. To begin, draw the center lines: a horizontal center line $m\,n$, Fig. 31, $3\frac{1}{4}''$ (full size) from the upper border line across the whole sheet, serving for both the left-hand and right-hand views; a vertical center line $p\,q$, $4\frac{1}{2}''$ from the left-hand border line, representing the joint of the two halves of the coupling; and a third center line $r\,s$, drawn vertically $5\frac{3}{8}''$ from the

FIG. 30

right-hand border line for the right-hand figure, or side view. The scale to be used is $6'' = 1$ ft.

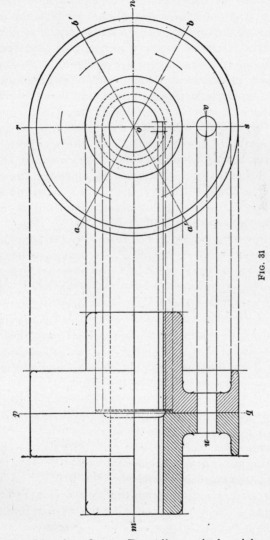

FIG. 31

Draw the side view first. Describe a circle with a radius of $2\frac{1}{2}'' \div 2 = 1\frac{1}{4}''$ from the intersection o of the center lines mn and rs as a center; this represents the bore for the shaft. Next draw in the keyway, $\frac{1}{2}''$ wide and $\frac{1}{4}''$ deep. Two circles described from the same center and having radii of $5'' \div 2 = 2\frac{1}{2}''$ and $10\frac{3}{4}'' \div 2 = 5\frac{3}{8}''$, represent the side view of the hub and the outside of the flanges, respectively. By reference to the lower half of the elevation it will be seen that the flanges are recessed, leaving a rim of only $\frac{3}{8}''$ in thickness. Hence, with a radius of $5\frac{3}{8}'' - \frac{3}{8}''$ $= 5''$ and a center o, draw a circle concentric with the outside circle, to represent the inside edge of the rim. By means of the 60° triangle draw the remaining center lines ab, $a'b'$ of the bolt holes and intersect them by circular arcs having a radius of $3\frac{3}{4}''$. Draw in the bolt holes in the lower half of the figure by drawing circles $1''$ in diameter. Draw the end view of a nut on the middle one of the lower three bolt-hole centers, according to directions given in connection with Plate 1003.

The elevation is now to be drawn. On either side of the vertical center line pq lay off $5''$, the length of hubs of the coupling, and draw vertical lines through the points obtained. Lay off similarly $2\frac{1}{8}''$ and $1''$ on either side of the vertical center line and draw vertical lines to represent the edges of the flanges and the thickness of the webs of the flanges, respectively; the latter lines may, however, be quite short, as they appear only in the lower half of the figure. Now carry over from the side view, by means of the T square, two horizontal lines tangent to the outside circle intersecting the vertical lines limiting the width of the flanges. Carry over similarly horizontal lines tangent to the circle representing the side view of the hub. These will intersect the vertical lines limiting the lengths of the hubs; the lower horizontal will also intersect the verticals that limit the thickness of the webs of the flanges. A tangent carried over horizontally from the bottom point of the circle representing the outer outline of the rim will also intersect the verticals in the elevation completing the sectional outline of the coupling. Carry over the horizontal center line uv of the bolt from the end view and complete the drawing of the bolt in the usual manner. Round off all sharp corners, using radii as given on the plate. The right-hand half of the coupling has a circular recess 4″ in diameter and $\frac{3}{16}$″ deep bored in it; draw this by laying off on either side of the horizontal center line mn, $4″ \div 2 = 2″$, and on the right of the vertical center line pq (or, what is the same thing, the face of the flange), lay off $\frac{3}{16}$″, and draw the horizontals and a vertical, respectively, through the points. Represent this recess in the side view also, by drawing a dotted circle with a $4″ \div 2 = 2″$ radius. Into the recess of the right-hand half of the coupling just drawn fits a boss projecting $\frac{1}{8}$″ from the face of the left-hand half of the coupling; represent this by drawing a vertical line $\frac{1}{8}$″ to the right of the vertical center line pq. The verticals representing the bottom of the recess and face of the boss are dotted in the upper half of the figure, as they are hidden there. The left-hand half of coupling has also a circular recess turned in, smaller in diameter than the boss, namely $3\frac{1}{4}$″; it is $\frac{5}{16}$″ deep measured from the face of the boss. Draw in this recess and round its bottom corners; also represent it in the side view by a dotted circle of proper diameter. Next carry over the top line of the shaft bore horizontally from and tangent to the circle representing the bore in the end view; this line must be dotted in the upper half of the elevation, as it is hidden from view. Finally carry over the bottom lines of the shaft bore and the keyway, shown in full in the lower half of the elevation. Put in the section lining and dimensions.

87. Part 4 on this drawing is a self-alining, self-oiling, dynamo bearing for a $2\frac{1}{2}$″ shaft. In Fig. 30 a half-tone reproduction of a photograph of this piece is given to enable the student to form a correct idea of its actual appearance. A shaft bearing, generally speaking, is a stationary machine part having a hole into which fits, and in which turns, a movable cylindrical piece, the shaft. Upon a shaft are carried other machine parts designed to turn with it, as, for instance, the armature in a dynamo. There are generally two bearings to a shaft of a machine, one on each side of the part carried by the shaft. In order that the shaft may turn freely, the two bearings must be exactly

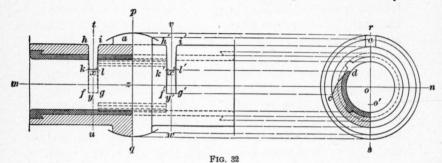

FIG. 32

in line all the time. To insure this against any possible distortion of the machine frame or bending of the shaft, bearings are often made, as the one here represented, self-alining; that is, they are so located in the frame that they

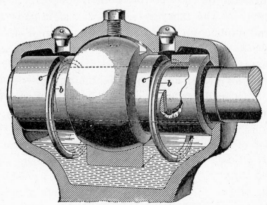

FIG. 33

can adjust themselves to any slight variations. The bearing here shown has for the purpose a spherical* boss a, called

---

*Strictly speaking, the boss is not spherical, being only a part of a sphere. However, for practical purposes, it is very convenient to refer to any part of a sphere, except half a sphere (hemisphere) as a sphere or ball, and this practice will be followed throughout this paper in cases of this kind, unless some other designation is considered advisable.

the *ball*, Fig. 32, the center of which rests in a correspondingly hollow seat, called the *socket*, in the machine frame,
shown in Fig. 33.   As it rests there, movable of course,
friction would be liable to cause the bearing to turn with
the shaft.   To prevent this, a slot is cut across the boss
at *a*, Fig. 32, into which fits a pin projecting from the stationary frame, Fig. 33.

When two surfaces move, one on the other, they
necessarily rub each other, producing friction, and this
not only consumes power, but creates heat and is liable to injure the surfaces.   The amount of friction varies
between different materials, certain combinations offering
less friction than others.   It has been found that steel
shafts move with a comparatively small amount of friction on a softer metal.   So bearings are usually lined
with Babbitt or similar material.   The great expedient,
however, to reduce friction, is lubricating the surfaces
with oil, which lubrication must be kept up constantly.
To reduce the necessary labor of the attendant and to
insure constant regular lubrication, bearings are often
made self-oiling; that is, are provided with means by
which the oiling is done automatically.   In the bearing
shown this is done by hanging over the shaft loose rings *b*
that dip into a reservoir of oil, as indicated in Fig. 33.
When the shaft turns the rings turn with it by adhe-
sion and carry enough oil from the reservoir to the top
of the shaft to properly oil it.   In order that the rings
may rest on the top of the shaft, the bearing proper
must have slots *c c* cut into it, as shown in Figs. 32 and 33,
and on the plate.   The bearing shown is made of cast iron
and is babbitted inside, the Babbitt being held in place
by dovetailed circular recesses at the ends, shown in the
left-hand half of the elevation, and longitudinal recesses
$\frac{3}{8}''$ wide and $\frac{3}{16}''$ deep, shown in the side view; the bab-
bitting is ordinarily done on a mandrel smaller in diameter
than the finished bore of the bearing.   After being babbitted the bearing is accurately bored and finally finished
on the outside.

The left-hand half of both views is shown in section, the right-hand half giving the external view. Oil grooves are not shown in the drawing and are omitted from all working drawings when regular shop practice is to be followed, only being added to drawing if special instructions are to be given.

88. In delineating the bearing, which is drawn half size, proceed in much the same manner as with the coupling. Draw the center line $m\,n$ (Fig. 32) $2\frac{5}{8}''$ from bottom border line and two vertical center lines, one $p\,q$ $4\frac{5}{8}''$ from the left-hand border line for the elevation, and another $r\,s$ $10\frac{3}{4}''$ from the left-hand border line for the side view. Begin with the end view, completing it as far as possible, before starting the other view. Thus draw circles with o as a center, $5\frac{1}{8}''$, $4''$, $3\frac{3}{8}''$, $3''$, and $2\frac{1}{2}''$ in diameter to represent, respectively, the circular outlines of the spherical boss in the center of the bearing, of the body of the bearing, of the outside of the Babbitt lining, and the bore. Next lay off $\frac{7}{8}''$ from o downwards and draw, with o' as a center, a circular arc with a radius of $2''$. This circular arc cuts into the circles representing the body of the bearing and the bore at c and d. Round off the sharp corner at d. Draw the $\frac{9}{16}''$ slot on top of the rounded boss. Draw the longitudinal recesses for the Babbitt $\frac{3}{8}''$ wide and $\frac{3}{16}''$ deep, their centers 45° from the horizontal center line $m\,n$. Section-line the Babbitt and bearing section. This view is now complete with the exception of one circle, namely, that representing the edge of the boss, the radius of which will have to be obtained from the other view, now to be drawn. Carry over horizontally from the end view the lines limiting the diameters of the boss, bearing, Babbitt lining, and bore, tangent to the circles representing these parts in the end view. Lay off right and left from the center line $p\,q$ the various distances limiting the length of the body of the bearing, the boss in the middle, and the lengths of the dovetails of the Babbitt lining. Likewise, lay off $2''$ on either side of $p\,q$ for the center lines $t\,u$ and $v\,w$ of the oil-ring slots. Lay these out next. It will be noticed that they are narrower inside, near the shaft by $\frac{1}{16}''$ than at the surface of the bearing. Carry over from the side view a horizontal line through d, which will intersect $t\,u$ and $v\,w$ at x and x', respectively. Lay out the bottom width of the slots at this point, $\frac{7}{16}''$, thereby finding the points k, l, k', and l'. Carry over a horizontal from the side view through c, which intersects $t\,u$ and $v\,w$ at y and y', respectively. Lay off the width of the slots at this point, $\frac{1}{2}''$. Draw verticals from the points f, g, f', and g' to the upper limiting line of the bearing and intersecting it; from the points of intersection h, i, h', and i' draw lines to the points k, l, k', and l'; also, lines $f\,k$, $g\,l$, $f'\,k'$, and $g'\,l'$. With z, the intersection of the center lines $m\,n$ and $p\,q$, as a center, draw circular arcs limiting the outside of the spherical boss, the radius being obtained by carrying over from the side view or by measurement, $5\frac{1}{8}'' \div 2 = 2\frac{9}{16}''$. The arcs intersect the verticals limiting the length of the boss in points which finally give the radius for a circle to be drawn in the side view to represent the edge of the round boss. Put in the section lining, using the proper lines for cast iron and Babbitt. Notice that the boss is section-lined all through in the bottom half of the figure, but only up to the bottom line of the slot a in the top half, showing that the slot runs all the way through the boss.

In completing the drawing, fill in the title and note that two patterns are necessary for the coupling, pattern for **1**, being A, and for **2**, B. Also note that six 1" bolts $3\frac{1}{4}''$ long with nuts are required and are called for in title or bill of material.

The part numbered **4** is made of cast iron, from pattern C, the Babbitt afterward being melted and poured about the mandrel previously spoken of, this mandrel being held in position inside of the casting while the bearing is being babbitted.

PLATE 1007, TITLE:

COMMUTATOR

89. This Plate shows the detail drawings and the assembly drawing of an electric railway-motor commutator.

It is composed of a shell, part **1**, a clamping ring, part **2**, these two parts being drawn together by eight bolts, thereby clamping the 100 commutator bars shown by the part **3**. The latter are separated from each other by mica insulation sheets .03″ thick and are also insulated both from the shell and the clamping ring by mica rings

FIG. 34

$\frac{3}{32}$″ thick. An idea of the general appearance of the commutator may be had from Fig. 34.

90. The commutator shell, part **1**, is to be shown in the right-hand upper corner of the Plate by means of an end view and a sectional elevation. Eight holes for the clamping bolts are symmetrically arranged in the manner shown and are to be countersunk. The shell is made of steel, cast from pattern *1007–A*. A keyway is cut in one end of the shell, extending into it for a distance of $2\frac{1}{2}$″, being $\frac{3}{8}$″ deep and $\frac{5}{8}$″ wide. In the sectional elevation no outlines of hidden parts are shown, except such as may serve to make the drawing clearer. This is always desirable when lines unnecessarily complicate the drawing without adding any information of value regarding the

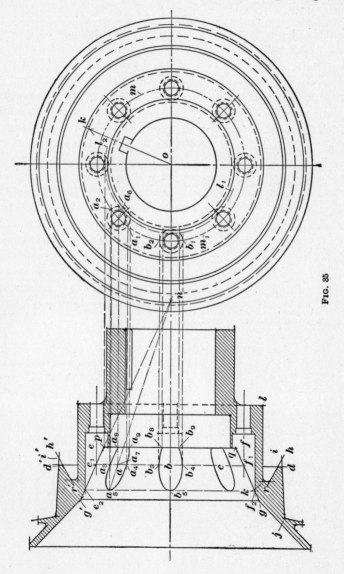

FIG. 35

construction of the piece represented. This part is to be

39—11

finished all over, as indicated by the note between the
two views.

91. Begin by drawing a horizontal center line $3\frac{5}{8}''$ below
the upper border line, extending across the whole width of
the Plate. Draw the vertical center line of the end view $3\frac{1}{4}''$
from the right-hand border line and with the intersection o,
Fig. 35, of these lines as a center draw the various circles
outlining the bore and the receding surfaces of the shell,
with the diameters given in the sectional view of the drawing. The scale to be used is $6'' = 1$ ft. With a radius of
$6\frac{3}{8}'' \div 2 = 3\frac{3}{16}''$, draw a circle, around which the centers of
the eight holes for the clamping bolts are to be symmetri-
cally located and which are spaced equally distant apart,
as indicated. The position of the center line $o\,k$ for the
keyway is obtained by drawing two circular arcs with a
radius greater than half the distance between two adjoining
holes and connecting the point of intersection k with the
center o. It will be noticed that each full-line circle
representing a bolt hole is concentric with two dotted circles, which represent the outlines of the countersunk parts
of the holes.

92. Next proceed to draw the sectional elevation of the
shell by drawing a vertical line, representing its right-hand
end, $\frac{3}{8}''$ to the left of the end view. Draw another vertical
line $9\frac{1}{8}''$ to the left of the first, thus obtaining two lines that
limit the length of the shell. Parallel with these lines
draw others that pass through the various external edges of
the shell. By projecting horizontal tangents from the top
and bottom points of the circles in the end view which represent similar edges, and letting them intersect corresponding
verticals in the sectional elevation, the exact locations of the
edges are determined. Proceed to outline the internal surfaces of the shell, the bore, and the keyway in a similar
manner.

93. It will be noticed that on this Plate several dimensions are given to thousandths of an inch. Most of these

dimensions refer to the clamping surfaces of the shell, clamping ring, and commutator bars. These parts are turned to fit gauges prepared by the toolmaker, who lays out the gauges and makes them suit the dimensions given. The purpose of giving these dimensions so exactly is to call attention to the fact that great accuracy is required and that measurements at these places are to be determined either by gauges or with micrometers. This practice of giving *accurate* dimensions in decimals and *approximate* dimensions of a machine part in halves, quarters, eighths, sixteenths, etc., of an inch, is now largely adopted in the better class of drafting rooms, the purpose of its adoption being to show the workman at a glance which parts of a machine part require to be very accurate and which do not, thus tending to prevent the waste of time incidental to needless accuracy.

In regard to laying off on the drawing dimensions given in decimals, lay off to the nearest 64th inch, actual measurement. This is ascertained in the following manner: Consider the dimension $9.416''$ in the sectional elevation of part **1**. As the scale used for drawing this is $6'' = 1$ ft., or one-half size, the actual distance to be laid off using a full-size scale is $9.416'' \div 2 = 4.708'' = 4'' + .708''$. But $.708''$ expressed in 64ths is $.708'' \times \frac{64}{64} = \frac{45.312''}{64} = \frac{45}{64}''$ to the nearest 64th inch. Hence, the actual distance, measured with a full-size scale, is $4\frac{45}{64}''$. Again, part **3** is drawn full size; hence, the dimension $1.594''$ expressed to the nearest 64th inch is $1\frac{38}{64}''$, since $.594'' = .594'' \times \frac{64}{64} = \frac{38.016''}{64} = \frac{38}{64}''$ to the nearest 64th inch.

To find the nearest 64th inch corresponding in value to a dimension given in thousandths of an inch consult Table V, found at the end of this paper under Useful Tables.

94. Among the parts demanding great accuracy is the clamping surface indicated by the lines $r\,h$ and $r'\,h'$, Fig. 35. The correct position and inclination of this surface is determined in the following manner: Draw a vertical line at a distance of 3.692″ from the left-hand end of the shell and intersect this line with two horizontal lines 9.710″ apart and equidistant from the horizontal center line, thereby locating the two points i, i'. From these points draw lines $r h$ and $r' h'$ at angles of 30° with the axis of the shell or with a line parallel to the axis, such as the line $k l$. Now draw a vertical line $d d'$ $3\frac{7}{16}″$ from the left-hand edge of the shell and find by trial a radius and center such that an arc can be described tangent to $d d'$, $h r$, and $i j$. Also, draw a line parallel to and $\frac{5}{8}″$ to the left of $d d'$ and with a radius of $\frac{3}{16}″$ find a center from which an arc may be described tangent to this line and tangent also to $h r$ and $l k$. So proceed with the upper half.

95. As the countersunk parts of the holes intersect the inside of the shell where it is cone shaped, the outlines of the holes will appear elliptical instead of circular, as indicated by the curves a, b, and c.

The outlines of the apertures a, b, and c have been carefully defined by a number of points found by the principles of projection. It is not necessary for the student to repeat this construction; he may limit himself to a few points only and by means of these draw the curves, approximately, freehand. The method of laying out the curve for the aperture a is identical with that for b and c. Connect the points e_2 and f_2 by a straight line; the extreme points of the curves will be situated on this line. Likewise connect points e_1 and f_1, on which line, points limiting the width of the various curves are to be located. The line $e_1 f_1$ is the end view of the circle $m m_1$. From the points $a_1 a_2$, where this circle intersects the largest of the circles representing the hole a, draw perpendiculars to the line $e_1 f_1$. The points of intersection a_3, a_4 are two points on the curve, limiting its extreme width. To find the point a_5 at the extreme end of the curve, produce the line $e_1 e_2$ until it intersects the horizontal center line of the two views at n. Project the center a_6, in the end view, on the line $e_1 f_1$; the points of intersection a_7 will be the center of the curve. Draw a line through n and a_7, intersecting line $e_2 f_2$ at a_5; this point is the extreme end of the curve. Assuming that the corner at point p is a sharp corner, project this point to the vertical center line of the end view, and through the point thus found draw the circular arc $l_1 l_2$ with o as a center. This is part of the end view of a circle represented by the line $p\,q$. From the points where this arc intersects the circle $a_1 a_2$, draw perpendiculars to the line $p\,q$; the points of intersection a_8 and a_9 will then locate the inner ends of the curve. Connect the points a_8, a_3, a_5, a_4, and a_9 by a curved line, drawn freehand; the result is the outline of the aperture a.

The location of the curve representing aperture b is somewhat easier to find. From the points of intersection b_1 and b_2 between the circle $m\,m_1$ and the circle indicating the hole b in the end view, draw perpendiculars to the line $e_1 f_1$, thereby locating the points b_3, b_4. The point of intersection between the line $e_2 f_2$ and the horizontal center line of the views gives point b_5. To locate the points b_8, b_9, draw perpendiculars, intersecting the line $p\,q$ from the points of intersection between the arc $l_1 l_2$, and the circle $b_1 b_2$.

It should be noted that while the lines $e_2 p$ and $f_2 q$ are here represented as straight lines, they should in reality be flat curves with their convex sides toward the horizontal center line of the view, because the elliptical curve, here shown in side view, is not located in a plane, but on a conical surface.

Attention is also called to the fact that while in this case the left-hand part of the end view has been used for projection, it is really the right-hand half that is represented in the sectional elevation. The left-hand half was used to avoid drawing projection lines across the whole of the end view.

Outlines of holes, as the above, or curves indicating the junction between intersecting parts, are generally drawn in the manner just described, partly to save time and also because such curves are bound to appear with the proper outlines and in the correct positions on the finished part, as a result of the process of manufacture, irrespective of how they are indicated on the drawings. But there are occasions when the draftsman desires to project such curves in their true form, and he should therefore be prepared to do this with ease and accuracy.

96. The clamping ring, part **2**, is also made of steel, cast from pattern *1007–B*, and slips over the shell at *d*, as shown in Fig. 38. It is shown in a sectional elevation and an end view, and the horizontal center line, common for both, should be $3\frac{1}{16}''$ above the lower border line. First

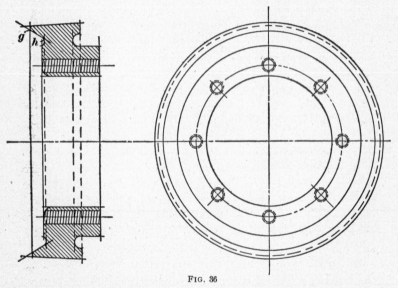

FIG. 36

draw the end view, locating its vertical center line $6\frac{7}{16}''$ from the left-hand border line. It is noticed that the circles in full lines, indicating the holes, arc surrounded by circles in dotted lines. The latter indicate the diameter at the bottom of the thread in the hole, here $\frac{9}{16}''$, or what is the same thing, the diameter of the bolts at the top of the thread. The full-line circles indicate the top of thread in the hole or the diameter of the drilled hole, which is .454″, or

about $\frac{29}{64}''$. A space of $1\frac{3}{16}''$ (full size) should be left between
the end view and the sectional view of the clamping ring.
In the latter view the tapped holes, shown in cross-section,
should in reality have 12 threads per inch, but owing to the
small scale to which they are drawn, it is difficult to represent the full number, and they were therefore drawn as
shown. The method of laying out the surface gh, Fig. 36,
with an inclination .of 30° to the horizontal center line, is
similar to the one described with reference to Fig. 35.

97. The commutator bar, part **3**, is shown in an elevation, an end view, and in a sectional view taken on line kl,

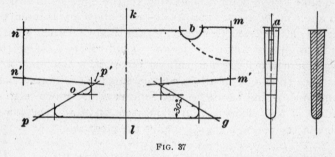

FIG. 37

Fig. 37; it is drawn full size. These commutator bars are
made in long strips and are sawed off to proper length.
After being assembled mica strips are placed between the
bars, and then the ends of the assembled bars are turned to
fit the clamping ring and shell. The majority of the
dimensions are very important and are therefore indicated
by inches and decimals. Locate the bottom, or base,
line pg of the commutator bar $3\frac{3}{4}''$ (full size) above the
lower border line and draw the vertical center line kl
$5\frac{7}{16}''$ from the right-hand border line. Locate the center
lines of the end view and sectional view $2\frac{1}{4}''$ and $1\frac{1}{4}''$,
respectively, from the right-hand border line. The com-
mutator bar is provided with the dimensions required by the
toolmaker for making the gauges and by the machinist for
turning it to size; consequently, some of the dimensions
required for drawing it must be obtained by calculation.

The height of the bar along the line $k\,l$, Fig. 37, is given in the sectional view as $1\frac{13}{16}''$, but the length of the side $m\,m'$ and the distance of the point m above the line $p\,g$ must be found by calculation. The point m' is located on a circle the diameter of which is $9.980''$; as $p\,g$ is tangent to a circle of $8.375''$ diameter, the distance of m' above $p\,g$ is: $\dfrac{9.980'' - 8.375''}{2} = .8025''$. The length of the side $m\,m'$ is found in the same manner and is: $\dfrac{12.125'' - 9.980''}{2} = 1.0725''$.

With the exception of the side $m\,m'$ and the recesses a and b, the two parts of the bar, as divided by the center line $k\,l$, are alike. The point o is located on the line $p\,p'$, drawn at an angle of 30° to $p\,g$, and its distance above $p\,g$ is found by means of the diameters given on the Plate. Other points, such as p', are found by means of intersecting lines, the location of which are determined either by a diameter or a distance from one of the boundary lines. The dotted bottom line of the recess in the side $m\,m'$ is drawn with a radius of $1\frac{5}{32}''$ from a center located on $m\,m'$, the lower edge of the recess being $\frac{11}{16}''$ below the point m.

98. Part 4 is one of the copper washers that fit under the heads of the clamping bolts, thereby making the commutator oil-tight and preventing oil getting from the bearing back of the commutator into the armature. The washer is shown in a plan view and a sectional elevation. The vertical center line, common for both, should be $5\frac{3}{16}''$ from the right-hand border line and the center of the plan view should be laid off on this line $1\frac{3}{8}''$ above the lower border line. A space of $\frac{7}{16}''$ should be left between the two views.

The construction of parts 4 and 5 is not explained by means of any text illustrations, as the student should be able to complete the drawings of both without any supplementary instructions.

99. Part 5 is one of the clamping bolts, the heads of which fit into the holes a, b, c, e, f in the shell, as shown in

Fig. 35. These bolts screw into the clamping ring, and the remarks made about the threaded holes, as to threads per inch, apply also to the bolts. The center line should be $6\frac{15}{16}''$ from the right-hand border line and the under side of the head should be $2\frac{5}{8}''$ above the lower border line.

100. The assembly drawing is to be located in the upper left-hand corner of the plate, on the same center line as the

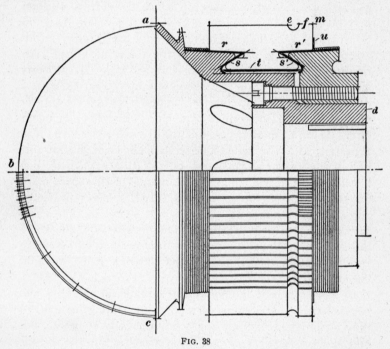

Fig. 38

shell, with a space of $\frac{3}{8}''$ between its left-hand boundary line and the left-hand border line. The upper half of this assembly drawing is shown in cross-section. Begin by drawing the shell in the upper half, projecting the various diameters over from the adjoining sectional elevation; then draw the clamping ring and the clamping bolt. The relative positions of these parts are clearly indicated by the dimensions given in the assembly drawing. In Fig. 38 the various mica rings, required for insulating the commutator bars from the shell and clamping ring, are indicated by letters r, r', s, s', t, and u. Each of these rings has a thickness of .063''; this dimension has been slightly exaggerated on the drawing, which is permissible on working drawings. Those parts of the two mica rings r, r' that extend beyond the ends of the commutator bars are securely fastened in place by twine, well shellaced.

The lower half of this view, in which the vertical outlines may be obtained by projection from the upper half, may now be drawn. But few commutator bars are shown in this assembly drawing, as it is not customary to spend the time required to indicate the position of all the bars. To properly space the latter draw the semicircle $a b c$, Fig. 38, with a diameter of 12'', that being the diameter of the commutator at the middle of the commutator bars. Divide the quarter circle bc in 5 equal parts, and the part next to b again in 5 parts. At either side of these division lines, lay off one-half of the insulation thickness which leaves in each division a space equal to one bar. At the middle of this space mark off the width of the recess; viz., .102''. Lines projected across from the first 12 divisions will locate the first three bars in the assembly drawing. The projection of the arcs e are flat curves near the center line, gradually increasing in curvature as the segments get farther away, as indicated.

In cases where it is desirable to lay off all the bars and every part of the same correctly, the following method may be pursued : Draw the semicircle $a b c$ as before, but add the two quarter circles, shown in Fig. 38, the outside one having a radius equal to the distance of the point m from the commutator center, and the inside one with a radius equal to the distance between the bottom of the recess e, near the ear f and the commutator center. Divide the quarter circle $b c$ as before, but continue the subdividing down to point c and make the dividing lines long enough to intersect all three arcs. In Fig. 38 this has been done only in the upper fifth of the arc. Projecting lines are now drawn, as before, those from the inner arc indicating the lowest points in the groove. Through these points and the adjoining edges draw circular arcs, the radii of which may be found by trial.

The pencil drawing is now complete and the Plate is ready to trace.

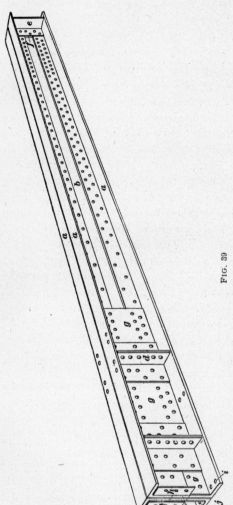

FIG. 39

PLATE 1008,

TITLE:

STEEL GIRDERS

101. The methods and conventions employed in making mechanical drawings are not all universally used in the various branches of engineering, as, for instance, in structural engineering, which concerns itself mainly with the construction of columns, girders, braces, etc. used in the construction of bridges, modern office buildings, etc. As an example of structural construction, the shop or working drawing of several special, built-up steel girders has been selected, by means of which the methods employed in the execution of this class of drawings will be shown.

Before proceeding with the drawing the student should familiarize himself with the names and purposes of the several parts, as given in the following description.

102. Referring to Fig. 39, a perspective view of a girder, the angles marked a, a are the **flange angles,** the upper pair forming the **top chords** and the lower the **bottom chords** of the girder. Connecting these chords is the **web-plate** b, while the vertical angles c, d, and e are known as **stiffeners.** The latter are required at the ends of the girder at c and e for the purpose of strengthening the web at the points where the girder is supported. At d stiffeners are also placed to reenforce the web, because at this point the upper chord of the girder is supporting the concentrated load presented by a column. At f, f are shown packing pieces, commonly called **fillers,** from the fact that they are used to fill a space otherwise open, which is undesirable where a compactly built-up part is required. These fillers are used wherever it is necessary to rivet through a space that would otherwise be vacant. **Reenforcing plates,** such as g, are frequently used to further stiffen the web of a plate girder, at the places adjacent to the points of support and beneath concentrated loads. The end j of the girder is to be secured to a structural steel column, and for this purpose the angle-iron **clips** h, h and the holes i, i through the lower flange angles are provided.

The structural girder under consideration is peculiar in that its depth is very small in comparison with its span, in consequence of which the girder is heavy for the load it is required to support. The necessity for keeping the girder shallow is that it may not diminish the **headroom** or height of the room beneath.

103. All the little circles shown on the chord and stiffeners (see Plate 1008) represent rivets. Attention is called to the fact that some of these are shown black. Whenever a blackened circle is shown it indicates a hole and not a rivet and that the rivets belonging to these holes are to be

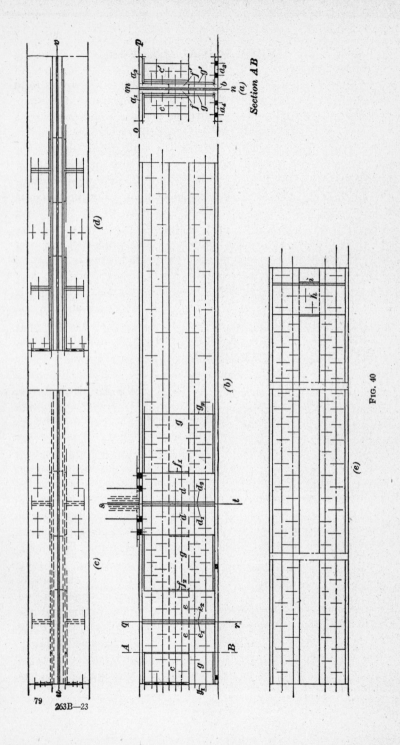

Section AB

(a)

Fig. 40

driven during erection; they are therefore known as **field
rivets.** All other rivets are to be driven in the shop.
When shown in elevation these holes are indicated by a
blackened rectangle. Holes for field rivets are shown in
the upper chord, Fig. 39, over the stiffener d and in the
lower chord to the left of c and d; also in the clips h.
Wherever the field-rivet holes are hidden behind some
other parts the holes are not blackened. For instance, in
the main elevation of the girder, Fig. 40 (b), four rivet
holes are shown above the stiffener d. Of these the two
central ones are partly hidden by the angles of the post
resting at this place; one-fourth of each hole is therefore
not blackened. As these four holes are not shown in section they should in reality be indicated by dotted lines; but
in order to make the field rivets more conspicuous to the
workmen the ordinary rules are departed from and the conventional method here shown is adopted, to indicate simply the *position* of the rivets.

104. The Plate represents the working drawings of four
separate girders, the shortest being 15 ft. 2″ and the longest
17 ft. 3½″ in length. It would evidently be impossible to
show each of these girders complete and at the same time
to a scale large enough to make a readable drawing, without
requiring an unnecessarily large sheet. To obviate this the
girders have been divided into several sections and some parts
broken away, as being simply duplicates of the part remaining. In this manner one drawing may be made to represent
four different girders. The method of indicating the places
where breaks occur differs from that heretofore described.
It is here indicated by drawing a line consisting of a long
dash and a dot along the adjoining parts of the break.
Adjoining sections need not necessarily be arranged in one
row, but may be placed in several rows, in this manner
making the drawing still more condensed. On this Plate
the first section is placed by itself and the line of break
marked with the line XX. The remaining three sections
are placed in a row below, in which the first section also has

a line XX indicating that this end is to be considered as contiguous to the one similarly marked. The parts removed by the two breaks in the lower row contain a number of rivet holes, which are spaced similarly to those in the remaining parts; it would therefore be superfluous to show them. The scale to be used is $1\frac{1}{2}'' = 1$ ft.

105. The distance between the centers of two rivets is called their **pitch**, commonly designated on the drawing by the word **space**. The space need not necessarily refer to the spaces between rivets in one row, but may also refer to spaces between alternate rivets in two parallel rows. For instance in the upper elevation, near the middle, are shown several spaces marked $4\frac{1}{2}''$, meaning the spaces between two alternate rivets in separate rows. In the lower elevation, beginning at the left, is found the note "31 alt. spaces @ $2\frac{1}{4}'' = 5'-9\frac{3}{4}''$"; this means that the drawing should show thirty-two rivets alternating in two rows and spaced $2\frac{1}{4}''$ apart. The rivets in each row have a pitch of $4\frac{1}{2}''$. The saving in length by this method is evinced by the fact that the drawing shows only nineteen spaces of the thirty-one required. It is customary to indicate not alone the space between the rivets and the total number in each series, but also the total distance between centers of the first and last rivet in one series, the note "$5'-9\frac{3}{4}''$" in above note referring to this distance. Each series is made up of as many rivets as possible without including rivets of a different pitch. As soon as a change takes place in the pitch a new series is arranged, as found, for instance, to the right of the note just referred to, where the following note is found: "17 alt. spaces @ $1\frac{1}{2}'' = 2'-1\frac{1}{2}''$," meaning that the spacing has been reduced from $2\frac{1}{4}''$ to $1\frac{1}{2}''$.

106. In the drawing, the four girders are designated by the marks $E\,1$, $E\,2$, $F\,1$, and $F\,2$, but these marks are only to be found under the lower three sections, at which place all changes have been made both as to spacing of rivets and difference in length of girders. The left-hand parts of all four girders, Fig. 40 (*b*), are alike and no distinction need therefore be made between them at this point. The marks *E 1*, *E 2*, *F 1*, and *F 2* are shop marks and are usually painted on the work in white lead before they leave the mill. To them the erector refers in placing the work in position, as the marks correspond with similar marks on an assembly drawing used in erecting the work in the field.

107. The dimensions of the various angles used in constructing the girder are not given in detail, they being unnecessary on a working drawing. All that is required is to give the size of the angles. The note on top of the left-hand part of the girder, "2 **Ls** $6'' \times 3\frac{1}{2}'' \times \frac{3}{8}''$—$0'$–$9''$ long," means that the part indicated is made up of two angles, or **Ls**, having legs $6''$ and $3\frac{1}{2}''$ long, respectively, each of which is $\frac{3}{8}''$ thick. These angles come in lengths of about 15 to 20 feet and can afterwards be cut in smaller lengths, to one of which the length "$0'$–$9''$" refers.

The fillers are also cut from long bars varying in width and thickness according to the space to be filled. For instance, the note "$3\frac{3}{4}'' \times \frac{3}{4}''$ Pl $1'$–$6''$" at the head of the girder means that the filler plate is to be cut from a bar $3\frac{3}{4}''$ wide by $\frac{3}{4}''$ thick, and to a length of 1 ft. $6''$.

It will be noted that the manner of indicating dimensions given in feet and inches on this Plate differs from that used on the other Plates described in this paper. Thus, instead of expressing 5 feet $6\frac{1}{4}$ inches as 5 ft. $6\frac{1}{4}''$, it is here expressed $5'$–$6\frac{1}{4}''$, in conformity with the working drawing from which the Plate was made. The former method is to be preferred (see Art. **20**), but if the latter is used, never omit the short dash between the feet and inches.

In order to aid the student in drawing the angles in the chords, the dimensions of which are not fully given on the Plate, a sectional view of one, fully dimensioned, is given in Fig. 41. The radii of the fillet and corners are more or less arbitrary, the various rolling mills having their own standards.

The rivets used in this girder have $\frac{3}{4}''$ and $\frac{7}{8}''$ shanks with heads $1\frac{1}{4}''$ and $1\frac{7}{16}''$ in diameter and $\frac{9}{16}''$ and $\frac{39}{64}''$ high, respectively. The holes for the rivets are generally punched $\frac{1}{16}''$ larger than the shank, the size of a rivet being indicated by the diameter of the shank *before* the rivet is driven. All $\frac{3}{4}''$ rivets require holes $\frac{13}{16}''$ in diameter. The rivets when driv-

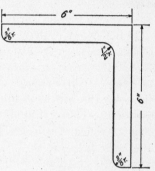

FIG. 41

en fill these holes; consequently the *driven* size of a rivet = nominal size $+ \frac{1}{16}''$. At the places where field rivets are to be driven, the notes "$\frac{15}{16}''$ holes" are to be found, indicating that $\frac{7}{8}''$ rivets are to be used.

108. To draw the Plate, begin by drawing the sectional elevation of the girder, Fig. 40 (*a*). This section is taken along the line *A B*, Fig. 40 (*b*), and shown as it would appear when looking along the girder from the right-hand end. Locate the center line *m n* $1\frac{11}{16}''$ from the right-hand border line, and the top line *o p* $3\frac{3}{4}''$ below the upper border line. Lay off one-half the thickness of the web-plate *b* to either side of center line and draw the four angles a_1, a_2, a_3, and a_4, according to the dimensions given in Fig. 41.

Between the upper and lower angles insert the two fillers *f, f'*; then add the reenforcing plates *g, g'*, and, finally, the clips *c, c'*. It should be noted that the reenforcing plates extend only to where the curve of the fillets on the chord angles begin, while the stiffeners have to extend clear to the angles of the top and bottom chords, and for this reason have their inner corners chipped off. Draw the center lines of the rivet holes, and indicate their location by blackened rectangles or circles (see Plate) where field rivets are to be indicated. Where the rivet heads are shown in side view indicate them by means of semicircles with diameters, as given above. On structural drawings it is not customary to indicate cross-sections by section lines; they are usually left blank or filled in entirely, either with ink or some dark color. If thus filled in, the spaces indicating field rivets are left white.

The note "Finished Third-Floor Line," found over the sectional elevation, means that the floor above the girder, when laid, will come to a height indicated by the line of dashes.

109. Next draw the elevation of the first section of the girder, locating its left end $\frac{7}{8}''$ from the left-hand border line. The limiting lines of the top and bottom angles may be projected from the section just drawn, likewise the lines limiting the width of fillers and reenforcing plates. Next locate the center lines $q\,r$ and $s\,t$ of the stiffeners d and e, Fig. 40 (b), and lay off their total width; also the sides of the legs d_1, d_2, e_1, and e_2, which project outwards at right angles to the plane of the paper. Lay off the clips c, one leg of which is seen to project a distance of $\frac{1}{8}''$ beyond the end of the girder. By referring to the sectional elevation, it will be noticed that the top of the clips is $1''$ below the upper side of the chord. Draw the reenforcing plate g extending from g_1 to g_2. The note "$2 - 14\frac{1}{2}'' \times \frac{3}{8}'' - 4'-4\frac{1}{2}''$ long," just below the lower chord, refers to this part. Indicate the fillers f_1 and f_2, the first being of a length equal to the width of d, and the latter of a length equal to the combined width of c and e. These fillers are covered both by the stiffeners and the reenforcing plates, and must therefore be indicated by dotted lines, which are shown beyond the edges of the stiffeners in order that they may be seen, though in reality they coincide with the edges of the stiffeners. Lay off the section line $X X$ at a distance of 8 ft. $5\frac{1}{4}''$ from the left-hand end of the girder.

All the rivets are located in six horizontal rows at the distances from upper side of girder indicated on the Plate. Draw these horizontal center lines. Select any one of these lines, as for instance the lowest, and lay off on same the distance between centers of rivets, as given in any one of the rows below the girder, all of which are seen to be alike. From the lowest center line, verticals are drawn by means of the **T** square and triangle to the other center lines, inter-secting them at the proper places and thereby locating the

centers of the various rivets.   It is unnecessary in the pencil drawing to draw the circle representing the rivets; this
may be postponed to the making of the tracing, when the
intersections of the rivet center lines will indicate the positions of the centers around which to draw the little circles.
In some shops it is customary to omit these circles altogether
and simply indicate the positions of the rivets by their
center lines.

110.   The first of the two plan views of the girder, shown
in the upper part of the Plate and in Fig. 40 (c) may now be
drawn by first laying off the center line $u\,v$ $1\frac{11}{16}''$ below the
upper border line.   Locate the left-hand end by drawing a
vertical line from the corresponding end in the elevation and
locate the section line at its right-hand end, 8'' from the
left-hand border line.   The length of those angle legs which
stand at right angles to the center line $u\,v$ may be found
by consulting the notes in the elevation.   The holes for the
field rivets will in this view appear as circles which are to
be blacked in.   The locations of the other limiting lines are
found partly by projection from the elevation and partly by
transferring the measurement from the sectional end view,
Fig. 40 (a).

111.   The other plan view, see also Fig. 40 (d), shows
the girder in a sectional view taken along an imaginary
horizontal center line in the elevation.   The view is similar
to the one previously drawn, except that some of the parts
are shown in full instead of dotted lines.   Most of the
limiting lines are found by projecting horizontals from the
other plan view, the position of the remaining limiting lines
being determined by direct measurement; all dimensions
extending in a horizontal direction are found in this manner.
Those field rivets in the lower chord that are not visible in
the other plan are here indicated, likewise those in the end
stiffener.

112.   Next proceed to draw the right-hand parts, see
also Fig. 40 (e), of the four girders.   Locate the lower side

of the same $2\frac{3}{8}''$ above the lower border line, letting the left-hand end lie in a line with the same end of the other elevation. This elevation is divided in three sections. Make the first section $3''$, the second $4''$, and the third $2\frac{25}{32}''$ long, leaving a space of $\frac{5}{32}''$ between each section. In other respects this elevation is drawn in the same manner as the one immediately above it. Locate the stiffener h, $3''$ from the right-hand end and add the filler i, here shown in full lines.

113. The dimensions may now be added to the various views, attention being given to the method of arranging the dimension lines that indicate the lengths of the complete girder and girder sections. Between the break line XX of the lower elevation and its right-hand end there are found three pairs of dimension lines, the first of which refers to the girders marked $E1$ and $E2$, the second to girder $F2$, and the third pair to girder $F1$. In each pair the upper line refers to the spacing of rivets and the lower to the total length of the section. Locate the first dimension line $\frac{1}{2}''$ below the girder, the second line $\frac{7}{16}''$ below the first, and leave a space of $\frac{3}{16}''$ between each of the remaining lines. The dimension lines found under the other elevation of the girder, represented by Fig. 40 (b), are supposed to be continuations of these six lines and should be located in the same manner. Draw the other dimension lines and insert corresponding dimensions, following closely the method used on the Plate as to their location and style of lettering. Add the notes referring to rivets and holes and the one referring to number and marks on girders. Lay off the space required for bill of materials and divide it into the necessary number of vertical and horizontal spaces. The abbreviations "Fill" and "Stiff" refer to fillers and stiffeners, respectively. R and L means right and left. When parts symmetrically placed are marked in this manner, it calls attention to the fact that they are not alike and that care should be exercised in order to put them in their proper places.

PLATES 1009 AND 1010, TITLE:

BENCH-VISE DETAILS

114. These two Plates, together with Fig. 43, give the details and assembly drawing of a bench vise. In actual practice the assembly drawing, Fig. 43, would be drawn first, but in this case it is desirable to draw the details first, as a clearer understanding will then be had of the parts constituting the assembly drawing. Plates 1009 and 1010

FIG. 42

may both be sent to the Schools for correction at one time, or separately, as the student prefers.

A general idea of the external appearance of the vise may be had from the half-tone view, Fig. 42, while the assembly view, Fig. 43 (*c*), which is a longitudinal section, will indicate the internal construction. It consists of the front jaw *1*, that works through an opening in the back jaw *2*. Motion is imparted to jaw *1* by means of the screw *17*, located inside part *1*, which is cored out for this purpose. The screw engages the nut *9*, which lies in a groove in part *2*, where it is held in position by means of the pin *12*. When an outward motion is given to the jaw *1* by turning screw *17* to the left, the jaw is assisted in its motion by the expanding spring *13*, while the screw is held in position, relative to the jaw, by the guard *14*. Both jaws are provided with steel facings *11*, secured by screws *18*.

The back jaw *2* rests on the base *3*, to which it is clamped by bolt *6* in such a manner as to leave it free to swing around the latter. A sleeve nut *7* engages with a clamping bolt *8*, whose head is held in a circular T-shaped groove in the base. A loosening of the nut by means of handle *10* allows the whole vise to be swung into any position desired, in which it may be retained by tightening the nut *7*. The advantage of this arrangement is that it enables the workman to turn any side of the work in the vise to the front without having to rearrange it in the jaws.

115. Begin by drawing the front jaw *1* on Plate 1009, shown in four views: A side elevation, an end elevation, a plan, and a section taken on line *A B* of the side elevation. Lay off the horizontal center line, common to the two upper views, $3\frac{3}{8}''$ from the upper border line, and the vertical center line of the end elevation $9\frac{1}{2}''$ from the left-hand border line. This center line, if produced, will also serve for the sectional view. Another horizontal center line, $5\frac{15}{16}''$ from the upper border line, will define the positions of the lower views. Allow a space of $\frac{3}{4}''$ between the two upper views. All the views on this Plate are drawn half size.

Draw the end elevation first, then the side elevation, defining some of the dimensions in the latter by projection from the first view. The radii of the curves defining the sides of the jaw in the end view are not to be inserted in the drawing made by the student, as they are given simply to aid him in constructing them. Ordinarily the determination of curves of this nature is left to the judgment of the patternmaker, unless there are special reasons why they should be exactly defined. Next draw the plan view, which is a bottom view showing the groove in same. Some of its dimensions will have to be taken from the side elevation

and some from the sectional view, which is to be drawn last.
It is seen that the horizontal part of the jaw is cored out
along its whole length, and that this cavity is partly rectangular and partly circular in section. The full-size view
of the jaw proper, shown in the upper left-hand corner of
the Plate, will apply to both jaws. Draw the vertical side
of the jaw $2\frac{1}{2}''$ from the left-hand border line, and its upper
corner $\frac{3}{4}''$ below the upper border line.

116. To draw the rear jaw, part *2*, shown in a side and
a front elevation, lay off their horizontal center lines
$2\frac{5}{8}''$ from the lower border line, and the vertical center line
of the front elevation $8\frac{3}{8}''$ from the left-hand border line.
The extension of the front jaw is to fit the cavity of the
rear jaw, but it is observed that part *1* is made slightly
narrower to allow it a freer motion.

It will be observed that the hole in the center of the base is
threaded as is further shown by the note, "Tapped for
$\frac{3}{4}''$ bolt." On working drawings, a thread is rarely shown in
a hole which is to be tapped; the general rule is to draw two
lines at a distance apart equal to the outside diameter of the
thread, and to place a note on the drawing stating the size
of tap to be used. It has been shown on this Plate, however, for the sake of completeness.

117. The base, part *3*, is shown in two views: a plan
view and a side view, the latter being half in section and
half in elevation. Lay off their vertical center line $3''$ to
the left of the right-hand border line, and the horizontal
center line for the plan view $2\frac{1}{2}''$ below the upper border
line. Leave a space of $\frac{3}{4}''$ between the two views. The square
hole indicated in the upper part of the plan view serves the
purpose of allowing the insertion of the bolt *8* from below
into the **T** slot.

118. The parts on Plate 1010 are drawn full size, except
those numbered *9*, *13*, *15*, *16*, and *17*, which are drawn half
size. Locate the tops of the views in the upper row

$1\frac{1}{8}''$ from the upper border line, and equalize the spaces between them, similar to those on the Plate. In drawing the knurled portion of part 7, draw, first, horizontal lines indicating the upper and lower borders, thereby making sure that the borders will appear even.

The lower part of the nut 9 is dovetailed into the groove situated in the base of part 2, but this groove is made $\frac{1}{16}''$ wider to give a certain amount of play to the nut.

119. Draw the center line of the jaw facing 11, $5\frac{3}{4}''$ below the upper border line, and draw the end view $1\frac{1}{2}''$ from the left-hand border line, leaving a space of $1''$ between this and the rear elevation. The note " scored face " indicates that the face of the jaw is to be provided with a series of shallow grooves cut at right angles to each other. The appearance of this surface is indicated in Fig. 42. It should be noted that the arcs outlining the upper and lower surfaces of this part are not concentric. The center for the arcs of the lower surfaces is found by drawing a line parallel with the face at a distance from it of $\frac{1}{4}''$, then, with a radius of $1\frac{9}{16}''$ and the lower edge of the face as a center, draw an arc intersecting the parallel line. The point of intersection is the center of these arcs. The center of the upper arcs is found if the vertical line, indicating the face, is produced and intersected by an arc having a radius of $3\frac{1}{4}''$, and its center in the upper edge of the face.

120. The horizontal center line for the two views of the handle 10 is located $6\frac{5}{8}''$ below the upper border line, leaving a space between the end view and the right-hand border line and between the two views, of $1''$ and $\frac{5}{8}''$, respectively. The right-hand end of the handle has been drawn in section, to show the threaded hole. In the free space above these views, locate the views of parts 8, 12, and 13.

121. Draw the horizontal center lines of parts 16 and 17, $1\frac{3}{8}''$ and $3\frac{7}{8}''$, respectively, above the lower border line, and leave a space of $\frac{7}{8}''$ between them and the left-hand border

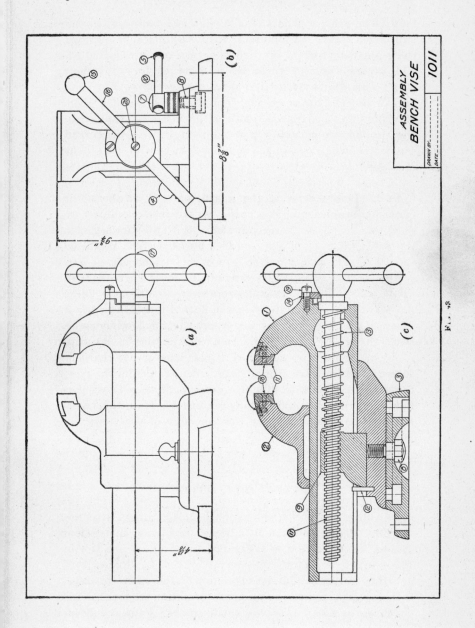

line. The head of part *17* is not spherical, as the left-hand half is outlined by a semicircle with a radius of $1\frac{1}{4}''$, while the right-hand part is outlined by two arcs of $1\frac{7}{8}''$ radius. The extreme end of the head is flattened for a distance of $\frac{1}{2}''$, corresponding to the diameter of the countersunk part of the hole for screw *20*. The thread on the vise screw is made in a conventional manner, somewhat similar to Fig. 7, with the exception that the rear parts of the thread are not shown. Locate the end and side view of part *15* as indicated.

122. Before drawing the guard, part *14*, it should be carefully studied, for its shape is somewhat difficult to ascertain from the two views given. The upper view is a front elevation and the lower a bottom view. The parts difficult to locate are the two shoulders on the rear surface. These are shown in dotted lines in the eleva-tion, but appear in the lower view as continuations of the sides. By con-sulting Fig. 44, where the guard is shown in perspective as it appears when seen from the rear, the student should be able to interpret the two views cor-rectly. Draw their vertical center line $6\frac{3}{4}''$ from the right-hand border line and locate the base lines of the views $3\frac{1}{4}''$ and $1\frac{7}{8}''$ from the lower border line.

Fig. 44

PLATE 1011, TITLE:

ASSEMBLY, BENCH VISE

123. Plates 1009 and 1010 being completed, the student should next make the assembly drawing, which forms Plate 1011. As all the details are given on Plates 1009 and 1010, no specimen plate is sent the student in this case, he being expected to get all his information from the detail drawings and Fig. 43. The small circles, $\frac{3}{16}''$ in diameter, enclosing figures and placed near the various details are reference circles; they indicate the proper position of the details in the assembly views, and the numbers correspond to those given in the bill of materials.

To draw the assembly views, Fig. 43, locate the horizontal center line of the upper views $3\frac{1}{2}''$ below the upper border line, and leave a space of $\frac{1}{2}''$ between these views and their adjacent vertical border line. The lower view should be $3\frac{3}{8}''$ above the lower border line, and a space of $\frac{1}{2}''$ left between it and the left-hand border line.

Insert the reference numbers at their respective parts and place the title in the lower right-hand corner as indicated. The reference letters referring to center lines in these and the following plates should be omitted on the drawings made by the student, and only such letters should be inserted that refer to section lines, such as A B on part 1.

PLATE 1012, TITLE:

SHAFT HANGER

124. In connection with Plate 1006 it was shown that shafts must be supported in bearings, and also how the latter may be made to conveniently effect alinement of the shaft. It was explained how shafts may be used to convey motion from one point to another, as, for instance, from an engine to the various machines to be driven by it. Such long shafts—with their couplings, if any are used—are called *line shafting*. They may be supported on the floor or from the ceiling of the building in which they are placed. In the latter case the supports are called **hangers,** and contain the bearings proper, which may easily be alined. This Plate shows a drawing of a common form of such shaft hangers. As the material list shows, it consists of nine parts, some of which occur but once, others twice, and one four times in the construction, so that the structure consists of fourteen parts, counting every single piece by itself. The part numbered 1 on the drawing is the hanger proper, which is fastened to the ceiling by strong bolts passing through holes in the base. Extending downwards, this

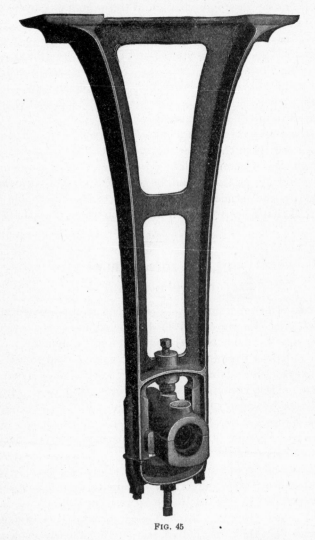

FIG. 45

hanger terminates in a square-shaped frame open at the lower end, in which is placed a *shell* made in halves, parts *6* and 7 on the Plate. Within this shell is located the bearing proper, numbered *4* and *5*, also made in halves. The aforesaid square-shaped frame is closed, after the shell with the bearing is inserted, by a *cap*, part *2*, secured by two studs, part *3*, and nuts, part *9*. The studs are cast into the hanger, first having been flattened at the end, as directed by the note near the detail of the hanger. Two setscrews, part *8*, serve to adjust the shell containing the bearing proper to correct alinement with the other hangers used to support the same line of shafting. The whole structure put together appears as shown in the half tone, Fig. 45. The student will notice that there are very few finish marks on the drawing, from which it is plainly evident that a large portion of the dimensions are for the foundry, and that there is very little machine finish. The bearing proper, parts *4* and *5*, and the shell, *6* and *7*, are finished where they join together, parts *6* and *7* being also faced off at the ends. Parts *1* and *2* are drilled and tapped for the $\frac{5}{8}''$–11 setscrew used to adjust the height of the bearing, and oil holes are drilled in part *4*. With these exceptions there is no machine work to be done on the hanger. Parts *4* and *5* are lined with Babbitt, the same process being followed as that described in connection with the bearing shown in Plate 1006, although the absence of finish marks indicate that the bearing is not to be bored.

125. All the parts are drawn on the Plate in detail, by themselves, except the setscrews, the nuts, and the main frame or hanger proper, which is represented in two views drawn to a scale of $3'' = 1$ ft. This figure shows the whole structure assembled.

The dimensions given on the assembly are leading dimensions only, the few detail dimensions of the main frame given and placed near the foot being added because the size of the sheet did not permit the portion of part *1* being shown in detail in any other position. The other dimensions of the main frame, or part *1*, are given in the two views located in the lower left-hand corner of the Plate.

126. All the details are to be drawn first, and to a scale of $6'' = 1$ ft. Start with the bearing proper, parts *4* and *5*. The student will readily perceive the similarity of this piece with the one drawn on Plate 1006. There are these differences, however: In the present case the bearing consists of two parts, while the former was one piece only. The present bearing is not self-oiling, so that there are no slots for oil rings, little oil holes being provided instead. The means for preventing the bearing from turning in its seat is in the

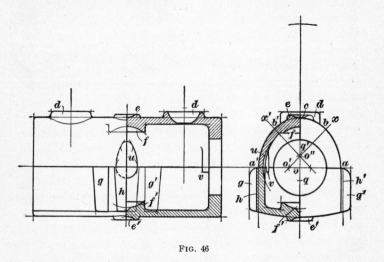

Fig. 46

present case a small boss, or teat, at the bottom of the rounded central portion, which is also called the *ball*. This small teat fits into a recess provided for it at the bottom of the lower shell, part 7. For convenience the two halves of the bearing are drawn together, the finish mark placed on the dividing line indicating that both surfaces are to be finished. Both halves are shown half in section. With the instruction given for the similar piece on Plate 1006, the student should have no difficulty in drawing the bearing. Place the center lines $1\frac{1}{2}''$ from the bottom border line, and the vertical center lines $8\frac{7}{8}''$ and $5\frac{7}{8}''$ from the right-hand border line, respectively.

127. The shells *6* and *7*, Fig. 46, are drawn in much the same manner as the bearing. The two halves are also shown together, as were those of the bearing; they are also shown in a perspective view, Fig. 47, partly broken away. Draw the horizontal center lines $5\frac{1}{8}''$ from lower border line, and the vertical center lines $5''$ and $1\frac{1}{2}''$ from right-hand border line, respectively. Begin with the right-hand, or end, view. Draw the circular opening from the center *o* (see Fig. 46). Next draw the outline of the shell, which is dome-shaped

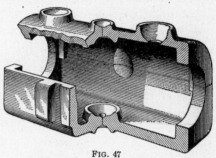

FIG. 47

in the upper half and box-shaped in the lower half. The outline of the upper half is composed of circular arcs of different radii, one drawn with a radius of $2\frac{1}{8}''$ from a center *o'* and $\frac{7}{16}''$ from *o* on the horizontal center line; the other with *o''* on the vertical center line as a center, $\frac{7}{16}''$ from *o*, with a radius of $1\frac{1}{2}''$. Lay off *o'* and *o''* first. Draw a line *o' o''* through these points and prolong it, say, to *x*. When curves of different radii are joined together, as in this instance, their point of junction should lie on a line passing through the centers of the arcs, such as line *o' x*. Draw one arc from *a* till it intersects *o' x* at *b*; then draw the other arc from *b* to *c*. Draw similar arcs on the left-hand side of the figure.

On top of the upper shell place the boss for the oil cup *d*, whose diameter is $1\frac{5}{8}''$ and whose top line is $\frac{1}{4}''$ above the crown of the shell, as seen in the other view. The boss is cupped, the cup having a radius of $\frac{11}{16}''$ and being $\frac{1}{2}''$ deep. Next add, in similar manner, the boss *e* for the end of the setscrew to bear against, $1\frac{1}{16}''$ in diameter and $\frac{1}{8}''$ high. This boss is also cupped, the cup having a radius of $\frac{9}{16}''$ and being $\frac{1}{8}''$ deep. This cup is not visible in the right-hand half of the end view, as the whole boss is hidden by the oil-cup boss and must be shown in dotted lines.

The outline of the lower, box-shaped half of the shell is now to be drawn. Carry straight lines down from a and a', one full and one dotted, as shown, the latter being hidden by a projecting lug. The bottom line of the lower shell is a circular arc having a radius of $7\frac{1}{2}''$. Its center is obtained by laying out the bottom point $1\frac{5}{16}''$ below the horizontal center line, and from there going up $7\frac{1}{2}''$ on the vertical center line. Draw the boss e' at the bottom. The lower shell has on each side three projections g, g' and h, the lugs g and g' protruding $\frac{3}{8}''$, and the raised surface h only $\frac{1}{16}''$. The outlines of the lugs appear in the end view in full, in both halves of the figure, while the raised surface h appears as a full line on the sectional, or left, side and as a dotted line on the right side, being there hidden by the lug g'. Round off the lugs with the proper radii. The projecting lugs $g\,g'$ just drawn, together with the raised surfaces h, hold the shell in proper position in the main frame, keeping it from moving endwise and sidewise respectively.

Next define the thickness of the shell in the left-hand side of the figure by drawing concentric arcs and parallel lines to the outlines already drawn. The thickness is $\frac{1}{4}''$, as given in the other view at the bottom, it being understood that the general thickness of shell is the same throughout. On the inside of the shells are placed bosses f and f', cupped to receive the ball, or rounded middle, portion of the bearing. These cups have, however, a smaller radius than the ball, for the following reason: As has been said, these surfaces are not finished. It

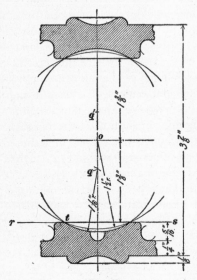

Fig. 48

would, therefore, not be practical to cast them so as to make them exactly coincide. By making the cups of smaller radius, the surfaces will be in contact only at the rim of the cup, as shown in Fig. 48. The radii of the cups are given as $1\frac{1}{16}''$; to find their centers, q and q', proceed as follows: With o as a center draw a circle with a radius of $1\frac{1}{2}''$, as shown in Fig. 48; next lay off $1\frac{3}{8}''$ from o downwards along the vertical center line, and draw a horizontal line $r\,s$ marking the top of the cupped boss. With the point of intersection t as a center and a radius of $1\frac{1}{16}''$, strike an arc cutting the vertical center line at q; with q as a center, draw the arc defining the bottom of the cup. Draw the upper cup in the same manner. Draw the little recess in the lower cup for the teat referred to in Art. **126.** The thickness of the shell is changed at two other places, namely, at u, Fig. 46, and at the corresponding point opposite, being recessed $\frac{1}{16}''$ deep and $\frac{7}{8}''$ wide to accommodate the ball, as the shell is only $2\frac{7}{8}''$ wide in the clear, while the ball is $3''$ in diameter. The top sleeve 6 is held in position, in relation to bottom sleeve, part 7, by four projections v, one placed at each corner of the top half and slipping into the bottom half.

128. The other view is now easily drawn. Carry over from the end view horizontal lines limiting the inside and the outside of the shell, the tops and bottoms of the bosses for the oil cups and ball cups, keeping in mind the fact that the line representing the inside of the top of part 6 is not found by projecting horizontally from the end view, as the top point there represents the bottom point of the cup f. The inside top line in the side view must be found by laying off a point $\frac{1}{4}''$ below the outside of the shell, and through this drawing a horizontal. Lay off the center lines and centers of the oil cups and draw their outlines. Carry over the centers of the ball cups and draw their outlines, also those of the setscrew cups. Lay out the lugs g and g', the raised surface h, the recess u, and the projections v, the latter visible only in the right-hand or sectional half of the figure. Round off the corners and draw the fillets.

39—13

The outlines of the recess u is found by ascertaining the intersection between the ball of the bearing and the inside of the shell.   The student is not required to determine the intersecting points by means of projection, but may draw an approximate curve in the following manner.   With the intersecting point of the two center lines as a center, draw an arc with a radius of $\frac{7}{16}''$.   Lay off another center $\frac{3}{4}''$ above the first and draw another arc with a radius of $\frac{1}{4}''$.   By means of the irregular curve draw two curves tangential to the two arcs.

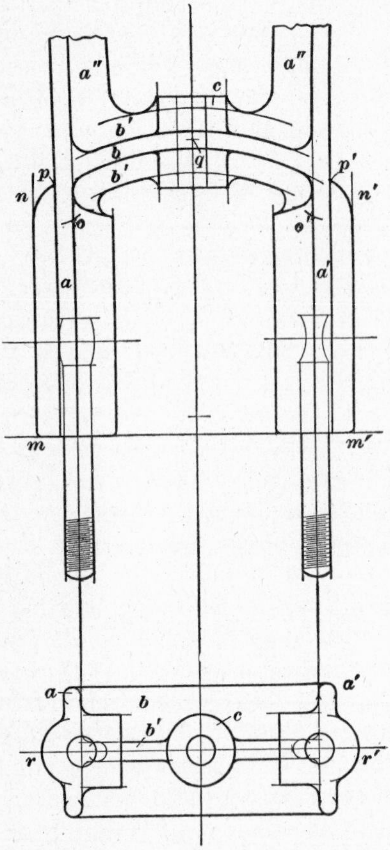

FIG. 49

129. Now draw the detail numbered *1* and *3* (see also Fig. 49), which is the lower portion of the main frame, with its bolts cast into it.   It will be noticed that the detail drawing of parts *1* and *3* shows only a portion of the frame, and that it is drawn to a larger scale than the frame shown in the assembly drawing.   This is another illustration of the practice referred to in the description of the enlarged cross-section of the pulley rim, Plate 1005.   The size of the Plate would not permit of drawing the entire frame to the scale used for the details; hence, the upper part only is shown, drawn to the enlarged scale, the dimensions necessary for the foot of the frame being given on the assembly.   Commence with the top view or elevation. Draw a vertical center line $2\frac{7}{16}''$ from left-hand border line.   Draw parallel to it the center lines of the bolts $5\frac{3}{16}''$ $\div 2 = 2\frac{19}{32}''$ from it, on either side.   Draw a horizontal line $m\,m'$, Fig. 49, which determines the bottom, and is $4\frac{1}{2}''$ (actual measurement) from the lower border line.   Lay out the inside and outside dimensions ($3\frac{1}{2}''$ and $6\frac{15}{16}''$) of the uprights and draw their vertical out-lines $m\,n$, $m'\,n'$.   The uprights have ribs a and a', the inside edges of which coincide with the center lines of the bolts; the ribs are $\frac{3}{8}''$ thick.   These ribs extend to the upper part of the frame, while the thick parts of the uprights terminate on the outside in caps which are partly spherical and have a radius of $\frac{7}{8}''$, with centers on the inside edges of the ribs. To locate these centers, lay off from $m\,m'$ the height $5\frac{5}{16}''$ on the outside edges of the ribs to p and p'; with these points as centers cut the inside edge line of the ribs with arcs struck with a radius of $\frac{7}{8}''$, obtaining centers o and o' of the caps.   A ribbed bridge $b\,b'$, having a cylindrical boss c in the center for the setscrew, connects the two uprights. This bridge is curved to a circular arc, the upper edge of the central horizontal rib b having a $6''$ radius, whose center is located $\frac{3}{8}''$ from the line $m\,m'$.   The lower edge of the central rib b is $\frac{3}{8}''$ away from the upper, and is struck from the same center.   The remainder of the bridge should be readily drawn.   Draw the cylindrical boss c by locating a point q in the middle of the rib b and laying off points $\frac{3}{4}''$ to the right and left of the vertical center line, and $\frac{15}{16}''$ above and $1''$ below point q.   Now put in the fillets joining the various parts, and round off the corners.   Next draw in the hole for the setscrew in the boss c, and finally the studs s. The flattening of the studs is shown in a conventional manner without dimensions, this being safely left to the blacksmith.

Begin now with the bottom view.   Carry down vertically the center lines of the studs, having previously drawn a horizontal center line of the whole figure $1\frac{3}{16}''$ (actual measurement) from the lower border line.   Draw the circles representing the studs, the threaded setscrew hole, and the cylindrical boss c.   Carry down the outside edges $m\,n$ and $m'\,n'$ of the uprights from the upper figure to the lower, intersecting the horizontal center line in r and r', through which points draw arcs of circles with a $\frac{11}{16}''$ radius to represent the plan of the uprights.   Carry down the inside edges of the uprights and lay off their width, which is $1\frac{1}{2}''$.   Carry down the edges of the ribs a and a' and make their width $2\frac{3}{4}''$. Finally, draw the rib b', $\frac{3}{8}''$ thick.   Round off corners and put in fillets.

130.   The next part to be drawn is the cap 2, also shown in Fig. 50.   Draw center lines $7\frac{3}{8}''$ from the left-hand border line and $6''$ from the bottom border line, respectively.   It is best to start with the upper view or plan.   Establish the stud-hole centers; draw the circles representing the stud holes, the set-screw boss, and the set-screw hole.   Lay out the outside and inside dimensions of the body and rib of the cap as well as their width; the dimensions $6\frac{15}{16}''$, $3\frac{1}{2}''$, $2\frac{3}{4}''$,

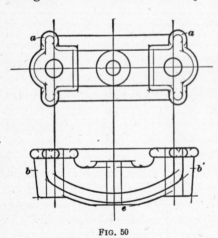

FIG. 50

and $1\frac{1}{2}''$ will be found to be the same as the corresponding dimensions of the uprights of part 1.   These outlines will be partly dotted lines, being hidden by a half-round molding $a\,a$ $\frac{3}{8}''$ wide carried all around.   In the plan, this molding shows in parallel lines and concentric circles to the outlines of the body proper and $\frac{3}{16}''$ away from them.   Now draw the lower view or elevation.   It is drawn in a manner similar to the bridge portion in part 1.   Notice that the body tapers on the sides b and b' and that it is flattened at the bottom

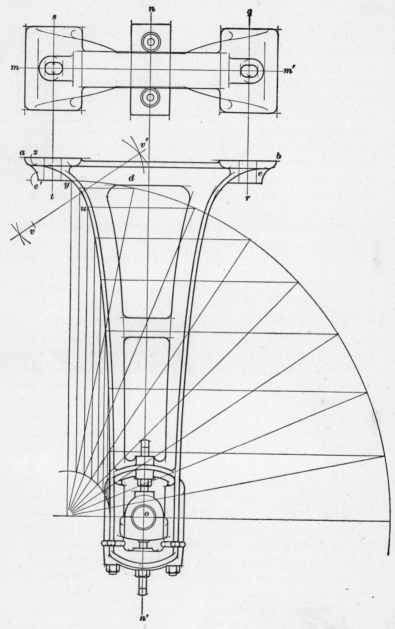

FIG. 51

at *c* for the nut of the setscrew.   Put in circles for fillets and round off the corners with proper radii.

131. All that now remains to be drawn is the assembly shown in two views and in four sections through the frame and web.   Start with the elevation, beginning at the left. Draw the horizontal center line *n n'*, Fig. 51, 3″ from the upper border line, and a base line *a b* 7⅜″ from the left-hand border line, draw center lines *q r* and *s t* for the bolt holes; lay out the thickness of the base and of the bosses *e* and *e'*, and draw in the bolt holes.   The top of the rib *d* is parallel to the base line; the rib itself is 1½″ high, as indicated on the section along *A B* shown at the left-hand upper corner of the Plate.   Lay off 30″ from the base line to locate the center of the shaft; this distance is called the *drop* of the hanger.   Draw a vertical center line through *o* and complete this end of the hanger from dimensions on the details previously drawn.   The scale to be used is 3″ = 1 ft.   The curve of the side of the hanger is partly that of an ellipse, half the diameters of which are 3¾″ and 28¼″.   Use for its construction the first of the two methods given in *Geometrical Drawing*, as shown in Fig. 51.   From *u* to *z* the curve is a circular arc tangent to the ellipse at *u* and to the bottom of the base at *z*, and passing through the end *y* of the long diameter of the ellipse.   If the circles used for the construction of the ellipse are divided into the same number of parts as shown in *Geometrical Drawing*, then the point *u* is located at the end of the third line from the left in Fig. 51. The center of the curve *u z* may be found in the following manner: Draw a perpendicular *v v'* that will bisect an imaginary straight line connecting points *u* and *y*, in the manner described in *Geometrical Drawing*.   Any arc with its center on line *v v'* will pass through points *u y*.   The center of an arc that will also pass through point *z* can be found either by trial or according to the method described in *Geometrical Drawing* for passing a circle through three points not in the same straight line, the three points here being *u*, *y*, and *z*.   The other construction dimensions can be obtained from the cross-sections and the over-all dimensions given on the assembly. The bottom plan, to the left of the figure just drawn, is easily made by carrying over, horizontally, all dimensions from the elevation that can be so obtained, and laying off the others from center line $m\,m'$, $5\frac{1}{2}''$ from left-hand border line.

Finally draw the four sections of the main frame at the left-hand upper corner of the Plate. The student should have no difficulty with these.

In lettering the title, note that part *8* is called for twice, it being plainly evident from the assembly that two adjusting screws are necessary, and also that four hexagonal nuts, part *9*, are required for parts *8* and *3*. Six patterns are called for to complete the hanger, although part *4* could be produced from pattern *D*, which is made for part *5*. It is probable, however, that on standard parts of this sort, large numbers will be made, and it is therefore advisable to call for patterns for each part.

PLATE 1013, TITLE:

GEAR-TEETH PROFILES

132. The style of drawing shown in Plates 1013, 1014, and 1015 is somewhat different from that shown in the preceding Plates. Plate 1013 is more of a diagrammatic nature, its purpose being to show the theory and construction of gear-teeth in general, while Plates 1014 and 1015 are intended to illustrate the use of shade lines in drawings. When shade lines are used, the outlines of an object are given by means of two varieties of lines, one lighter and one heavier than that previously adopted as the standard. The function of shade lines is to differentiate between such surfaces that are illuminated by rays of light, assumed to come in a certain direction, and other surfaces not exposed to such rays. A detailed description of this subject has already been given in *Geometrical Drawing*.

While there is no doubt of the fact that drawings containing shade lines will greatly assist in giving a clearer idea of the shape of the objects represented, such lines are, however, going out of use more and more, principally because more care and time is required to execute a drawing in this manner. But as some drawing offices still continue their use and as there are cases when they *must* be used, as for instance in drawings intended for the U. S. Patent Office, it is well for the student to familiarize himself also with this method. The three Plates are drawn full size.

If a circle is rolled on a straight line without sliding, a point on the circumference of the circle will describe a curve called the **cycloid.** The circle is called the **generating circle.** The shape of the curve and the manner of drawing it are shown in Fig. 1. Let O be the center of the generating circle, which is $1\frac{1}{4}''$ in diameter, P the point on the circumference of the generating circle, and $A B$ the straight line on which the generating circle is rolled and which is equal in length to the circumference of the generating circle, or $1\frac{3}{4}'' \times 3.1416 = 5.4978$, say $5\frac{1}{2}''$. The generating circle should be so placed that its center O lies over the center of the line $A B$, as shown. Divide the generating circle into any number of equal parts, in this case 12, or $P1$, 1–2, 2–3, 3–4, etc., and through these points draw lines $C D$, $E F$, $G H$, etc., parallel to the line $A B$. Through the center O of the generating circle draw the radius $O\,6$. Divide each half of the line $A B$ into half the number of equal parts that the generating circle is divided into, as $A\,1$ 1–2, 2–3, etc., and through these points draw lines perpendicular to $A B$ terminating in the line $G H$, as $A\,G$, 1–$1'$, 2–$2'$, 3–$3'$, etc. From the point $1'$, with a radius equal to the radius of the generating circle, as $O\,6$ or $1'$–1, describe an arc intersecting the line $K L$ in the point P^1; from the point $2'$, with the same radius, intersect the line $I J$ in the point P^2; from the point $3'$, with the same radius, intersect the line $G H$; continue in a similar manner with the remaining points $4'$, $5'$, $7'$, $8'$, etc., intersecting the lines EF and CD in the points P^4, P^6, P^7, P^8, etc. The points A, P^1, P^2, P^3, etc. are points in the curve through which the cycloid may be drawn. It will be noticed that when the center O of the generating circle coincides with the point G, the point P on the circumference of the generating circle coincides with the point A; and that when the generating circle is revolved toward the right, without sliding, until the center O coincides with the point $1'$, the point P will coincide with the point P^1. Thus it is seen how the point P passes through all the points from A to B, namely, A, P^1, P^2, P^3, etc., when started at A and revolved toward the right to B.

133. If the generating circle is rolled, without sliding, on the outside of the circumference of an arc of a circle supposed to be at rest, instead of being rolled on a straight line, the curve described by a point P of the generating circle will be an **epicycloid**.

The manner of drawing such a curve is shown in Fig. **2**. AB is the arc upon which the generating circle is rolled, its center being at S and its radius being $3\frac{1}{2}''$. The diameter of the generating circle is in this case the same as in Fig. **1**, or $1\frac{3}{4}''$. Make the lengths of the arcs $6 A$ and $6 B$ equal to half the length of the circumference of the generating circle, by first calculating the length of half the circumference of the generating circle and drawing a straight line tangent to the arc $A 6 B$ at 6, making it equal in length to half the circumference of the generating circle. Then make the arc $6 A$ equal to this line by means of the approximate method given in *Geometrical Drawing*. Divide the arc $A 6 B$ and also the generating circle into the same number of equal parts, in this case 12, as $A 1$, 1–2, 2–3, etc., and $P 1$, 1–2, 2–3, etc., and draw radii from the center S to the points of division on the arc $A 6 B$. During the revolution of the generating circle, the center O will describe an arc $m O n$ concentric with the arc $A 6 B$ and having the same number of degrees in it as $A 6 B$. Produce the radii just drawn to the arc of center positions $m O n$, intersecting this arc in the points m, $1'$, $2'$, $3'$, $4'$, etc. Through the points of equal divisions, 1, 2, 3, etc., of the generating circle pass concentric arcs having the center S, as CD, EF, GH, IJ, and KL. With the points $1'$, $2'$, $3'$, $4'$, etc. as centers and radii equal to the radius of the generating circle describe arcs cutting the arcs KL, IJ, GH, etc. in the points P^1, P^2, P^3, etc., which are points on the epicycloid.

134. When the generating circle rolls on the inside of the arc, the curve described by a point on the circumference is called a **hypocycloid.** The method of drawing it is similar in all respects to that just given for the epicycloid. The student should be able to construct it from the drawing without further explanation. The diameter of the generating circle is $1\frac{3}{4}''$ as before.

135. Suppose that a string is wound on a cylinder and that the end of the string is at the point P in Fig. **3.** If this string is unwound from the cylinder, keeping it constantly tight, the end P will describe a curve known as the **involute of the circle,** or, more simply, the **involute.** To construct it geometrically, let O be the center of the given circle representing the cylinder, which, in Fig. **3,** is $2\frac{1}{2}''$ in diameter, and P the free end of the string when wound on the cylinder. Divide one-half of the given circle representing the cylinder into any number of equal parts, in this case 6, as $P1$, 1–2, 2–3, etc., and through each of these points draw tangents to the circle, as P^1, P^2, P^3, etc. To draw these tangents, first draw the radii $O1$, $O2$, $O3$, etc. and then draw the tangents $1P^1$, $2P^2$, $3P^3$, etc. at right angles to them. By means of the approximate method given in *Geometrical Drawing,* find the length of the arc $1P$ and make the length of the tangent $1P^1$ equal to this length; of the tangent $2P^2$ equal to twice this length; of the tangent $3P^3$ equal to three times this length, and so on. The curve drawn through the points P^1, P^2, P^3, P^4, etc. will be the required involute. The use of these curves will now be explained.

136. On Plate 1014, in Fig. **1,** is shown one-half of **two spur gear-wheels** in mesh.   The two dotted circles tangent to each other at P are struck from the centers of the gear-wheels and are called the **pitch circles.**   The diameter of any gear-wheel is always understood to be the diameter of its pitch circle unless it is specified as **diameter at root,** or **diameter over all.**   The length of that part of the pitch circle between the centers of any two consecutive teeth is called the **circular pitch,** or simply the **pitch.**   Thus, in Fig. **1,** Plate 1014, the length of the arc $a\,b$ is equal to the pitch of either gear-wheel.   When the gear-wheels are cut in a gear-cutter, the width of the tooth $c\,d$ on the pitch line is equal to the space $d\,f$; that is, the arc $c\,d$ is equal to the arc $d\,f$, and each is equal to half the pitch.   When the gear-wheels are cast, that is, when they are not cut in a gear-cutter, clearance is given between the back of one tooth and the front of the tooth following, to allow for inequalities in casting.   This clearance, or **backlash,** as it is usually termed, is generally made equal to 4 per cent. of the pitch. This is done by making the thickness of the teeth $c\,d$ equal to .48 of the pitch.

The part $C\,C_1$ of the tooth that lies beyond the pitch circle is called the **addendum,** and the part $C\,C_2$ that lies below it is called the **root.**   The **face** of the tooth is the part $C\,C_1\,C'\,C$, Fig. **2,** of the tooth above the pitch circle, extending the whole width of the tooth.   The **flank** is the part $C\,C_2\,C''\,C$, Fig. **2,** of the tooth below the pitch circle, extending the whole width of the tooth.   The terms addendum and root mean distances only, while face and flank mean surfaces.

The usual practice is to make the addendum equal to $.3\,P$, and the root equal to $.4\,P$. $P =$ the circular pitch. The distance $C_1\,C_2$ is called the whole depth of the tooth. The method of describing the curves of teeth shown on the Plate 1013, Fig. **4,** is a convenient way of drawing the **cycloidal,** or **double-curved teeth.**   Cycloidal teeth are constructed by making the outline of the face a part of an epicycloid and the flanks a part of the hypocycloid, hence the name double-curved teeth.

137. In Fig. 4, Plate 1013, let AB be part of a pitch circle struck with a radius of, say, $5\frac{1}{2}''$. For convenience in drawing the tooth, let the pitch be $2''$. With O as a center, which is the center of the gear-wheel, and a radius equal to $5\frac{1}{2}''$, describe the arc AB, part of the pitch circle. Through O draw a straight line OS, cutting AB in P. Take the radius of the generating circles SP and $S'P$ equal to $1\frac{7}{8}''$ for this case and describe arcs having centers at S and S' on the line OS. With O as center and OS as radius describe the arc $S_2 S_1$. In connection with the gear-wheel teeth, the generating circles are frequently called **describing circles.** Roll the outer describing circle upon AB in such a manner that the center S will move in the direction of the arrow along the arc $S_2 S_1$. By means of the method given in Fig. **2**, find the points P^1, P^2, P^3, etc. on the epicycloid described by the point P. Trace a faint curve through the points just found and measure off on the pitch circle the thickness of the tooth.

$$PD = .48p = .48 \times 2'' = .96''$$

Make $EF =$ the addendum $= .3 \times p = .3 \times 2'' = .6''$. With O as a center and OF as a radius describe an arc cutting the epicycloid in G. Now roll the inner describing circle on AB, so that its center S' moves in the direction of the arrow, and find the points P_1, P_2, P_3, etc. of the hypocycloid described by the point P, through which trace a faint curve. Make EF' equal the flank of the tooth $= .4p = .4 \times 2'' = .8''$, and with O as a center and OF' as a radius describe an arc cutting the hypocycloid in G'. PG' is the outline of the flank of the tooth and PG that of the face. Since it would be a tedious operation to draw all the tooth curves in this manner, it is usual to approximate the curves by means of circular arcs; that is, to find by trial a center Q and a radius QP such that an arc described from this center and with this radius will pass through the points on the curve GP and coincide with that curve as closely as possible; also, to do the same with regard to the curve PG', using the center Q' and the radius $Q'P$.

To find the center Q or Q' of these circular arcs proceed as follows: With P and G as centers and any radius describe arcs intersecting in C and C'. Draw a straight line through C and C'; the center Q must line on $C\,C'$ to the left of $G\,P$. Try different points 1, 2, 3, 4, etc. on this line as centers and $1\,G$, $2\,G$, etc. as radii, and see if one of the arcs struck with either one of these centers and radii will coincide with the epicycloidal curve $G\,P$. Make this circular arc fit the curve for a short distance beyond G—as far as P^3, for example; this will insure the arc being more nearly correct. This should be done in every case when finding an approximate radius of this kind. Continue in this manner until the point Q is found such that an arc struck with Q as a center and $Q\,G$ or $Q\,P$ as a radius will coincide as closely as possible with $G\,P$. If a circle were drawn with O as a center and $O\,Q$ as a radius, the centers of all the circular arcs of the faces of the teeth would lie in this circle, and the radii of these arcs would be equal in length to $Q\,P$. Hence, to find the center Q_1 of the arc $D\,H$ forming the back of the tooth, take D as a center and $Q\,P$ as a radius and describe a short arc cutting, in Q_1, the circle passing through Q. Then, with Q_1 as a center and the same radius describe the arc $D\,H$. In a similar manner find the center Q' and describe $P\,G'$, also $D\,H'$. Instead of letting the flank form a sharp corner at the bottom of the tooth, as shown dotted at G', it is usual to put a small fillet there, as shown by the full line. This makes the tooth stronger and less liable to break or to crack in casting. The entire tooth outline or curve $G\,P\,G'$ or $H\,D\,H'$ is called the **profile** of the tooth.

138. A **rack** is a part of a gear-wheel whose pitch circle is a *straight line;* the tops of the teeth all lie in the same plane.* A portion of a rack and one tooth are shown in Fig. 5. Take the pitch the same as before, then the addendum and root are also the same, that is, $.6''$ and $.8''$. Take

---

* As the radius of a circle is increased indefinitely, any arc of the circle approaches more and more to a straight line; and when the radius becomes infinite, the arc becomes a straight line.

the radius of the describing circles $1\frac{7}{8}''$, as before. It is evident that the tooth profile will be formed of parts of cycloids formed by rolling the describing (generating) circle upon the pitch line $A\,B$. Draw a small part of the cycloidal curves, as shown in the figure, by the method given in Fig. **1**; lay off the addendum and root and find the approximate radius in the same manner as in the last figure. The centers of the curves for the faces and flanks of all the teeth of the rack will evidently lie on the straight lines passing through Q and Q', respectively, and parallel to the pitch line $A\,B$.

139. In Fig. **6** is shown the manner of drawing the **involute,** or **single-curve tooth.** The profile in this case is formed of a portion of an involute curve and a portion of the radius of the pitch circle. The circle from which the involute is constructed is called, in this case, the **base circle.** To find it draw the pitch circle, of which the arc $A\,B$ is a part, with a radius equal to $5\frac{1}{2}''$ and having its center at O. Draw any radius $O\,W$ cutting the arc $A\,B$ in D. Through D draw the straight line $E\,F$, making an angle of 75° with $O\,W$. With O as a center and a radius to be found by trial, draw a circle tangent to $E\,F$. This circle, of which the arc $H\,G$ is a part, is the base circle, and cuts $O\,W$ in P. Upon this circle construct, in exactly the same manner as was shown in Fig. **3,** a portion of an involute curve passing through P. Lay off the addendum $I\,K = .6''$, and with O as a center and $O\,I$ as a radius describe an arc to form the top of the tooth, intersecting the involute in L. That part of the flank below the base circle is straight and is a part of the radius drawn to the point P. $K\,I'$ is the root. The tooth has a fillet at L' and R', as in cycloidal teeth. A circular arc is passed through the points L and P, coinciding as nearly as possible with the involute curve $L\,P$. Its center Q is found in the same manner as in Fig. **4.** For involute teeth it is only necessary to find the one center Q; the centers for all the remaining teeth lie on a circle having O as a center and passing through Q. To draw the other side of the tooth, lay off on the pitch circle $MN = .96''$, as before. With M as a center and $QN = QP$ as a radius draw an arc cutting, at Q_1, the circle passing through Q; with Q_1 as a center and the same radius describe the part $P'R$ of the tooth profile above the base circle. The part $P'R$ below the base circle is a part of the radius OP'.

140. In drawing any of the curves previously described, the greater the number of parts into which the describing or base circles are divided, the greater will be the accuracy obtained. The profile of the rack tooth used for involute gears is a straight line making an angle of 15° with a line drawn perpendicular to the pitch line. Its construction is shown in Fig. 7.

DEFINITIONS AND CALCULATIONS

141. When a revolving shaft transmits motion to another shaft parallel to it by means of gear-wheels or tooth-wheels in such a manner that two corresponding points, one on each gear-wheel, always lie in the same plane, the two gears are called **spur gear-wheels.** When the shafts are not parallel, but their axes intersect in a point, as O in Plate 1015, they are called **bevel gear-wheels.** If two bevel gear-wheels that work together have pitch diameters of the same size, they are called **miter gear-wheels.**

From what has preceded, it is evident that *the circular pitch multiplied by the number of teeth equals the circumference of the pitch circle.*

Let p = circular pitch of gear-wheel;
          n = number of teeth;
          d = pitch diameter;
          π = 3.1416 (π is pronounced **pi).**

Then, $$d = \frac{pn}{\pi} \qquad (1)$$

or, *the diameter of the pitch circle equals the circular pitch multiplied by the number of teeth divided by 3.1416.*

$$p = \frac{d\pi}{n} \qquad (2)$$

or, *the circular pitch equals the pitch diameter multiplied by 3.1416 divided by the number of teeth.*

$$n = \frac{d\pi}{p} \qquad (3)$$

or, *the number of teeth equals the pitch diameter multiplied by 3.1416 divided by the circular pitch.*

When constructing cycloidal teeth for gear-wheels, the diameters of the describing circles are usually made equal to one-half the diameter of the pitch circle of a gear-wheel having 12 teeth of the same pitch as those of the gear-wheel about to be made.

Let d' be the diameter of the describing circle; then,

$$d' = \frac{12\,p}{\pi} \times \tfrac{1}{2}, \text{ or } d' = \frac{6\,p}{\pi} \qquad (4)$$

Addendum = $.3p$; root = $.4p$; thickness of teeth for cast gears is $.48p$, and for cut gears $\tfrac{1}{2}p$.

PLATE 1014, TITLE:

GEAR AND PINION

142. This Plate shows the halves of two cast **gear-wheels** having cycloidal teeth, which work together, a cross-section of each gear being also given. The drawing is full size, the wheels not being shown entire for want of room; to have done so it would have been necessary to make the drawing to a reduced scale. The pitch is $1''$, the number of teeth in the large gear is 36, and in the small one 18. The pitch diameter of the large wheel is found by formula **1** to be

$$d = \frac{1 \times 36}{3.1416} = 11.46'', \text{ nearly}$$

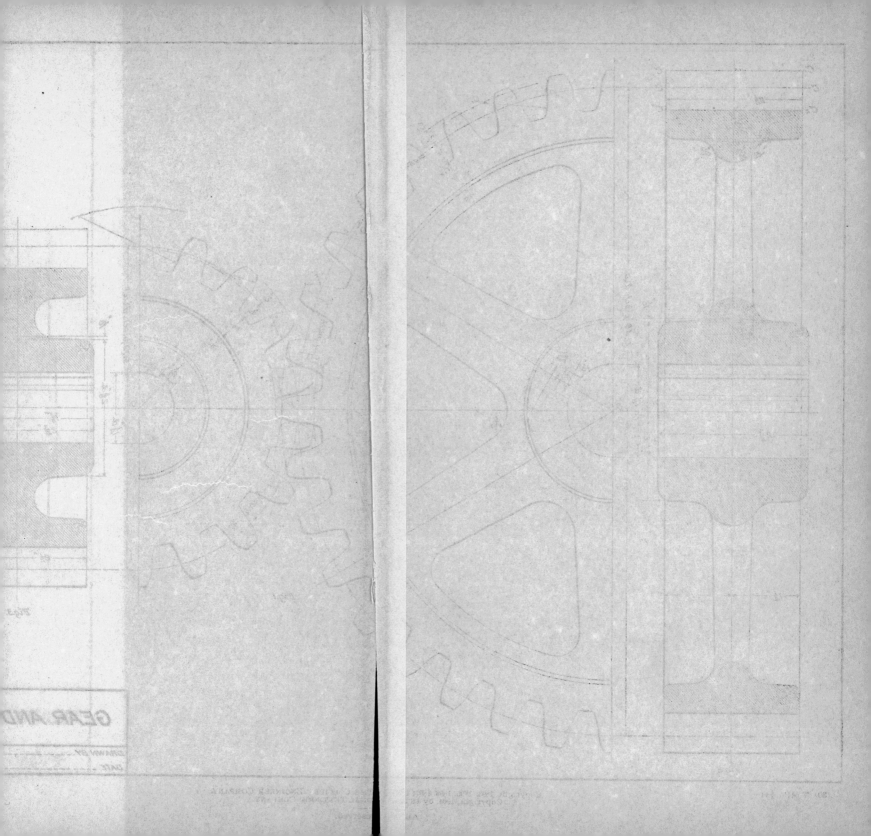

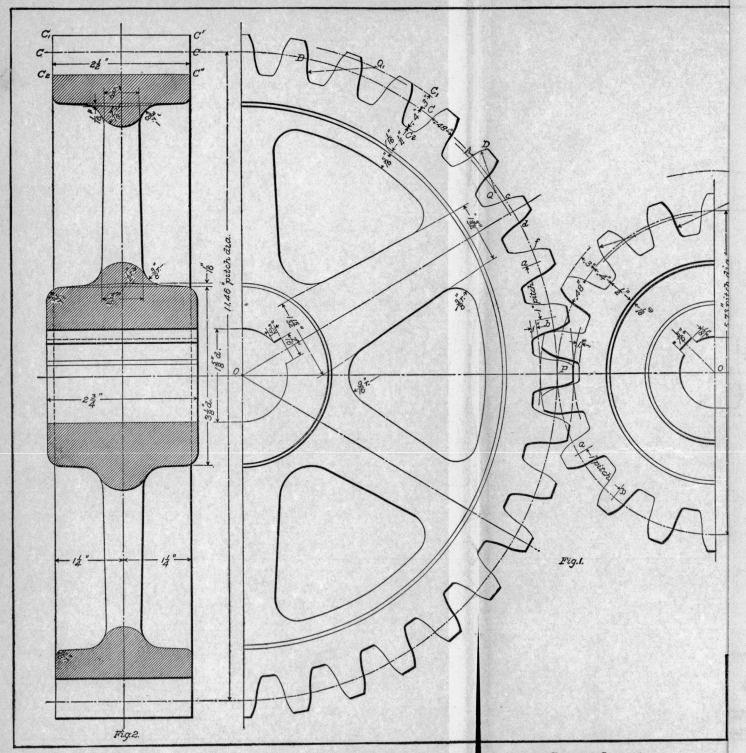

Fig.1.

Fig.2.

The pitch diameter of the small gear

$$= \frac{1 \times 18}{3.1416} = 5.73'', \text{ nearly}$$

The diameter of the describing circle is found by formula **4** to be

$$d' = \frac{6 \times 1}{3.1416} = 1.91''$$

For all practical purposes, the diameter of the describing circle may be taken to the nearest 16th inch. For circular pitches under $\frac{1}{2}''$, approximate the diameter of the describing circle to the nearest 32d inch. To find the nearest 16th or 32d, multiply the decimal part of the diameter by 16 or 32 and take the nearest whole number of the product as the number of 16ths or 32ds that the decimal represents. Thus, in the above, the decimal part of the diameter is .91''; .91 × 16 = 14.56. The nearest whole number to 14.56 is 15; hence, the diameter of the describing circle is $1\frac{15}{16}''$. If the diameter had been required to the nearest 32d, .91 × 32 = 29.12; 29 is the nearest whole number; hence, the diameter would be $1\frac{29}{32}''$. In this case, take the diameter as $1\frac{15}{16}''$, approximating to the nearest 16th for all circular pitches above $\frac{1}{2}''$. The addendum will be .3 × 1'' = .3''; the root = .4 × 1'' = .4''; and the thickness of the tooth on the pitch circle = .48 × 1'' = .48''.

Draw the line of centers $O\,O'$ between the two axes. With O as a center describe a semicircle having a diameter of 11.46'', cutting $O\,O'$ in P. With O' as a center describe a semicircle having a diameter of 5.73'' which shall be tangent to the first circle; this semicircle also cuts $O\,O'$ in P. These are the pitch circles. Divide the larger pitch circle into $\frac{36}{2}$, or 18 equal parts by using the protractor.

This is accomplished by laying the protractor on the drawing in such a manner that the center of the protractor coincides with the center O of the gear-wheel and then laying off on the drawing 18 divisions, each equal to 10°. The reason for this will be clear when it is remembered that there are 360° in a circle, or $\frac{360°}{2} = 180°$ in a semicircle, and as there are 18 teeth in the semicircle, $180° \div 18 = 10°$, which is the angle between two lines drawn from the centers of any two consecutive teeth to the center O. In a like manner, any circle may be divided into parts by using the protractor. Make $C C_1 = .3'' =$ addendum, and $C C_2 = .4'' =$ root. With O as a center and $O C_1$ and $O C_2$ as radii, describe light circles, called **addendum** and **root circles,** to represent the tops and bottoms of the teeth. Consider the points of division just laid off on the pitch circle as the centers of the teeth, and lay off on each side one-half of the thickness $c d$ of the tooth, or $.48 \times \frac{1}{2} = .24''$. Upon another sheet of paper strike a short arc of the pitch circle and construct the profile of the tooth as described in Plate 1013, using describing circles $1\frac{1}{16}''$ in diameter. Having found the centers Q and Q_1 of the circular arcs used for the profiles of the teeth, draw circular arcs through these centers, as previously described; then, with O (see Plate 1014) as a center and the same radii describe circles; these circles will contain the centers of the circular arcs which form the teeth profiles. With the point A as a center and a radius equal to the radius of the face of the tooth (found on the other sheet of paper), describe an arc intersecting the circle of face centers at Q. With Q as a center and the same radius, describe the arc $A D$ for the face of the tooth, the point D being the point of intersection of $A D$ with the addendum circle. In the same way draw the remaining faces of the teeth. To draw the flanks take a point representing the intersection of a tooth profile with the pitch circle (the point B, for example) as a center and a radius equal to the radius of the flank found on the other paper on which the tooth profile was drawn, and describe an arc intersecting the circle of the flank centers in Q_1. With Q_1 as a center and the same radius, describe the flank curve, stopping at the root circle. Draw the flanks of the remaining teeth in the same way and then put in the fillets. The remaining part of Fig. 1 can be easily drawn from the dimensions given.

Fig. 2 is a conventional method of drawing cross-sections of gears. The hubs and rims are sectioned, but the teeth and arms are not. This is similar to the wheel shown on Plate 1005. This method of sectioning makes the views clearer and saves the time spent in sectioning.

In Fig. 3 the entire gear is sectioned, except the teeth. The student should now be able to finish the Plate without further instructions.

PLATE 1015, TITLE:

BEVEL GEARS

143. To draw in section and projection two cast **bevel gears** whose axes intersect at right angles: The number of teeth in the large gear is 20, in the pinion 16.   The circular pitch is $1''$; the teeth are to be of the cycloidal form, having a face $2''$ wide. In any kind of gearing, whether spur, bevel, or spiral, the smaller wheel is called the **pinion.**

Calculate the pitch diameters, addenda, roots, and describing circles by the same rules that were given for spur gears.

$$\text{Diameter of pinion} = \frac{16 \times 1''}{3.1416} = 5.09''$$

$$\text{Diameter of the large gear} = \frac{20 \times 1''}{3.1416} = 6.37''$$

$$\text{Diameter of describing circle} = \frac{6 \times 1''}{3.1416} = 1.91''$$

Take this as $1\frac{15}{16}''$, as in the last Plate.

Addendum $= .3''$; root $= .4''$. The sectional view, Fig. **1,** must be drawn first.   Draw PP' and through some point P' on this line draw $P'P_1$ perpendicular to it. Lay off PP' equal to the diameter of the pinion $= 5.09''$; also $P'P_1$ equal to the diameter of large gear $= 6.37''$. Bisect PP' and $P'P_1$, and draw OM and ON perpendicular to those lines at the point of bisection; they intersect in O. $O M$ and $O N$ are the axes of the two gears and intersect at right angles as required. Draw $P O P_1$ and $P' O$. Through P draw $A P M$ perpendicular to $O P$. Through P' draw $M P' N$ perpendicular to $O P'$ and through P_1 draw $P_1 N$ perpendicular to $O P_1$. $P M$ and $P' M$ intersect at M on the line $O M$; $P' N$ and $P_1 N$ intersect at N, on the line $O N$. Lay off $P' C'$, $P C$, and $P_1 C_1$, each equal to $2''$, or the width of the face of the teeth; these lines are called the **pitch lines,** and the width of the face of the teeth is always measured on these lines. Lay off $P A$ equal to $.3'' =$ the addendum, and $P B$ equal to $.4'' =$ the root. Lay off $P' E$ and $P' D$ for the addendum and root of the other side, and $P' E'$ and $P' D_1$ for the addendum and root of the large gear. All these addenda and roots are each equal to $.3''$ and $.4''$, respectively. In bevel gears, all straight lines of the tooth profiles pass through the point of intersection O of the axes; hence, draw $A O$, and $A A'$ will be the projection of the top of the tooth. Draw $B O$, and $B B'$ will represent the bottom of the tooth, the line $A' C B'$ being perpendicular to $O P$. Make $B F'$, $D F$, $D_1 F_1$, etc. each equal to $\frac{1}{2}''$, according to dimensions. Join F', F, F_1, and F_2 with O, intersecting the perpendiculars through C, C', and C_1 (namely, the lines $A' C B'$, etc. produced) at G', G, G_1, and G_2. G', G and $G_1 G_2$ will represent the bottom of the gears. The rest of the sectional part can be drawn from the dimensions.

144. To show the shape of the teeth, proceed as follows: For the large gear, take N as a center, $N P'$ as a radius, and describe an arc. Choose a point H and lay off $H H'$ $= .48$ times the pitch $= .48''$, or the width of the tooth. With $N E'$ and $N D_1$ as radii, describe the addendum and root circles. Roll the describing circles upon the arc whose radius is $N P'$ and construct the tooth profile in exactly the same manner as in Fig. 4 of Plate 1013, $Q H$ and $Q_1 H'$ being the radii of the faces and flanks. To show the shape of the same tooth at C', draw $C' N'$ perpendicular to $O P'$, or, what is the same thing, parallel to NP'. With $N'C'$ as a radius and N as a center, describe an arc. Draw NH and NH', and the distance between the points of intersection on the arc just drawn, measured on that arc, will be the pitch of the gear at the bottom of the tooth. With the same center and $N'E_1$ and $N'E_2$ as radii, describe arcs representing the addendum and root circles. Draw NQ and NQ_1, also QH and Q_1H'. Through K draw KQ' parallel to HQ, and through K' draw $K'Q_2$ parallel to $H'Q_1$; the points of intersection Q' and Q_2 of these lines with NQ and NQ_1 are the centers for the face and flank of the tooth at K and K'. Circles passing through these points concentric with N contain the centers of all the circular arcs forming the tooth profiles that may be laid off upon the arc whose radius is NK. The whole process is called **developing the teeth of bevel gears.**

In the same manner construct the tooth curves for the pinion, using the same describing circles, $1\frac{5}{16}''$ in diameter, and MP', $M'C'$ as radii, instead of NP' and $N'C'$.

145. To construct the other view, draw first the projection of the pinion. Draw the center line mn. Produce the lines FF', DB, $P'P$, and EA across the drawing, as shown. Choose a point S on mn as a center and draw a quadrant with a radius equal to the radius of the pinion, as SP. Project the points D and E upon MO in D_2 and E_3. With S as a center and the distances E_3E and D_2D as radii, describe quadrants to represent the tops and bottoms of the teeth, that is, the projection of the addendum and root circles of the pinion in Fig. **2.** Since the whole pinion contains 16 teeth, the quadrant will contain 4 teeth; hence, divide the quadrant into 4 equal parts on the pitch circle to represent the centers of the teeth. Lay off on each side of the points of division distances ge and gb, each equal to one-half the thickness of the tooth. On each side of the points of division on the addendum circle lay off hf and hc, each equal to one-half the thickness of the top of the tooth JK, Fig. **1,** measured on the addendum circle. On each side of the points of division on the root circle lay off id and ia, each equal to one-half the thickness of the tooth at the root, as OP, Fig. 1, measured on the root circle.   Having now three points on each side of all the teeth to the right of the center line mn, project them upon the lines EA, $P'P$, and DB, produced as shown.   For example, project f and c upon EA in f' and c'; e and b upon $P'P$ in e' and b'; d and a upon DB in d' and a'.   Draw a curve through these points, either by using an irregular curve or by circular arcs. This remark also applies to the other curves shown in the quadrant.

146.   The tooth curves in Fig. 1 must be drawn as accurately as possible, but those shown in Fig. 2, being oblique projections, are drawn to satisfy the eye, and no particular accuracy is required.   To find the points on the tooth curves at the bottom of the pinion, describe a circle having a center O_2 upon mn, which shall be tangent to PP' and have a diameter equal to $6.37'' =$ the diameter of the large gear.   Through B' and A', Fig. 1, draw lines parallel to OO_2; also draw other lines through O_2 and the points d', f', c', etc., cutting the lines first drawn in d'', f'', c'', etc. Two points are considered enough in this case, as the curves are very short.   They may be drawn in with the irregular curve in the same manner as the tops.   The other teeth are drawn in a similar manner.   Draw the middle tooth first. The left-hand half of the pinion is exactly the same as the right-hand half.

147.   To draw the projection of the large gear, project the points E', D_1, L, and R upon the axis ON, in the points E_4, D_3, L_1, and R_1, and with O_2 as a center and radii equal to $E_4 E'$, $D_3 D_1$, $L_1 L$, and $R_1 R$, describe circles to represent the addendum and root circles of the tops and bottoms of the teeth in Fig. 2.   Divide the pitch circle into 20 equal parts, to correspond with the number of teeth in the large gear, beginning with the point of intersection of the pitch circle with the center line mn.   Lay off on each side of these pitch-circle divisions, distances equal to one-half the thickness of the teeth = one-half of HH' in Fig. **1**. By exactly the same method that was used to lay off the thickness of the teeth at the top and bottom on the quadrant, lay off the thickness of the top and bottom of the teeth on the addendum and root circles in Fig. **2**. Draw the bottoms of the teeth in exactly the same manner as the bottoms of the pinion teeth were drawn. All the teeth of the large gear are alike in the projected view.

148. Bevel gears are always measured according to their largest pitch diameter, as PP' and $P'P_1$. If a bevel gear were spoken of as 12″ in diameter, it would be understood that the largest pitch diameter was 12″.

PLATE 1016, TITLE:

DRIVING PULLEY, FLYWHEEL, AND CRANK-SHAFT

149. A steam engine has been chosen as a final example for this paper. The design is one that will give a great deal of practice in laying out various mechanical details and in making an assembly (Plate 1021) from the details found on Plates 1016, 1017, 1018, 1019, and 1020, which together form the complete drawings for this engine. On the various plates, the parts have been grouped so as to show their general relationship to each other. The scale used is, with some few exceptions, $3'' = 1$ ft.

150. Of the parts shown on Plate 1016, the pulley and flywheel should easily be constructed without any additional explanation, by simply following the instructions given in connection with Plate 1005. Locate their horizontal center lines $4\frac{9}{16}''$ below the upper border line and the vertical center lines of the two views of part *1*, $4\frac{5}{8}''$ and $7''$, respectively, from the left-hand border line. The vertical center lines of part *2* should be $4\frac{3}{8}''$ and $1\frac{3}{8}''$, respectively, from the right-hand border line.

Part *3* is a forged-steel crank-shaft, on one end of which is to be mounted the driving pulley and on the other end the flywheel, both held in position by keys partly sunk into the shaft and partly into the hubs. The crank-shaft consists of the shaft proper and of two arms projecting at right angles, called the *webs*, which are connected by a short stud-like part, the *crankpin*. The vertical center line of the flywheel is $11\frac{3}{8}''$ (see Plate 1016) from that of the crankpin, the latter center being coincident with that of the cylinder and connecting rod, while the center line of the driving pulley is $11\frac{1}{4}''$ to the other side of the crankpin center. It should be noticed that on the Plate the abbreviation $\mathcal{C}$ has been used for the term center line.

After the flywheel and driving pulley have been mounted on the shaft, the latter is placed in the bearings of the engine frame. The centers of these bearings are indicated as being $5\frac{1}{8}''$ to either side of the crankpin center. It will be noticed that the two keyways are not alike, the one for the driving pulley being cut clear to the end, while the one for the flywheel stops a short distance from the end. The stroke of the engine is determined by the distance between the horizontal center line of the crankpin and that of the shaft. This distance is here $4''$ and the stroke will therefore be $4'' \times 2 = 8''$.

The shaft is $2\frac{1}{4}''$ in diameter; the web is $2\frac{3}{4}''$ wide by $1\frac{1}{2}''$ thick and rounded off to a radius of $6\frac{3}{4}''$. Locate the center line of shaft $3''$ above the lower border line, and the vertical center line through the crank and end view of shaft $4\frac{15}{16}''$ and $9\frac{3}{4}''$, respectively, from the left-hand border line.

PLATE 1017, TITLE;

ENGINE FRAME

151. On this Plate are shown a plan, a side elevation, an end view, two cross-sections, and some details of the engine frame, all drawn to a scale of $3'' = 1$ ft. The elevation and plan are to be drawn together. Locate the center lines of these two views $2\frac{3}{4}''$ and $6\frac{3}{4}''$, respectively, below the upper border line and extend them the whole length of the Plate, as they are also to serve for the end views.   The vertical center line, which in both views passes

through the center of crank-shaft, should be $2\frac{1}{2}''$ from the right-hand border line. Locate the main horizontal dimensions from this center line.   Draw the base line of the elevation $9''$ (to scale) below the center of the crank-shaft and make the base of the pedestal at crank-shaft end of frame $11\frac{1}{2}''$ long and $15\frac{3}{4}''$ wide.   The position of the center line of the base at the cylinder end is found by laying off 3 ft. $3\frac{1}{8}''$ (the distance between shaft center and cylinder end of frame) and then measuring back $8''$; the base at this end is $14''$ long by $9\frac{1}{2}''$ wide.

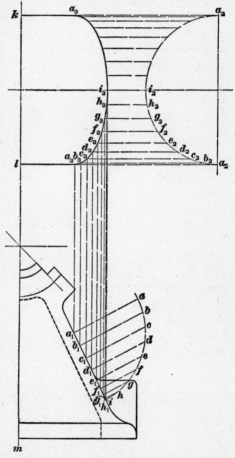

FIG. 52

The two cross-sections, one of which is taken at AA and the other at BB, indicate the shape of the frame, showing that the latter, on the whole, is cylindrical.   The elevation shows that the lower part of the frame curves downwards before joining the base under the crank-shaft.   The form of this curve as it appears in the elevation is determined by

locating a number of points from the vertical and horizontal
center lines and base line, as shown by the dimensions on
the drawing. The points are then joined by lines drawn
with the irregular curve. Before joining this curve to the
cylindrical part of the frame, draw first the bead-like rib
seen at this end, indicated by a circle $\frac{3}{4}''$ in diameter (see
section on BB) and draw the curve tangential to this
circle. The pedestal is pyramidal in shape, as seen in the
elevation, with a semicircular opening in the top. To
show this opening properly in the plan view, the special
construction shown in Fig. 52 is required, in which
the lower view represents the end of the frame in
elevation. The semicircle, $6\frac{3}{4}''$ in diameter, representing
the lower part of the opening, is supposed to have been
turned at right angles about its vertical radius so as to lie
in the plane of the paper. Only a quarter circle has been
shown—the other part being symmetrical to it—and this has
been divided into 8 equal parts, as shown at $a\,b,\ b\,c,\ c\,d$, etc.
From these division points, projectors are drawn at right
angles to side of frame, as indicated by lines $a\,a_1,\ b\,b_1,\ c\,c_1$, etc.

A plan view of the opening is now to be drawn above the
elevation by first drawing the semicircle $a_2\,i_2\,a_2$, representing
a plan of the opening, and dividing it in 16 parts, since the
whole semicircle is shown here. Draw horizontals from the
points $a_2,\ b_2,\ c_2$, etc., letting them intersect verticals from
the points $a_1,\ b_1,\ c_1$, etc., the points of intersection being
points on the curve, as shown at $a_3,\ b_3,\ c_3$, etc. Draw
horizontals through the two points a_3 toward the center
line, when the lines $k\,a_3$ and $l\,a_3$ will indicate the outline of
the opening as it will appear in the plan view. Verticals
have been shown as only intersecting the horizontals from
the lower half of the semicircle, but it is understood that
they should be continued so as also to intersect those in the
upper half, this part of the view being symmetrical to the
lower half.

152. The face of the crank-shaft bearing is inclined at
an angle of 45° with the horizontal, and has two $\frac{3}{4}''$ studs

tapped into the frame for each cap. The lower half of
the bearing and the cap are each lined with Babbitt $\frac{3}{8}''$ thick.
For aid in drawing these bearings in the plan view, the
student should refer to Fig. 53.   The method employed is

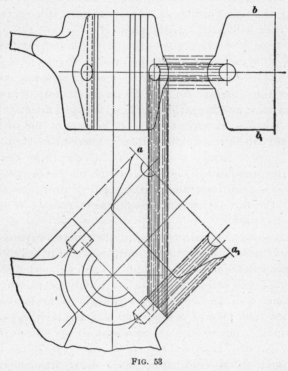

FIG. 53

identical with that used in Fig. 52, and for this reason it was
not thought necessary to supply it with reference letters or
to enter into any detailed description of same.   The dimensions of the plan view $a\,a_1$ shown in connection with the
main elevation in Fig. 53, are derived from the plan view of
the cap, part 2, the outlines being identical for both parts.
The outlines of the stud holes and the curved parts of the
frame adjoining same are divided into a certain number of
parts, not necessarily as many as are indicated in the illustration, and these points are projected to the main elevation.

Another plan view $b\,b_1$ located as shown, is subdivided in a similar manner, and from the points of division, horizontals are drawn intersecting vertical lines drawn from the elevation at the points indicated. When these points are joined by circular arcs, the centers of which must be found by trial, the true outlines of frame and holes will be found, and as they will appear in the plan.

153. The walls of the frame are $\frac{5}{8}''$ thick and have a raised surface that is bored for the crosshead slide, as indicated in the cross-section, and by means of dotted lines in the plan view and elevation. These surfaces are $12\frac{1}{4}''$ long and bored to a diameter of $6\frac{1}{4}''$, the centers of the surfaces being $15\frac{5}{8}''$ from the cylinder face. There is at the center of the upper surface a grease or oil receptacle through which the crosshead is oiled. Near the middle of the opening in the side of the frame will be seen the four bosses that support the valve-stem guide by means of four $\frac{1}{2}''$ hexagonhead bolts, part 7.

The boss on the cylinder end of the frame projects into the center bore of the cylinder, but an actual fit is only had along the small shoulder $\frac{1}{16}''$ high. The cylinder is held in position by the seven studs, part 5, which are tapped into the frame end. In the end view, shown to the left of the plan view, the plan of drilling and tapping for these studs is indicated, from which it is seen that all the studs are not equally spaced. Locate the vertical center line of this view $1\frac{15}{16}''$ from the left-hand border line. Next draw the crosssection taken on line $A\,A$ of the elevation, with its center line $2\frac{3}{16}''$ from the left-hand border line. This section is intended to represent the right-hand part of the elevation, but most of the parts beyond the plan of section have been omitted to avoid any superfluity of lines. Two of the bosses that support the valve-stem guide are also seen in this view.

Below and on the same center line the other sectional view is to be shown. The outlines of this section are circular arcs, the exterior one having a radius of $4''$. Locate its center $2\frac{1}{4}''$ above the lower border line. To define the height of this section draw a horizontal line at a distance above its lowest point equal to the height of the frame along the line BB (this distance should be measured on the drawing) in the elevation. BB should cut all four curves at as nearly right angles as is possible. The frame is $\frac{5}{8}''$ thick at this place and a circular arc with a radius of $3\frac{3}{8}''$ is therefore drawn concentric to the former arc. Tangential to this inner arc and to the horizontal, top, boundary line, draw two circles with a radius of $\frac{3}{8}''$; draw fillets between these circles and the outside arc.

154. Next draw the bearing cap, part *2*, shown in plan and elevation, with the grease cup, the top of which makes an angle of 45° with the horizontal and whose sides are outlined by a curve with $1\frac{3}{4}''$ radius. The reason for this inclination is the necessity of having the upper edge of cup horizontal when the cap is in position on the frame.

Part *3* is the gland that fits about the piston rod and holds the piston-rod packing in place in the stuffingbox. The latter is made by recessing the inside of the frame, as indicated by dotted lines at the cylinder end of the frame. The position and shape of this recess are shown by the dotted lines. Two $\frac{1}{2}''$ studs, part *4*, which are tapped into the frame at ff', support the gland.

PLATE 1018, TITLE:

VALVE GEAR

155. The cross-section assembly in the upper part of this Plate shows the relation and connection between valve, guide, slide, eccentric rod, eccentric strap, and eccentric sheave, all these parts being detailed elsewhere on the drawing. All the parts are drawn half size, except part *5*, drawn full size, and all are provided with reference numbers corresponding with those on the assembly. Draw the details first, then the cross-section assembly.

156. Part *1*, the valve, is made of cast iron from pattern *1018–A*. It is a cup-shaped device, through the top of which the valve rod, part *11*, passes. Its position in the steam chest regulates the entrance of the steam through the ports that connect with the ends of the cylinder and permits also the exhaust steam to pass from these ports into the exhaust port, which connects with the exhaust pipe.

Locate the horizontal center line of the valve-rod boss $3\frac{9}{16}''$ (actual measurement) below the upper border line, and the vertical center lines of the two views $2''$ and $4\frac{5}{16}''$, respectively, from the left-hand border line. The left-hand view is a side elevation and the other an end view. On top of the boss is seen a rib-like projection; this slides on a corresponding rib on the steam-chest cover, which serves to hold the valve in place.

157. Part *2*, the valve-stem slide, is supported by parts *3* and *4* which, in turn, are bolted to the engine frame through the four holes in the bosses shown in the center of the opening in the elevation of the frame, Plate 1017. The slide is square shaped, with a stud at its center to which the eccentric rod is connected. Draw the horizontal center line for the two views at a distance of $5\frac{1}{8}''$ (full size) below the upper border line and the vertical center lines $2\frac{13}{16}''$ and $6\frac{3}{16}''$, from the left-hand border line.

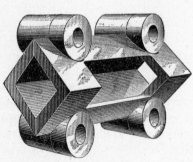

FIG. 54

Parts *3* and *4* are the two halves of the valve-stem guide, the exact shape of which is somewhat difficult to understand from the drawings alone. As an aid in gaining a clear conception of this part, the perspective view, Fig. 54, has been added. The junction of the parts is found along the center line common to the plan view and adjoining end view, part of each of the four bosses belonging to the front and part to the rear of the guide. The front of the guide has a rectangular opening $1\frac{1}{2}'' \times 3\frac{3}{4}''$. Locate the horizontal center lines of the two upper views $5\frac{1}{4}''$ and that of the lower view $3\frac{1}{8}''$ above the lower border line. Draw the vertical center lines $2\frac{1}{8}''$ and $5\frac{3}{8}''$, respectively, from the left-hand border line.

. 158. Part *5* is the clamping nut that locks the eccentric rod to the eccentric strap, part *9*. Locate the two views on the same center line as the lower view of part *4* and leave a space between the three views of $\frac{3}{4}''$ and $\frac{1}{4}''$ (full size), respectively. It is noticed that the hole in the nut is threaded only up to a distance of $\frac{3}{8}''$ from the outer end, this part being enlarged in diameter. According to a rule previously given, threads are to be omitted on tapped holes shown in elevation by means of dotted lines. Contrary to this rule threads have been added to some of the holes indicated on this Plate, as, for instance, on part *5*. Here the addition of threads brings out more clearly the fact that this hole is not threaded along its whole length.

Parts *6* and *7* are the eccentric rod and strap, the threaded end of part *6* being screwed into part *9*, while the other end, together with part *7*, is clamped about the stud on part *2*. The bolts, part *15*, pass through the strap and screw into the threaded holes in the rod. Locate the horizontal center line $1\frac{1}{16}''$ (full size) above the lower border line and leave a space of $\frac{5}{16}''$ between the first view and left-hand border line, and spaces of $\frac{19}{32}''$ and $\frac{1}{2}''$ between the first, second, and third views; make the latter $4\frac{1}{2}''$ long and leave a space between this and the fourth view of $\frac{9}{16}''$.

159. Part *8* is the eccentric sheave, which is fastened to the crank-shaft by means of the two setscrews *17* that pass through the tapped holes indicated. Its center is $\frac{7}{8}''$ to one side of the shaft center, this distance determining the *throw*

of the eccentric and the travel of the valve. Draw the
horizontal center line $2\frac{5}{16}''$ above the lower border line
and the vertical center line of the elevation $7\frac{1}{4}''$ from the
right-hand border line, leaving a space of $\frac{9}{16}''$ between
the two views of this part.

Parts 9 and 10 are the halves of the eccentric strap which
embraces the revolving eccentric sheave. They are prevented from sliding sidewise by the engagement of the central rib on the sheave with a corresponding groove in the
strap. Two bolts 16 are inserted through holes in the latter
and hold the halves together by means of nuts and check-
nuts. The lines of intersection between the oil cup and
strap, as shown in elevation, are indicated by two curves,
the radii of which have not been indicated, as it will suffice
if the student draw them approximately. The same remark
applies to the intersections shown in the end view. The
sectional view shown below the elevation is a section taken
along the horizontal center line. Locate it and also the
center line of the sectional view $5\frac{9}{16}''$ and $8\frac{5}{16}''$, respectively,
below the upper border line and lay off the vertical center
lines $6\frac{5}{16}''$ and $2\frac{5}{8}''$, respectively, from the right-hand border
line.

160. The valve rod, part 11, is shown in position in the
sectional assembly and is detailed in the upper part of the
Plate. It has two long threaded portions, one at each end,
on which the nuts 12, 14 and check-nuts 13 are screwed,
whereby the valve and slide may be secured to the rod and
the distance between the valve and slide adjusted. When
drawing part 11, locate its center line $\frac{3}{4}''$ below the upper
border line, its right-hand end $1\frac{3}{16}''$ from the adjacent border
line, and make the rod $5\frac{3}{4}''$ long (actual measurement).
The distance from end to end of the threaded portion should
be $1\frac{5}{8}''$.

In drawing the assembly, lay off the center line of the
valve rod $1\frac{3}{16}''$ below the upper border line and the vertical
center lines of the valve, slide, and shaft $2''$, $7''$, and $14''$,
respectively, from the left-hand border line

PLATE 1019, TITLE:

PISTON, CROSSHEAD, AND CONNECTING-ROD

161. In the sectional assembly, Fig. 55, is seen the pis-

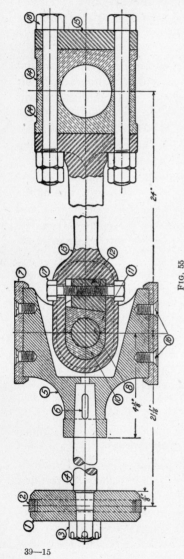

FIG. 55

ton *1*, which is given a reciprocating motion in the steam
cylinder by the steam acting
alternately on either side of
it.   Its motion is conveyed
by the piston rod *4* to the
crosshead *5*, the latter containing in its interior one end
of the connecting-rod *13*
swinging around a pin *8*,
while the other end has a
bearing *14* that embraces the
crankpin.   In this manner
the force acting on the piston
is transmitted to the crankpin, where the reciprocating
motion of the piston is
changed into a rotary one.
All the views on this Plate
are drawn half size, except
those of parts *3*, *4*, *6*, *8*, and *9*,
which are drawn full size.

162. The piston, part *1*
(see detail numbered *1*) is
made of cast iron and is provided on its outer edge with
a groove for the piston ring,
and with a central hole for
the piston rod.   The hole is
composed of a straight and a
tapered part, the straight
part extending to a point
$\frac{7}{16}''$ from one end.   The

diameter of the hole varies from $\frac{3}{4}''$ to $\frac{13}{16}''$, the latter dimension applying to a point $\frac{1}{16}''$ from end of hole at which place the hole is countersunk, enlarging the diameter to $1''$. Locate the horizontal center line of the two views, $2''$ from the upper border line, and the vertical center line $1\frac{11}{16}''$ from the left-hand border line, leaving a space of $\frac{7}{16}''$ between the two views.

163. The piston ring, part 2, fits in the groove around the outside of the piston; it provides a steam-tight fit between the piston and the cylinder walls, and is for this reason made expansible by leaving an opening of $\frac{25}{64}''$ between its ends. It will be noticed that the ring is larger in diameter than the inside one of the cylinder; but when sprung into place in the cylinder it will adjust itself to the cylinder bore and the two ends will approach each other, until they nearly touch. The horizontal center line of the two views may be drawn $5\frac{9}{16}''$ from the upper border line, and the vertical center line of the elevation placed $1\frac{13}{16}''$ from the left-hand border line; a space of $\frac{5}{16}''$ is left between these views.

The crown nut, part 3, fits the end of the piston rod and fastens the piston securely to the latter. To prevent an accidental turning of the nut, it is provided with a series of grooves into which fits a pin, which also passes through a hole in end of piston rod. The horizontal center line of these views is placed $2\frac{11}{16}''$ from lower border line, and the vertical one of the elevation $5''$ from the left-hand border line, leaving a space of $\frac{5}{8}''$ between the views.

164. The piston rod, part 4, is tapered at both ends, one to fit the piston and the other the crosshead. When the dimension of one end of a tapered piece is given, together with its length, the dimension of the other end may be found either by calculation or by construction. In the first case it is found by means of proportion. For instance: the taper at one end of the rod is 1 in 16, the full diameter of the rod $1''$, and the length of the tapered portion $2\frac{1}{4}''$.

The proportion $1 : 16 = x : 2\frac{1}{4}''$ gives a value for x of .1406; by subtracting this value from $1''$ it is found that the extreme end of the rod should be $1'' - .1406'' = .8594'' = .8594 \times \frac{64}{64} = \frac{55}{64}''$ in diameter.

If this diameter is found by construction, proceed as follows: A taper of 1 in 16 is, of course, equal to $\frac{1}{16}$ in 1. Multiply the fraction expressing the increase or decrease in $1''$ by some convenient length, preferably by some number that will divide the denominator without a remainder, in this case, by 4, obtaining $\frac{1}{16}'' \times 4 = \frac{1}{4}''$; this represents the difference in the diameters $4''$ apart. Hence, $4''$ from where the taper begins draw a line at right angles to the center line and lay off on it on either side of the center line $\frac{1}{2}'' - (\frac{1}{4}'' \div 2) = \frac{3}{8}''$. Join the points as laid off with the extremities of the line defining the beginning of the taper by straight lines, and measure back from this line the length of the tapered part $2\frac{1}{4}''$, drawing through this point a line perpendicular to the center line. At the other end of the rod the diameter is $\frac{3}{4}''$, and the taper is 1 in 12. This end is to fit the hole in the piston, part *1*, and as the diameters and length of the hole is given in the views of the piston, the tapered part of the piston rod may be drawn by means of these dimensions.

Locate the center line of the rod $1''$ above the lower border line; leave a space of $\frac{3}{4}''$ between the rod and the left-hand border line and make the rod $8''$ long.

165. The crosshead, part *5*, is fitted to the piston rod by the tapered key, part *6*, which is driven through it and the piston rod, the hole in the piston rod being indicated by dotted lines at the right-hand end, part *4*. The crosshead receives the end of the connecting-rod, which is kept in place by the crosshead pin, part *8*. The upper and lower interior surfaces of the crosshead taper toward the closed end, while the vertical sides are parallel and provided inside and outside with bosses around the holes for the pin. On top and bottom of the head, holes are tapped for the screws that hold the wearing strips, part *7*, in place. Lay off the center line for the elevation and end view $1\frac{3}{4}''$, and that of the sectional plan $4\frac{1}{4}''$ below the upper border line. Let the vertical center line of the two left-hand views be $7\frac{1}{4}''$ from the left-hand border line, and place the remaining view $\frac{11}{16}''$ to the right of the elevation.

166. The connecting-rod, part *13*, is shown broken, the size of the Plate not permitting it to be drawn full length. The method employed in laying off the correct taper of the remaining parts is similar to that explained in Art. **164.** The places where the tapered portion of the rod begins and ends are found by drawing verticals through the centers of the fillets at either end, which are struck with a radius of $\frac{7}{8}''$; the points of intersection between the verticals and the fillet arcs are the initial points of the tapered part. It is found by calculation that the total length of the tapered part is $16\frac{9}{16}''$. Knowing this length and the diameter at either end of this part the student should be able to construct the taper.

One end of the connecting-rod receives the bearings, parts *10* and *11*, which fit over the crosshead pin, part *8*. The other end of the rod is attached to bearings *14*, for the crankpin. The bearing, parts *10* and *11*, is prevented from moving sidewise along the crosshead pin, because its width is just equal to the distance between the inside surfaces of the bosses on crosshead. The two parts of the bearing are forced toward the pin by means of the wedge, part *12*, which may be raised or lowered by turning the adjusting screws, part *17*, in the proper direction. Notice that the holes through which these screws pass are countersunk about $\frac{3}{16}''$ for the screw heads; hence the two slight curves in the outer line defining the outline of the small end of the rod in the elevation. Draw the horizontal center line of the elevation and end view $6\frac{3}{16}''$ and of the bottom view $7\frac{13}{16}''$ below the upper border line. The vertical center line corresponding to the center of the crosshead pin is $9\frac{3}{8}''$ and the one through the end view is $3\frac{9}{16}''$ from the right-hand border line.

167. Next draw the crosshead pin, part *8*, with its center line $5\frac{3}{4}''$ from the right-hand border line and its top $4\frac{3}{16}''$ above the lower border line. Also the nut, part *9*, that screws on its lower end and locks the pin to the crosshead. Draw the center line for the nut $3\frac{1}{4}''$ above lower border line and locate the center line of the elevation $8\frac{5}{8}''$ from the right-hand border line; a space of $\frac{1}{2}''$ is left between the two views. Both of these views are drawn full size.

Draw the bearings, parts *10* and *11*, and also the wedge, part *12*. The center line of the first two views should be $1\frac{3}{8}''$ below the upper border line, and that of the right-hand view $3\frac{15}{16}''$ from the right-hand border line, leaving a space of $\frac{7}{16}''$ between the two views. In locating the views of the wedge, leave a space of $4\frac{1}{8}''$ between them and the right-hand border line. The top line of the upper view should be $2\frac{3}{4}''$ below the upper border line and a space of $\frac{1}{4}''$ left between the two views.

168. The halves of the bearing for the crankpin, part *14*, are symmetrical and only one of them need be shown. Locate the center line of the two upper views $1\frac{15}{16}''$ below the upper border line and the vertical center line of the right-hand view $\frac{3}{4}''$ from the right-hand border line; leave a space of $\frac{11}{16}''$ between the views. The center line of the lower view should be $4''$ below the upper border line.

Draw the connecting-rod strap, part *15*. The bolts, part *18*, pass through this strap and the connecting-rod, holding the bearings, part *14*, in position and clamping them to the crankpin. Draw the center line of the strap $6''$ below the upper border line and locate the views $1\frac{13}{16}''$ and $\frac{9}{16}''$, respectively, from the right-hand border line.

169. Part *7*, the wearing strip mentioned above, is somewhat peculiar in form and the three views should be studied carefully in order to obtain a clear idea of its true shape. Place the center line of the upper views $4\frac{3}{8}''$ above the lower border line and let the vertical center line of the plan be $1\frac{3}{8}''$ from the left-hand border line; leave a space of

$\frac{1}{2}''$ between the two views. Place the third view $\frac{5}{8}''$ below the plan view.

In drawing the remaining detail, part *6*, locate the upper side of the elevation $5\frac{15}{16}''$ below the upper border line. Leave a space of $4\frac{3}{8}''$ between the left-hand border line and the view next to same, and a space of $\frac{3}{8}''$ between the views themselves. The end view may be placed $\frac{3}{8}''$ below the others. The taper can be laid off directly from the dimensions; if, however, one of the dimensions, say the one marked $1\frac{3}{16}''$ had been omitted, the extreme left-hand vertical line would be drawn first, next the line whose dimension is marked $1\frac{1}{16}''$ laid off, and a perpendicular drawn downwards through its right-hand extremity, then the length of the lower side may be found in the following manner: A taper of 1 in 8 is equal to $\frac{1}{4}''$ in $2''$; hence, lay off $2''$ downwards on the perpendicular last drawn, draw a horizontal line through point just laid off, and measure off to the left of this point $\frac{1}{4}''$; the point so determined is the other extreme point of the taper.

170. All necessary information required in explanation of the sectional assembly has already been given in connection with the various parts and partly also in Art. **161.**

PLATE 1020, TITLE:

CYLINDER AND VALVE-ROD STUFFINGBOX

171. On this Plate are given four views of the cylinder, part *1*. Taken from left to right there is a sectional plan, a sectional elevation, a bottom plan, and, below the first view, a front view of the steam chest. The first view is also made to serve as an assembly, as the position of the various parts located in or on the cylinder are indicated by means of dotted lines. These lines are not to be reproduced by the student, as they are simply inserted to aid him in understanding the relation between the various parts.

The cylinder is of cast iron and hollow; on one side it has a box-like extension, called the steam chest, with a boss *i*,

Fig. 56 (*b*), on its upper side, into which the steam pipe is to be screwed. The steam enters the steam chest through this pipe and passes from here through either of the

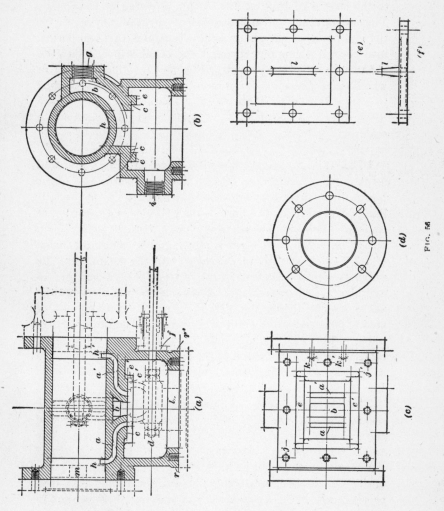

ports *a*, *a'*, Fig. 56 (*a*), into one end of the cylinder bore, the valve *d* determining by its position through which of the ports the steam shall enter and how long its flow is to continue.   In Fig. 56 (*a*), the steam has entered through port *a*, driving the piston to the right; but in the present position of the valve the latter has already advanced so far to the left as to shut off the steam, allowing it to expand. The steam that at the previous stroke has been acting on the right side of the piston is now escaping through port *a'* into the valve and out through the exhaust port *b* into the exhaust pipe, screwed on at *g*, Fig. 56 (*b*).   The manner in which valve *d* receives its motion has already been described in connection with Plate 1018.   Parts *1*, *2*, and *3* are to be drawn to a scale of 3″ = 1 ft.; parts *4*, *5*, and *6* to a scale of 6″ = 1 ft.

172.   The sectional plan view is to be drawn first and located on a horizontal center line $2\frac{1}{4}''$ below the upper border line; draw its vertical center line $2\frac{9}{16}''$ from the left-hand border line.   The bore of the cylinder is $4\frac{3}{4}''$ for $8\frac{3}{8}''$ of its length and is enlarged to $4\frac{13}{16}''$ at a distance of $1\frac{3}{4}''$ from either end.   The walls are $\frac{5}{8}''$ thick and the flanges at each end $1\frac{5}{16}''$ thick and $9\frac{7}{8}''$ in diameter.   In the steam chest the valve travels on a seat *c c'*, $4\frac{1}{4}''$ from the center line of cylinder.   The center line of the valve stem is $2\frac{1}{8}''$ from the valve seat, it being understood that the center lines of steam pipe and valve stem are located in the same vertical plane.   The valve is prevented from moving sidewise by two ribs *e*, *e'*, $\frac{1}{2}''$ high and $5\frac{5}{8}''$ long.   One of these is shown at *e'*, Fig. 56 (*a*), and both are shown in section at *e*, *e'*, Fig. 56 (*b*), and in plan at Fig. 56 (*c*).

The exhaust port *b* is $1\frac{1}{8}''$ wide and separated from the steam ports by webs $\frac{1}{2}''$ thick.   It follows a path around the lower part of the cylinder and has walls $\frac{5}{8}''$ thick.   The steam ports have a $\frac{3}{4}''$ opening 3″ wide, and follow a curved path through the walls of the cylinder.   The straight parts of these ports are centrally located in said walls and are joined to the ends of the ports by curves having their centers in the valve seat and cylinder bore, respectively.   The steam-chest walls are $\frac{5}{8}''$ thick, with an extension of $\frac{1}{4}''$ at *r* and *r'* to permit a machine finish to match steam-chest cover.

At f is a boss of equal thickness to be finished as a seat for the valve-stem stuffingbox, an opening being provided for the valve steam $\frac{41}{64}''$ in diameter. In the front of the steam chest is an opening $6\frac{1}{2}'' \times 5\frac{1}{2}''$. Dimensions for locating the stud holes in the cylinder flange for the cover are found on the drawing of part 2, and the distance between the stud holes in the steam-chest flange is found on the elevation of the steam chest.

173. In the sectional elevation, to be drawn next, the section is taken through the vertical center line of the sectional plan. The bore of the cylinder, thickness of walls, and connections between the exhaust port and the exhaust pipe are clearly shown. The width of the valve seat and of ribs e, e' are also given, showing that the valve has a clear bearing on either side of the ports of $\frac{1}{2}''$. This and the following view are both located on the extended center line of the first view. Draw the vertical center line $7\frac{1}{8}''$ from the left-hand border line.

The bottom plan of the cylinder may now be drawn, locating its vertical center line $3\frac{7}{8}''$ from the right-hand border line. Little need be said in explanation of this view. The exhaust-pipe opening is shown by full-line circles and the steam-pipe opening by dotted circles. One half of the plan for drilling the cylinder head is shown to the right, the other half being symmetrical.

174. On a center line $7\frac{3}{4}''$ below the upper border line locate the fourth view of the cylinder, the longitudinal dimensions of which may be projected directly from the first view. Through the opening in the front of the chest the steam and exhaust ports may be seen, likewise a plan of the valve seat and the ribs $e\,e'$, Fig. 56 (c). The drilling plan for the eight studs, over which the steam-chest cover fits, is shown at $j\,j'$, also the drilling $k\,k'$ for the two studs, which hold the stuffingbox in place. The frame-end drilling plan is shown to the right of this view in Fig. 56 (d). The location of the holes corresponds with the position of the

studs that are tapped into the engine frame and support the cylinder. Locate the center line of this plan $6\frac{1}{8}''$ from the left-hand border line.

175. The steam-chest cover, part *3*, is next drawn in elevation and end view. Locate the vertical center line of these views $7\frac{5}{16}''$ from the right-hand border line and the horizontal center line of the elevation $6\frac{1}{16}''$ above the lower border line, leaving a space of $\frac{11}{16}''$ between the views. The projection *l*, Fig. 56, (*a*), (*e*), and (*f*), holds the valve in place. The cover is recessed inside and out to obviate the finishing of any part but those that fit the steam chest and on which the nuts for the studs are seated.

176. Part *2* is the cylinder head, which is bolted to the cylinder by means of the eight studs, part *7*. The latter are fastened in the end of the cylinder before the cylinder head is put in place. The cylinder head is slightly recessed on the outside, the finish mark applying only to the raised portion. At *m*, Fig. 56 (*a*), is a recess in the cylinder head to make room for the nut on end of piston rod when the piston is at the end of its inward stroke.

177. The views along the lower border line are all located on a center line $1\frac{13}{16}''$ above same. Begin with part *4*, the valve-rod stuffingbox, and locate the two views at distances of $1\frac{1}{8}''$ and $3\frac{1}{4}''$ from the left-hand border line. The stuffingbox is bolted to the steam chest at *f*, Fig. 56 (*a*), by means of studs $\frac{3}{8}''$ in diameter, part *9*.

Part *5* is the gland that compresses and holds the packing in place in the stuffingbox, the purpose of the packing being to make the fit between piston rod and stuffingbox steam-tight. It should be noticed that those ends of the stuffing-box and gland that face each other are countersunk, the object being to force the packing toward the piston rod. Locate these views $5\frac{15}{16}''$ and $7''$ from the left-hand border line.

Part *6* is the clamping nut that holds the gland, part *5*, in position and by means of which the latter may be forced

more tightly against the packing. Let the center line of the right-hand view be 6″ from the right-hand border line, and leave a space of $\frac{7}{8}$″ between the two views.

The remaining parts, *7, 8,* and *9,* are studs, the uses of which have been described. It will be noticed that the studs for *7* are specified as follows: $2\frac{3}{8}$″ long, thd. $\frac{3}{4}$″ × $\frac{7}{8}$″, indicating that the studs are threaded for $\frac{3}{4}$″ at one end and $\frac{7}{8}$″ at the other end.

PLATE 1021, TITLE:

ASSEMBLY OF HORIZONTAL STEAM ENGINE

178. From the details given on Plates 1016 to 1020, inclusive, the student is required to make an assembly drawing giving a general view of the engine in a plan and a side elevation.

That he may have an idea of what he is expected to do, a reduced copy of the Plate is given in Fig. 57, in which all dotted lines indicating parts not visible have been omitted in order to simplify the work. In order to get the drawing within the same limits as were used on the preceding Plates, it is necessary to use a $\frac{1}{5}$ scale; that is, a scale of 2.4″ = 1 ft. It will be necessary, therefore, for the student to construct a scale of this kind, according to instructions given in Art. **11.**

When making an assembly view from several detail sheets, it is often possible to use the latter directly for tracing purposes, if both are drawn to the same scale. In that case the various detail views are successively laid under the tracing cloth and adjusted into such a position that their center lines will coincide with those of the views in the assembly in which they are to be inserted, after which they are pinned to the board. Considerable dodging is sometimes required in order that the tracing cloth may be so arranged, relative to the board, that overhanging parts do not interfere with the free use of the **T** square. Those parts of the tracing cloth that extend beyond the edges must be handled with care, so as not to tear or wrinkle it.

If the assembly had been drawn to a scale of $3'' = 1$ ft. it would have been possible in the present instance to trace some of the details directly into the assembly, as, for instance, the engine frame, but being drawn to a scale differing from any of the details it is not possible in this case to make any direct use of the detail views in this manner.

179. Draw the two horizontal center lines $3\frac{1}{4}''$ and $8\frac{7}{8}''$ from the upper border line and lay off the vertical center line through center of cylinder $3\frac{1}{4}''$ from the left-hand border line.   Locate the vertical through center of crank-shaft at a distance from the other vertical corresponding to that given in engine frame.   Draw the side elevation of the bed-plate with the bearing caps in position, from the dimensions given on the detail sketches, taking care to make the parts that are likely to be hidden by the flywheel, eccentric rod, etc. light so that they may be easily erased before tracing. The drawing may be traced without removing the unnecessary construction lines, but it is better to remove them,

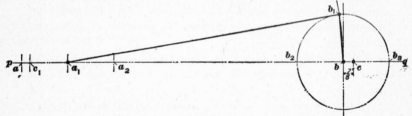

Fig. 58

since it lessens the liability of inking in lines that will have to be erased from the tracing.   Draw the plan of the bed-plate with the bearing caps, studs and nuts, foundation-bolt holes, etc. shown in their proper places and positions.

180. Returning to the elevation, draw the crank and crank end of the connecting-rod in the position shown in the general drawing.   The method by which to determine the position of center of crankpin is shown in Fig. 58, where $b\,b_1$ represents the distance between centers of shaft and crankpin and $b_2\,b_3$, the two dead centers of the engine.   The

length of the stroke is indicated by the points a, a_2, the
piston rod in this instance occupying a middle position at
point a_1. To find the corresponding position of the crankpin, draw the circle $b_2 b_3$ with $b b_1$ as a radius; this radius is
the length of the crank between center of shaft and center
of crankpin, or $4''$ (see Plate 1016). Then with a radius
equal to the length of the connecting-rod between its centers, and with b as a center, draw a small arc intersecting
the line $a b_2$ at a_1; this determines the center position of the
piston rod. With the same radius $a_1 b$, but with a_1 as a
center, draw the arc $b b_1$; the point of intersection b_1 with
the circle $b_2 b_3$ will be the point sought, viz., the center of
crankpin, when the center of the crosshead pin is at a_1.
A line connecting a_1 and b_1 will be the center line of the
connecting-rod.

181. Draw the crosshead, obtaining the dimensions
from the detail sketch. Complete the connecting-rod in
both views, and draw the piston rod $1''$ in diameter. Draw
both views of the cylinder with the nuts and the steam pipe
in their proper position, getting all dimensions from the
detail sketches.

Draw the center line of the valve stem in the plan view,
and draw the stuffingbox, valve stem, valve-stem slide and
its guide in both views. In order to determine the position
of the valve-stem slide, it is necessary to locate the center
of the eccentric. Referring to the general drawing, it is
seen that the eccentric is on the dead center farthest from
the cylinder. The offset of the eccentric is given as $\frac{7}{8}''$ in
the detail sketch; hence, when in this position, the center
of the eccentric strap will be situated at c, $\frac{7}{8}''$ to the right of
the crank-shaft center on the line $p q$, Fig. 58. With this
point as a center, and a radius equal to the distance between
the centers of the eccentric strap and the hole in the stud
end of the eccentric rod (see detail sketch), in this
case 2 ft. $1\frac{1}{8}''$, describe an arc cutting the center line $p q$
in c_1; c_1 will be the center of the pin on the valve-stem
slide, which may be completed with the aid of the detail

sketch. Complete the drawing of the eccentric, eccentric strap, and eccentric rod in both views.

Finally draw in the bandwheel and flywheel (see general drawing for position). The flywheel will be of the same diameter as the bandwheel, but only 3″ wide.

READING A WORKING DRAWING

182. The following general method of procedure has, by experience, been shown to be conducive to the accurate and rapid reading of a drawing made in projection. *First*, if the drawing is dimensioned, ignore the existence of the dimension lines and dimensions entirely until after the general shape of the object is fixed on the mind. *Second*, by referring to the several views, form an idea of the shape of the main body of the object; that is, observe if its outline shows it to be a cube, a sphere, a cylinder, a cone, a pyramid, etc., or a combination of several of these elementary forms. The shape of the main body having been impressed on the mind, observe how it is modified by details, determining, by reference to the several views, whether they project from the main body or are recesses, or holes. *Finally*, by referring to the dimensions, form an idea of the relative sizes of the component parts. Pay due regard to all conventional representations that may have been used; for instance, do not become confused if the arm of a pulley, or a rib, which, truly speaking, should have been in section, is shown in full. If two half sections are placed on either side of a common center line, remember that each half must usually be viewed independently of the other and must be mentally completed.

183. When reading a drawing in which the views are correctly placed, it is often a great aid, when the shape of some part is doubtful, to project with a straightedge points or edges of it over to another view, in order to find the location of the doubtful part. When the views are not placed in their correct relative positions, this cannot be done. An example of a case of this kind is given in Fig. 59, and in reading a drawing with the view thus placed, the reader is supposed to constantly imagine that the views are in their correct relative positions; with a little practice this will be found to be quite easy.

In a case of this kind, it is manifestly impossible to project points or lines from one view to the other by means of a straightedge, and a different method must be followed. Select some surface whose projection appears in both views, or a center line; now place a pair of dividers so that one

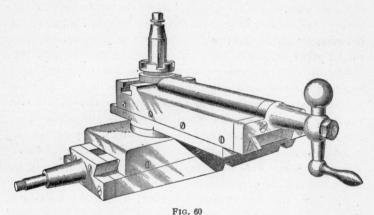

FIG. 60

point rests on the projection of the surface or center line selected, and open them until the other point reaches the point or line whose projection it is desired to find in the other view. Then place one point of the dividers on the line representing the selected surface in the second view, and move the dividers along this line until a line, or the projection of a line, is found to coincide with the other point of the dividers. Examples of this will appear later on.

In order to aid the student in reading a drawing, we have selected the compound rest, Fig. 59, and will show in detail by what process of reasoning this drawing is read. To aid the student in obtaining a correct idea of the location and shape of the various parts, a perspective view of the compound rest has been given in Fig. 60.

184. To find the shape of the different parts and also to discover, if possible, the relation between them, we must commence our investigation somewhere. Let us choose the bottom of the front view. Looking at this, it is noticed that a partial section is shown, from which, by reason of the section lining running in opposite directions, we conclude that A and B are separate parts. At the right and left of the front view, the full lines c, c show that some part of A is higher than the bottom of B, but we do not know whether these lines denote the top surfaces of projecting parts between which B is fitted, or if c is the top surface of a raised strip of some kind that extends clear through the inside of B. In order to settle this question, we note whether the top surface is continued somewhere. Looking at the front view it is seen that the line c is dotted clear through B, which settles conclusively that the part whose top surface is shown by the line c is a raised strip extending clear through B; this fact immediately implies that B has a groove of some kind running through it longitudinally in order to admit the raised strip.

Referring now to the sectional view, which, as previously stated, is a view taken on the line $a\,b$ of the front view, and everything to the right of this line being removed, we may choose the bottom line d' of the sectional view as a base from which to make measurements. From the fact that the section is taken on the line $a\,b$, we know that the line just chosen is the projection of the intersection d of the plane represented by $a\,b$ with the bottom of A. Measuring from d' upwards to the highest line c' of A in the sectional view, and placing one point of the dividers on d in the front view, it will be seen that the other point coincides with the dotted line forming a continuation of $c\,c$; this shows that c' is the projection of c. In a similar manner, we determine that e' is the projection of e, and tracing the outlines of A in the sectional view, we notice that the raised strip on A has inclined sides. We also notice that B is cut out to suit the profile of A, except that on one side a steel part L is interposed between the inclined sides of A and B; it is also seen that a screw rests with its point against L.

Referring now to the front view, and knowing from inspection of the sectional view that the upper and lower surfaces of the steel part L are flush with c' and e', or c and e in the front view, to determine the length of this part, notice if any dotted or full lines showing its length are shown anywhere at a right angle to c and e. None being found, the conclusion to be drawn is that either the steel part L is as long as A or has the same length as B. A person without any practical experience might conclude that the length is the same as that of A; but any one having engineering instinct or practical knowledge would immediately notice that, as the steel strip has setscrews which evidently push it against the inclined side of A, it would be unnecessary to make the strip the length of A, and hence would immediately conclude that its length is the same as that of B. This latter conclusion is the one the draftsman desired to convey.

185. Looking at the sectional view of A again, we notice that a groove, open on top, is cut into A. To find its length we must find lines corresponding to it in the front view. Measuring from d' upwards to the bottom of the groove and transferring the measurement to the front view, we find that the dotted line gg represents the bottom and end of the groove, which at the left is also shown to be open at the bottom, since the dotted line g curves around and continues to the bottom of A. This is also indicated by the dotted lines g' that form an extension of the sides of the groove in the sectional view; measuring from c' downwards to the horizontal dotted line joining the ends of $g'\,g'$, and then passing along c in the front view, the point of the dividers will be found to coincide with the point where the dotted line g meets the bottom of A. From this the conclusion is drawn that the dotted horizontal line

39—16

joining $g'g'$ in the sectional view is the bottom edge of the opening.

186. Looking at the front view we notice a left-handed screw C that is placed within the slot just investigated. Knowing that, in a view in line with its axis, the outline of a screw will be a circle, and knowing that this circle will be found inside of the slot, the screw is readily found in the sectional view. Now, experience teaches us that when a screw is shown in place in a machine drawing, there must also be somewhere along its axis a threaded hole (or a nut) to receive it. Looking at the sectional view we see the outline of something (marked "*Bronze*") that surrounds the screw. Now, this part, at first glance, appears to be a continuation of the pin E directly above it; there are two reasons, however, why this is not the case. In the first place, the part E is sectioned for steel; this immediately shows that E and the part under investigation are separate parts. Furthermore, when tracing out the shape and positions of the objects in the front view, they will be seen neither to be in line nor to have any connection with each other. To find the part under investigation in the front view, we may take, in the sectional view, a measurement from the center of the screw downwards to the lowest point of the part we are investigating, and then, referring to the front view, proceed along the center line of the screw C until we strike the dotted line h. Since the sectional view shows only things to the left of the line ab, we know that as the part being investigated shows in the sectional view, we must look for it to the left of ab in the front view. At the ends of the horizontal dotted line h we notice two vertical dotted lines that show the length of the part under investigation; since these lines terminate against the line c, we know that the part butts against the surface of B.

This latter conclusion is further confirmed by examining, in the sectional view, the full outline of the part. Referring again to the front view, we see a screw thread indicated in B right above the part we are discussing, and in the absence of any indication to the contrary may justly assume that it is a threaded shank by means of which the part is attached to *B*. By this time we are probably convinced that the part we have been investigating is the nut we are looking for, but are not sure of it. To find out, let us try to investigate the whole of the screw. In the front view, the dotted lines *i, i* show that the screw has a bearing and also has a collar butting against part of *A*; beyond the bearing the screw shows in full and apparently has a seat for some kind of an attachment which must cause the screw to turn, since a dowel-pin is shown in the seat. Inspecting the sectional view we find a screw similar to the one under discussion, with a ball handle and retaining nut on the end of it. As we find a note "*Two Handles Machinery Steel, Finish all over,*" and as we cannot find any other place for the second handle, we naturally conclude that such a handle is to be placed on the end of the screw *C*. Now, from the fact that the screw is confined longitudinally by the collar and the ball handle, and that there is no thread on the part of the screw between them, we know that the nut must be to the right of the collar; since the part previously investigated is the only part we can find that directly surrounds the screw, we will now be justified in assuming that it is the nut we are looking for.

The fact that *A* and *B* are connected together by a screw provided with a handle for turning it will immediately suggest the idea that it is to be used for moving the part *B* along *A*, whence we conclude that *B* is a slide moving on *A*. Knowing this, the logical conclusion is that the piece *L* is a gib used for taking up the wear of the sliding surfaces, which view is proved to be correct when it is noticed, by reference to the sectional view, that a tightening of the setscrew will tend to draw the wearing surfaces together.

187. Looking now at the part *K*, at the left of *A*, in the front view, considering the part by itself, we cannot tell whether it is an integral part of *A* or a separate piece fastened to it. But as soon as we consider it in connection with the screw C, we see that the latter cannot be placed in position unless the part K is removable. From this we conclude that the part K is separate from A. The next question that suggests itself is: How is it fastened on? The note on the front view and the dotted screw heads in the sectional view show that screws with slotted heads are used.

As far as the shape of K is concerned, the front view shows that it is a cone joining some presumably flat part. Referring now to the sectional view, we discover by measuring successively from the center line and center of the screw C that the dotted horizontal line k' represents the lower surface of K, and the absence of any other dotted lines in this part of the sectional view indicates that the profile of the flat part of K is the same as that of A.

On examining the sectional view, it is seen that some part of D, which from the section lining we know to be separate from B, projects downwards from the main body of D and is in contact with the upper surface l' of the part B. Referring now to the front view and looking along l, we find that the part under discussion is cylindrical; this is inferred from the dimension " $4''$ *turned.*" The main body of D, and also the parts G, H, and J, may now be investigated in a manner similar to that in which the relation of A, B, C, and K was traced; it will then be found that D is a part similar to A. Furthermore, the investigation will show that G is a slide; this slide is movable by means of the screw H, which turns in the bearing J.

188. Referring again to the sectional view, we see that B and D are connected together by a pin E, the object of which is unknown as yet.   Examining this pin we notice that a hole is cut through its upper end and that a screw F, with a tapered shoulder to the right of its screw thread, passes through this hole. On close examination, we see that the hole in E is so placed that the tapered part of the screw F bears against the upper side of the hole. We further notice that the screw F is not used as a fastening device to hold any parts of D together; this conclusion is forced upon us by the fact that the sectional view shows D to be one piece. Now, we know from experience that a screw is used either as a fastening device or to transmit motion; as it obviously is not used for the purpose first mentioned, we conclude that it probably serves for the latter purpose. To make sure of this we trace out what will happen if the screw is rotated. We then notice that if the screw is screwed inwards, it will raise the part E; but as E cannot move upwards by reason of being confined by the collar on it, it shows to us that screwing F inwards will force D down on B. The logical inference is that E and F form a clamping device intended to clamp B and D together.

Examining the pin E again, we do not find anything that would definitely tell whether it is round or square. Here judgment must be used. An experienced person would know upon the first glance that the clamping arrangement shown is an expensive one to make and one not likely to be adopted when it is only required to fasten two pieces rigidly together, in which case E might be either round or square. The next inference would be that it is used in order to allow D to be rotated around E and to be clamped in any position. This supposition requires the pin E to be round and is correct in this case.

189. Referring now to the ball handle I, of which only one view is shown, the question of whether it is circular or square is immediately settled by experience teaching us that a handle having the shape shown is not likely to be anything else but round, and in the absence of any note or indication to the contrary, we would be justified in assuming it to be so.

190. As far as the part G is concerned, the sectional view shows it to be cored out in order to pass over the nut in which the screw H works. The width and profile of the coring must be obtained from the front view, which it will be remembered is a view at a right angle to the sectional view. The natural assumption to make is that the lines giving the width and profile of the coring will be found directly in the vicinity of the screw H in the front view. Measuring from the center line of this screw in the sectional view upwards to the line showing the height of the coring, and then transferring this measurement to the front view, we find the full circle n. Now, as the coring is beyond the bearing J, we know that its profile would show in dotted lines and conclude that the circle n represents some part of the bearing J. As this bearing has a conical projection, the inference is that the full circle represents the largest diameter of the cone, which is the case. Now, the absence of a dotted line showing the coring forces us to conclude that the dotted line would be directly behind the full circle n and is thus hidden. This conclusion is further strengthened by finding two vertical dotted lines r, r tangent to the circle n, and we finally decide that the groove has straight sides with a semicircular top, as given by the dotted lines r, r and the upper semicircle of n. By measuring again in the manner previously explained, we decide that the dotted line o is a front view of the nut in which H works.

At the right-hand end of the sectional view of G we notice a T-shaped opening. Referring to the front view we can easily discover, by transferring measurements, that the dotted horizontal lines p, p show the length of the slot, which is seen to extend clear across G.

191. Referring now to the drawing of the tool post, it will be observed that only one view is given. While this does not definitely settle that the post is circular in cross-section, common practice would justify a person in assuming, in the absence of any note or any other indication to the contrary, that such was the case. This view is strengthened by the fact that some dimensions are marked d, signifying diameter, which term is rarely applied to any but a round object.

192. The two views of the collar give its shape. Referring to the front view, while there is no definite note to that effect, it would be inferred from the fact that a thread is shown that the lower part is separate, being, in fact, a circular nurled nut threaded to receive the upper part.

193. While, generally speaking, any one can learn to determine the shape of objects from a drawing, there are cases that arise in practice where this is very difficult without further verbal or written instructions. The cases in which this usually happens are where coring has various odd-shaped curved surfaces that curve in different directions, as occurs, for instance, with the steam ports and other passages of steam-engine cylinders and other similar work. Practical experience with a certain line of work, and, frequently, a knowledge of the object of the doubtful part, will often enable the reader to form a correct idea of what the draftsman is trying to convey; when this experience or knowledge is lacking, *consult somebody who is likely to know.*

Furthermore, the shape of an object does not necessarily in itself always reveal its purpose. Ability to determine at sight what an object is to be used for involves either a thorough knowledge of a particular line of work—in which case the purpose of objects coming within its range can usually be determined at sight—or a very wide general knowledge of engineering construction.

BLUEPRINTING

194. Blueprinting is the process of duplicating a tracing by means of the action of light upon a sensitized paper. The following solution is much used for sensitizing the paper: Dissolve 2 ounces of citrate of iron and ammonia in 8 ounces of water; also $1\frac{1}{4}$ ounces of red prussiate of potash in 8 ounces of water. Keep the solutions separate and in dark-colored bottles in a dark place where the light cannot reach them. Better results will be obtained if $\frac{1}{2}$ an ounce of gum arabic is dissolved in each solution.

When ready to prepare the paper, mix equal portions of the two solutions, and be particularly careful not to allow any more light to strike the mixture than is absolutely necessary to see by. For this reason it is necessary to have a dark room to work in. There must be in this room a tray or sink of some kind that will hold water; it should be larger than the blueprint and about 6 inches deep. There should also be a flat board large enough to cover the tray or sink. If the sink is lined with zinc or galvanized iron, so much the better. There must be an arrangement like a towel rack to hang the prints on while they are drying. For the want of a better name, this arrangement will be called a print rack. The paper used for blueprinting should be a good, smooth, white paper, and may be purchased of any dealer in drawing materials. Cut it into sheets a little larger than the tracing, so as to leave an edge around it when the tracing is placed upon it. Place eight or ten of these sheets upon the flat board before mentioned, taking care to spread flatly one above another, so that the edges do not overlap. Secure the sheets to the board by driving a brad or small wire nail through the two upper corners sufficiently far into the board to hold the weight of the papers when the board is placed in a vertical position. Lay the board on the edges of the sink, so that one edge is against the wall and the board is inclined so as to make an angle of about 60° with the horizontal. Darken the room as much as possible and obtain what light may be necessary from a lamp or gas jet, which should be turned down very low. With a wide camel's-hair brush or a fine sponge, spread the solution just prepared over the top sheet of paper. Be sure to cover every spot and do not get too much on the paper. Distribute it as evenly as possible over the paper, in much the same manner that the finishing coat of varnish would be put on by a painter. Remove the sheet by pulling on the lower edge, tearing it from the nail that holds it, and place it in a drawer where it can lie flat and be kept from the light. Treat the next sheet and each succeeding sheet in exactly the same manner, until the required number of sheets has been prepared.

Unless a large number of prints is constantly used, it is cheaper to buy the paper already prepared. It can be bought in rolls of 10 yards or more, of any width, or in sheets already cut and ready for use. There is very little, if anything, saved in preparing the paper, and better results are usually obtained from the commercial sensitized paper, since the manufacturers have machines for applying the solution and are able to distribute it very evenly.

195. In Figs. 61 and 62 are shown two views of a printing frame that is well adapted to sheets not over $17'' \times 21''$. The frame is placed face downwards and the back A is

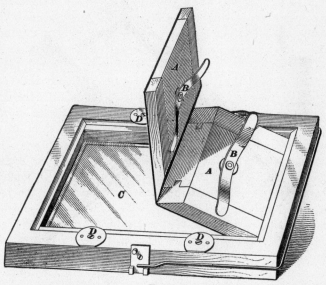

FIG. 61

removed by unhooking the brass spring clips B, B, and lifting it out. The tracing is laid upon the glass C, with the *inked* side touching the glass. A sheet of the prepared paper, perfectly dry, is laid upon the tracing with the yellow (sensitized) side downwards. The paper and tracing are smoothed out so as to lie perfectly flat upon the glass, the cover A is replaced, and the brass spring clips B, B are sprung under the plates D, so that the back cannot fall out. While all this is being done, the paper should be kept from the light as much as possible. The frame is now placed where the sun can shine upon it and is adjusted, as shown in Fig. 62, so that the sun's rays will fall upon it as nearly at right angles as possible. According to the conditions of the sky—whether clear or cloudy—and the time of the year, the print must be exposed from 3 to 15 minutes. The tray, or sink, already mentioned, should be filled to a depth of about 2″ with clear water (rain water if possible). The print having been exposed the proper length of time, the frame is carried into

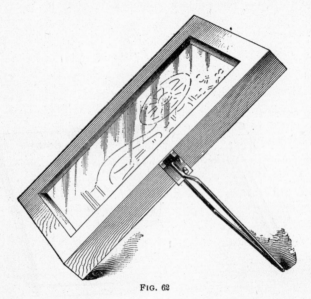

FIG. 62

a dark part of the room, the cover removed, and the print (prepared paper) taken out. Now place it on the water with the yellow side down and be sure that the water touches every part of it. Let it soak while putting the next print in the frame. Be sure that the hands are dry before touching the next print. The first print having soaked a short time (about 10 minutes) take hold of two of its opposite corners and lift it slowly out of the water. Dip it back again and pull out as before. Repeat this a number of times, until the paper appears to get no bluer; then hang it by two of its corners to dry on the print rack previously mentioned. If there are any dark-purple or bronze-colored spots on the prints, it indicates that the prints were not washed thoroughly on those spots. If these spots are well washed before the print is dried, they will disappear.

196. It is best to judge the proper time of exposure to the light by the color of the strip of print projecting beyond the edge of the tracing. To obtain the exact shade of the projecting edge, take a strip of paper about 12″ or 14″ long and 3″ or 4″ wide. Divide it into, say, 12 equal parts by lead-pencil marks, and with the lead pencil number each part 1, 2, 3, etc. Sensitize this side of the paper and, after it has been properly dried, place it in the print frame with the sensitized side and the marks and figures against the glass. Expose the whole strip to the light for 1 minute; then cover the part of the strip marked 1 with a thin board or anything that will prevent the light from striking the part covered. At the end of the second minute, cover parts 2 and 1; at the end of the third minute, parts 3, 2, and 1, etc. When 12 minutes are up, part 1 will have been exposed 1 minute; part 2, 2 minutes, etc., part 12 having been exposed 12 minutes. Remove the frame to a dark part of the room and tear the strip so as to divide it into two strips of the same length and about half the original width. Wash one of the strips as before described, and when it has dried, select a good rich shade of blue, neither too light nor too dark; notice the number of the part chosen, and it will indicate the length of time that the print was exposed. Examine carefully the corresponding part of the other strip, and the correct color of the edge of the print projecting beyond the tracing is determined. All prints should be exposed until this color is reached, no matter how long or how short the time may be; then they should be immediately taken out and washed.

197. In Fig. 63 is shown a patented frame which can be shoved out of the window and adjusted to any angle. When not in use, it can be folded up against the wall and occupies but little space. It is made in different sizes from 16″ × 24″ to 48″ × 72″. It is one of the best frames in the market,

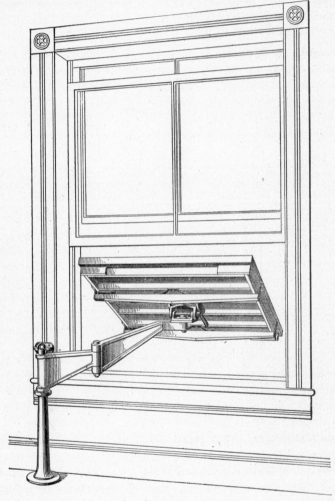

FIG. 63

and is placed in such a position relatively to the window that the window can be lowered to the top of the main arm, when it is desired to keep out the cold during the winter.

USEFUL TABLES

198. Forms of Bolt Heads, Nuts, and Screw Heads.
The information required for the construction of the standard forms of bolt heads, nuts, and the principal screw
heads is given in Fig. 64.   The several dimensions are indicated by capital letters in the diagrams and the relations
between these dimensions are stated either below each separate diagram or below each series of diagrams.   It is seen
that these dimensions are all based on the diameters of the
bolts or screws.

199. In order to avoid the calculations required to
use these diagrams, the standard dimensions of bolt heads,
nuts, and screw heads have been given in Table I, for the
sizes mostly in use.   Dimensions, corresponding with those
indicated by capital letters in the diagrams, are found in
the table in columns headed by similar letters.   For instance:
It is required to find the height of a hexagon head for a
bolt $1''$ in diameter.   In the diagram of a hexagon head
the letter F represents its height.   To find its numerical
value from the table, descend along the column A until the
diameter 1 is found.   Then pass in a horizontal direction to
the column F, where the value $\frac{13}{16}$ is found, which is the
dimension required.

200. Small, standard, machine or wood screws are indicated by gauge numbers instead of by diameters.   Table II
gives the gauge numbers and the corresponding diameters
of the sizes mostly used.   To draw a screw of a certain gauge,
find its diameter in the table, and lay out the head according
to the instructions given with the diagrams in Fig. 64.

201. Diameters of Small Holes.—The sizes of small
holes are generally indicated by the gauge number of the
drills used in drilling them instead of by their diameters.
Table III gives the gauge numbers and corresponding diameters of the Morse twist drills.   The table will also serve to
indicate the gauge numbers of ordinary steel wire.

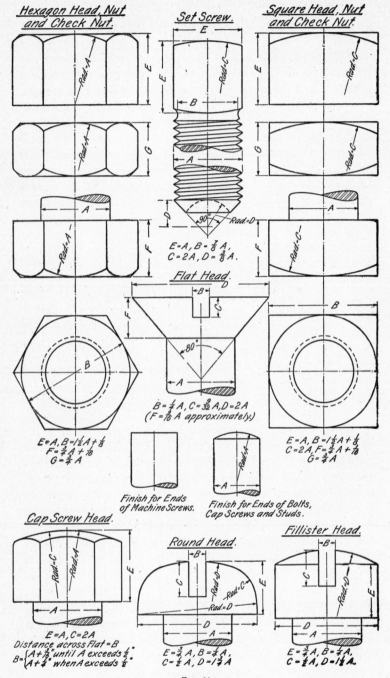

Hexagon Head, Nut and Check Nut.

Set Screw.

Square Head, Nut and Check Nut.

$E = A, B = \frac{3}{8} A,$
$C = 2A, D = \frac{3}{8} A.$

Flat Head

$B = \frac{1}{4} A, C = \frac{3}{32} A, D = 2A$
(F = $\frac{1}{16}$ A approximately.)

$E = A, B = 1\frac{1}{2}A + \frac{1}{8}$
$F = \frac{3}{4} A + \frac{1}{16}$
$G = \frac{3}{4} A$

$E = A, B = 1\frac{1}{2} A + \frac{1}{8}$
$C = 2A, F = \frac{3}{4} A + \frac{1}{16}$
$G = \frac{3}{4} A$

Finish for Ends of Machine Screws.

Finish for Ends of Bolts, Cap Screws and Studs.

Cap Screw Head.

$E = A, C = 2A$
Distance across Flat = B
$B = \begin{cases} A + \frac{1}{16}\text{" until A exceeds } \frac{5}{8}\text{"} \\ A + \frac{1}{4}\text{" when A exceeds } \frac{5}{8}\text{"} \end{cases}$

Round Head.

$E = \frac{3}{4} A, B = \frac{1}{4} A,$
$C = \frac{1}{4} A, D = 1\frac{1}{4} A$

Fillister Head.

$E = \frac{3}{4} A, B = \frac{1}{4} A,$
$C = \frac{1}{4} A, D = 1\frac{1}{4} A.$

Fig. 64

202. Pipe Threads.—The pitches and depths of the screw threads on pipes cannot be made according to the rules applying to ordinary screw threads, as in that case the depth of the thread would be greater than the thickness of the pipe.

Table IV gives the standard dimensions of pipe threads. By means of the data given under the head of Total Length of Thread and Length of Perfect Thread, it is possible to determine the length of the part containing imperfect threads. It should be noted that the number of the latter is a constant for all diameters; that is, according to the standard adopted, there should always be six imperfect threads, two of which are imperfect only at top, and four both at top and bottom. The number of perfect threads will vary according to the diameter of the pipe or nipple.

203. Decimal Equivalents of Parts of 1 Inch. Table V is intended to aid the student in finding the nearest 64th inch corresponding in value to a dimension given in thousandths of an inch.

The decimal fractions are printed in two sizes of type; the one in large type giving the exact value of the corresponding fractional part of an inch to the fourth decimal place. A given decimal fraction of an inch is rarely exactly equal to any of these values, but is either above or below it, and the question is then to decide to which of two values it is the nearest, whether to the preceding or succeeding one. For instance it is desired to lay off the fraction .1330" in 64ths of an inch. The nearest decimal fractions are .1250 and .1406, and the question is which of these to choose. By means of the decimal fractions, printed in smaller type, this question may be answered at once, as the value of any one of these is the mean of the two adjacent fractions printed in larger type. If therefore any of the given decimal fractions is *above* the mean in value it belongs to the succeeding decimal fraction, if *below* to the preceding one. In this instance the mean fraction is .1328, and as .1330 is greater than this, .1406" or $\frac{9}{64}$" will be chosen. In the same manner the nearest 64th inch corresponding to the decimal fractions .3670" and .8979" are found to be $\frac{23}{64}$" and $\frac{57}{64}$", respectively.

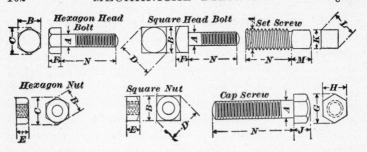

Hexagon Head Bolt　Square Head Bolt　Set Screw
Hexagon Nut　Square Nut　Cap Screw

TABLE I

DIMENSIONS OF STANDARD-FINISHED BOLTS, NUTS, SET, AND CAP SCREWS

A	Threads Per Inch	Bolt Dimensions					Cap-Screw Dimensions			Setscrew Dimensions		
		B	C	D	E	F	G	H	J	K	L	M
$\frac{1}{4}$	20	$\frac{1}{2}$	$\frac{37}{64}$	$\frac{45}{64}$	$\frac{1}{4}$	$\frac{1}{4}$				$\frac{1}{4}$	$\frac{23}{64}$	$\frac{1}{4}$
$\frac{5}{16}$	18	$\frac{19}{32}$	$\frac{11}{16}$	$\frac{27}{32}$	$\frac{5}{16}$	$\frac{19}{64}$	$\frac{37}{64}$	$\frac{1}{2}$	$\frac{5}{16}$	$\frac{5}{16}$	$\frac{7}{16}$	$\frac{5}{16}$
$\frac{3}{8}$	16	$\frac{11}{16}$	$\frac{51}{64}$	$\frac{31}{32}$	$\frac{3}{8}$	$\frac{23}{64}$	$\frac{21}{32}$	$\frac{9}{16}$	$\frac{3}{8}$	$\frac{3}{8}$	$\frac{17}{32}$	$\frac{3}{8}$
$\frac{7}{16}$	14	$\frac{25}{32}$	$\frac{29}{32}$	$1\frac{5}{64}$	$\frac{7}{16}$	$\frac{7}{16}$						
$\frac{1}{2}$	13	$\frac{7}{8}$	$1\frac{1}{64}$	$1\frac{15}{64}$	$\frac{1}{2}$	$\frac{7}{16}$	$\frac{7}{8}$	$\frac{3}{4}$	$\frac{1}{2}$	$\frac{1}{2}$	$\frac{45}{64}$	$\frac{1}{2}$
$\frac{5}{8}$	11	$1\frac{1}{16}$	$1\frac{13}{64}$	$1\frac{1}{2}$	$\frac{5}{8}$	$\frac{17}{32}$	$1\frac{1}{8}$	$\frac{7}{8}$	$\frac{5}{8}$	$\frac{5}{8}$	$\frac{7}{8}$	$\frac{5}{8}$
$\frac{3}{4}$	10	$1\frac{1}{4}$	$1\frac{7}{16}$	$1\frac{3}{4}$	$\frac{3}{4}$	$\frac{5}{8}$	$1\frac{5}{32}$	1	$\frac{3}{4}$	$\frac{3}{4}$	$1\frac{1}{16}$	$\frac{3}{4}$
$\frac{7}{8}$	9	$1\frac{7}{16}$	$1\frac{21}{32}$	$2\frac{1}{32}$	$\frac{7}{8}$	$\frac{23}{32}$	$1\frac{5}{16}$	$1\frac{1}{8}$	$\frac{7}{8}$	$\frac{7}{8}$	$1\frac{15}{64}$	$\frac{7}{8}$
1	8	$1\frac{5}{8}$	$1\frac{7}{8}$	$2\frac{9}{64}$	1	$\frac{13}{16}$	$1\frac{7}{16}$	$1\frac{1}{4}$	1	1	$1\frac{13}{32}$	1
$1\frac{1}{8}$	7	$1\frac{13}{16}$	2	$2\frac{3}{16}$	$1\frac{1}{8}$	$\frac{29}{32}$						
$1\frac{1}{4}$	7	2	$2\frac{5}{16}$	$2\frac{53}{64}$	$1\frac{1}{4}$	1	$1\frac{3}{4}$	$1\frac{1}{2}$	$1\frac{1}{4}$			
$1\frac{3}{8}$	6	$2\frac{3}{16}$	$2\frac{3}{4}$	$3\frac{1}{64}$	$1\frac{1}{2}$	$1\frac{3}{16}$						
$1\frac{1}{2}$	5	$2\frac{3}{8}$	$3\frac{1}{64}$	$3\frac{57}{64}$	$1\frac{3}{4}$	$1\frac{3}{8}$						
2	$4\frac{1}{2}$	$3\frac{1}{8}$	$3\frac{39}{64}$	$4\frac{3}{32}$	2	$1\frac{9}{16}$						
$2\frac{1}{4}$	$4\frac{1}{2}$	$3\frac{1}{2}$	$4\frac{3}{64}$	$4\frac{61}{64}$	$2\frac{1}{4}$	$1\frac{3}{4}$						
$2\frac{1}{2}$	4	$3\frac{7}{8}$	$4\frac{15}{64}$	$5\frac{3}{4}$	$2\frac{1}{2}$	$1\frac{15}{16}$						
$2\frac{3}{4}$	4	$4\frac{1}{4}$	$4\frac{59}{64}$	$6\frac{1}{4}$	$2\frac{3}{4}$	$2\frac{1}{8}$						
3	$3\frac{1}{2}$	$4\frac{5}{8}$	$5\frac{1}{16}$	$6\frac{3}{8}$	3	$2\frac{5}{16}$						
$3\frac{1}{4}$	$3\frac{1}{2}$	5	$5\frac{55}{64}$	$7\frac{5}{64}$	$3\frac{1}{4}$	$2\frac{1}{2}$						
$3\frac{1}{2}$	$3\frac{1}{4}$	$5\frac{3}{8}$	$6\frac{13}{64}$	$7\frac{1}{2}$	$3\frac{1}{2}$	$2\frac{11}{16}$						
$3\frac{3}{4}$	3	$5\frac{3}{4}$	$6\frac{41}{64}$	$8\frac{1}{8}$	$3\frac{3}{4}$	$2\frac{7}{8}$						
4	3	$6\frac{1}{8}$	$7\frac{5}{64}$	$8\frac{23}{32}$	4	$3\frac{1}{16}$						
$4\frac{1}{4}$	$2\frac{7}{8}$	$6\frac{1}{2}$	$7\frac{1}{2}$	$9\frac{3}{16}$	$4\frac{1}{4}$	$3\frac{1}{4}$						
$4\frac{1}{2}$	$2\frac{5}{8}$	$6\frac{7}{8}$	$7\frac{15}{16}$	$9\frac{3}{32}$	$4\frac{1}{2}$	$3\frac{7}{16}$						
$4\frac{3}{4}$	$2\frac{5}{8}$	$7\frac{1}{4}$	$8\frac{3}{8}$	$10\frac{1}{4}$	$4\frac{3}{4}$	$3\frac{5}{8}$						
5	$2\frac{1}{2}$	$7\frac{5}{8}$	$8\frac{13}{16}$	$10\frac{25}{32}$	5	$3\frac{13}{16}$						

TABLE II

STANDARD MACHINE AND WOOD SCREWS

Gauge No.	Diameter Inches	Threads Per Inch	Diameter of Round Head	Diameter of Filister Head	Diameter of Flat Head
000	.0315				
00	.0447				
0	.0578				
1	.0710				
2	.0842	64	.1544	.1332	.1631
3	.0973	48	.1786	.1545	.1894
4	.1105	36	.2028	.1747	.2158
5	.1236	32	.2270	.1985	.2421
6	.1368	32	.2510	.2175	.2684
7	.1500	32	.2754	.2392	.2947
8	.1631	32	.2936	.2610	.3210
9	.1763	32	.3238	.2805	.3474
10	.1894	32	.3480	.3035	.3737
11	.2026	24			
12	.2158	24	.3922	.3445	.4263
13	.2289	22			
14	.2421	20	.4364	.3885	.4790
15	.2552	20			
16	.2684	18	.4866	.4300	.5316
17	.2816	18			
18	.2947	18	.5248	.4710	.5842
19	.3079	18			
20	.3210	16	.5690	.5200	.6308
21	.3342				
22	.3474	16	.6106	.5557	.6894
23	.3605				
24	.3737	16	.6522	.6005	.7420

TABLE III

MORSE TWIST-DRILL AND STEEL-WIRE GAUGE

Gauge No.	Diameter Inch	Gauge No.	Diameter Inch	Gauge No.	Diameter Inch
1	.2280	33	.1130	65	.0350
2	.2210	34	.1110	66	.0330
3	.2130	35	.1100	67	.0320
4	.2090	36	.1065	68	.0310
5	.2055	37	.1040	69	.02925
6	.2040	38	.1015	70	.0280
7	.2010	39	.0995	71	.0260
8	.1990	40	.0980	72	.0250
9	.1960	41	.0960	73	.0240
10	.1935	42	.0935	74	.0225
11	.1910	43	.0890	75	.0210
12	.1890	44	.0860	76	.0200
13	.1850	45	.0820	77	.0180
14	.1820	46	.0810	78	.0160
15	.1800	47	.0785	79	.0145
16	.1770	48	.0760	80	.0135
17	.1730	49	.0730		
18	.1695	50	.0700		
19	.1660	51	.0670		
20	.1610	52	.0635		
21	.1590	53	.0595		
22	.1570	54	.0550		
23	.1540	55	.0520		
24	.1520	56	.0465		
25	.1495	57	.0430		
26	.1470	58	.0420		
27	.1440	59	.0410		
28	.1405	60	.0400		
29	.1360	61	.0390		
30	.1285	62	.0380		
31	.1200	63	.0370		
32	.1160	64	.0360		

TABLE IV

U. S. STANDARD STEAM, GAS, AND WATER PIPE

Sizes of Pipes Inches	Threads per Inch	Actual External Diameter Inches	Actual Internal Diameter Inches	Total Length of Thread	Length of Perfect Thread	Size of Hole for Tap	Diameter of Thread at End of Pipe	
							Outside	At Bottom of Thread
1/8	27	.405	.270	.41	.19	11/32	.393	.334
1/4	18	.540	.364	.62	.29	7/16	.522	.433
3/8	18	.675	.494	.63	.30	37/64	.658	.568
1/2	14	.840	.623	.83	.39	23/32	.815	.701
3/4	14	1.050	.824	.84	.40	59/64	1.025	.911
1	11½	1.315	1.048	1.03	.51	1 5/32	1.283	1.144
1¼	11½	1.660	1.380	1.06	.54	1 1/2	1.627	1.488
1½	11½	1.900	1.611	1.07	.55	1 47/64	1.866	1.727
2	11½	2.375	2.067	1.10	.58	2 7/32	2.339	2.223
2½	8	2.875	2.468	1.64	.89	2 5/8	2.820	2.620
3	8	3.500	3.067	1.70	.95	3 1/4	3.441	3.241
3½	8	4.000	3.548	1.75	1.00	3 3/4	3.938	3.738
4	8	4.500	4.026	1.80	1.05	4 1/4	4.434	4.234
4½	8	5.000	4.508	1.85	1.10	4 3/4	4.931	4.731
5	8	5.563	5.045	1.91	1.16	5 9/32	5.490	5.290
6	8	6.625	6.065	2.01	1.26	6 11/32	6.546	6.346
7	8	7.625	7.023	2.11	1.36	7 11/32	7.540	7.340
8	8	8.625	7.982	2.21	1.46	8 11/32	8.534	8.334
9	8	9.625	8.937	2.32	1.57	9 11/32	9.527	9.327
10	8	10.750	10.019	2.43	1.68	10 7/16	10.645	10.445

NOTE.—The taper of the threaded part is 1 in 16.

TABLE V

DECIMAL EQUIVALENTS OF PARTS OF 1 INCH

Fraction	Decimal	Fraction	Decimal	Fraction	Decimal	Fraction	Decimal
	.0078		.2578		.5078		.7578
$\frac{1}{64}$	.0156	$\frac{17}{64}$	.2656	$\frac{33}{64}$	.5156	$\frac{49}{64}$	.7656
	.0235		.2735		.5235		.7735
$\frac{1}{32}$	.0313	$\frac{9}{32}$	.2813	$\frac{17}{32}$	.5313	$\frac{25}{32}$	.7813
	.0391		.2891		.5391		.7891
$\frac{3}{64}$	.0469	$\frac{19}{64}$	.2969	$\frac{35}{64}$	.5469	$\frac{51}{64}$	.7969
	.0547		.3047		.5547		.8047
$\frac{1}{16}$	.0625	$\frac{5}{16}$	.3125	$\frac{9}{16}$	.5625	$\frac{13}{16}$	.8125
	.0703		.3203		.5703		.8203
$\frac{5}{64}$	.0781	$\frac{21}{64}$	.3281	$\frac{37}{64}$	.5781	$\frac{53}{64}$	.8281
	.0860		.3360		.5860		.8360
$\frac{3}{32}$	.0938	$\frac{11}{32}$	.3438	$\frac{19}{32}$	.5938	$\frac{27}{32}$	.8438
	.1016		.3516		.6016		.8516
$\frac{7}{64}$	.1094	$\frac{23}{64}$	.3594	$\frac{39}{64}$	.6094	$\frac{55}{64}$	.8594
	.1172		.3672		.6172		.8672
$\frac{1}{8}$	.1250	$\frac{3}{8}$	.3750	$\frac{5}{8}$	.6250	$\frac{7}{8}$	.8750
	.1328		.3828		.6328		.8828
$\frac{9}{64}$	.1406	$\frac{25}{64}$	.3906	$\frac{41}{64}$	.6406	$\frac{57}{64}$	.8906
	.1485		.3985		.6485		.8985
$\frac{5}{32}$	.1563	$\frac{13}{32}$	.4063	$\frac{21}{32}$	.6563	$\frac{29}{32}$	.9063
	.1641		.4141		.6641		.9141
$\frac{11}{64}$	.1719	$\frac{27}{64}$	.4219	$\frac{43}{64}$	.6719	$\frac{59}{64}$	.9219
	.1797		.4297		.6797		.9297
$\frac{3}{16}$	.1875	$\frac{7}{16}$	.4375	$\frac{11}{16}$	.6875	$\frac{15}{16}$	.9375
	.1953		.4453		.6953		.9453
$\frac{13}{64}$	.2031	$\frac{29}{64}$	.4531	$\frac{45}{64}$	.7031	$\frac{61}{64}$	.9531
	.2110		.4610		.7110		.9610
$\frac{7}{32}$	.2188	$\frac{15}{32}$	.4688	$\frac{23}{32}$	.7188	$\frac{31}{32}$	.9688
	.2266		.4766		.7266		.9766
$\frac{15}{64}$	.2344	$\frac{31}{64}$	.4844	$\frac{47}{64}$	.7344	$\frac{63}{64}$	.9844
	.2422		.4922		.7422		.9922
$\frac{1}{4}$	.2500	$\frac{1}{2}$	.5000	$\frac{3}{4}$	.7500	1	1.0000
	.2578		.5078		.7578		1.0078

SKETCHING

INTRODUCTION

1. In practice, the draftsman is required in most cases to draw from rough freehand sketches, made by himself or by some one else, either from an actual object or an imaginary one. For instance, suppose that a machine is in operation somewhere, of which the drawings never existed or were lost. For the purpose, say, of rebuilding or regularly manufacturing this machine, a set of working drawings is required. Suppose, as is most generally the case, that the machine is so located that it is not readily accessible to the draftsman at all times, so that he cannot take measurements while making the drawing, even if this were commendable. In such cases he must make **sketches,** that is, rough mechanical drawings freehand, from which later on he executes the regular drawings.

Again, suppose a certain change or modification is to be made in a machine, machine part, or mechanism, or a new one is to be made, and a working drawing is required. The idea is then made clear to the draftsman by means of sketches more or less complete, from which the regular drawings are subsequently elaborated.

2. A sketch must have all the essentials of a working drawing except that it is not made to scale, although the relative proportions of the object represented are maintained as near as this is possible by mere eyesight. As in a

§ 15

mechanical drawing, the sketch must clearly contain all the dimensions and explanatory notes necessary to enable the object to be made from it. To all intents and purposes, then, a working sketch could be immediately used as a working drawing, and is sometimes so used in cases of emergency. A regular working drawing is, however, generally more elaborate; not only is it drawn to scale, but generally a smaller number of views of the object are shown than are required in a sketch. In both, one endeavors to get along with as few views as are necessary to clearly represent the object, although in a sketch a multiplicity of lines is avoided by additional views and sections, which can be quickly drawn; also, various notes, short cuts, and conventional marks may be used more freely on a sketch than would be tolerated on a regular drawing.

3. Method of Procedure.—In sketching an object, it is first fully represented in as many views as are necessary to bring out all the details; the measurements are taken afterwards and written in. This is by far the best plan, as much time may be wasted by trying to take measurements and write dimensions as one sketches. Furthermore, by first fully completing the sketch a better general knowledge of the object is gained, which will help in distinguishing between dimensions that are essential and those that are not. Of this more will be said later.

SKETCHING MACHINE DETAILS

GENERAL REMARKS ON SKETCHING

4. Materials for Sketching.—All that is needed for making a sketch are a lead pencil, paper, and a soft rubber. It is convenient to have the rubber attached to the end of the pencil. Various rubber-tipped pencils are in the market and are readily obtainable from stationers. The paper is best used in letter size, $8'' \times 10''$ done up in pads, from which the single sheets can be detached one by one. The paper should be heavy, so that it will stand considerable abuse; Manila paper is very good for the purpose. Cross-section paper is well adapted to sketching; the little squares are a great aid in enabling the piece to be sketched in proper proportion and assist materially in producing rapidity. The kind that is divided into $\frac{1}{16}''$ squares is to be preferred. The student, however, is advised not to use it until he has become proficient in making sketches on plain paper, since in actual practice he will frequently be obliged to make sketches on plain paper, and he will find it very difficult to do this if he has learned to depend on cross-section paper. The student should not use it in the work done in connection with this paper. It must be kept in mind that the sketch is not a correct drawing to scale, and the student should be guided by the eye entirely, except when making various views of the same object correspond, of which more will be said presently.

5. Sketch of a Single Object Requiring But One View.—As previously stated, one should get along with as few views as possible; in some cases a single view will be sufficient for the sketch, while perhaps two might be called for in the working drawing made from it. Thus, the object illustrated in Fig. 1 can be fully represented by a side view, as shown in the sketch, Fig. 2; nor would the working drawing subsequently made from it require any more, since the view cannot be mistaken for anything else than a stud bolt with a hexagonal head. If the bolt had a square head, only one side would be shown; the fact that two sides are shown in the sketch indicates that the head is hexagonal.

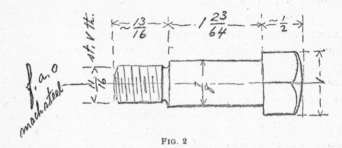

FIG. 1

6. Fig. 3 illustrates an object—a bushing —that might be sketched in a single view, but would probably in a working drawing be represented by

FIG. 2

both a section and an end view, to show that the two rectangles represent cylinders and that there are only two holes in the flange. In the sketch, Fig. 4, the end view may be dispensed with and a note substituted giving the information about the holes. That the body is cylindrical may be indicated conveniently by adding to some of the measurements the letter D, meaning diameter. While such a view is sufficient, an end view alone would clearly not be, as it would not disclose

FIG. 3

the length of the two cylinders, and would, even with the necessary information to that effect, be wholly inadequate to form at once a mental picture of the shape

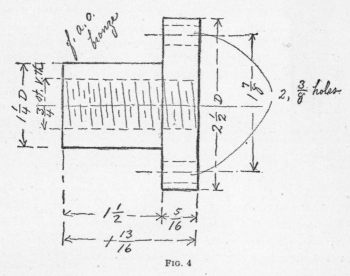

FIG. 4

of the body. It is thus seen that judgment must be used as to what view to sketch. Rather than leave any doubts, two views should be made.

7. Sketch of a Single Object Requiring Two Views.—Fig. 5 is an illustration of an object—a gripper from a printing press— that requires two views: a front view giving the peculiar outline of the piece, and an end view, or a bottom view, to show the width. See Fig. 6. While either the front view and the end view, or the front view

FIG. 5

and the bottom view, would suffice, an end view and

bottom view would not. The bottom view is shown in
dotted lines, and it is at once evident that this view

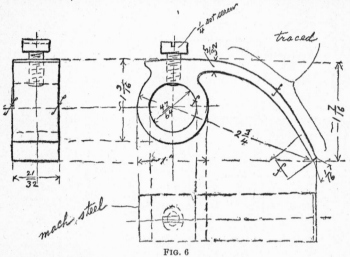

FIG. 6

and the end view would not show the shape of the object
in this instance.

**8. Sketch of a Single Object Requiring Three
Views.**—An object is represented in Fig. 7 that is simple in
appearance. However,
it is necessary to show
three views in order
that the drawing may
clearly bring out its
shape. The front view,
Fig. 8, is the main
view; the side view
and plan give the
depth of the uprights
and base, and they also
show, respectively, that
the uprights and ends of
the base terminate in
semicircles. These are features the front view does not show.

FIG. 7

9. Sketch of a Single Object Requiring a Section. Three outside views will, as a general rule, be sufficient to

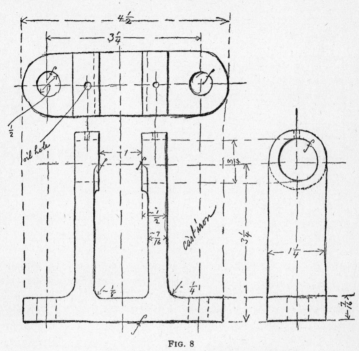

FIG. 8

clearly bring out the details of any object, even if the object is hollow and outlines are thus hidden from sight. In many cases, as, for instance, in the case of the bushing shown in Figs. 3 and 4, dotted lines may be employed to point out such hidden features. Often, however, many dotted lines become confusing, and it is then much better to make a section, that is,

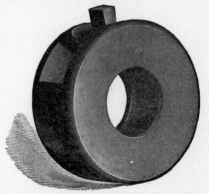

FIG. 9

to imagine the object cut along a certain plane and one of the parts removed, a sketch being made of the remaining part. Fig. 9 is an example of such an object—a safety collar.

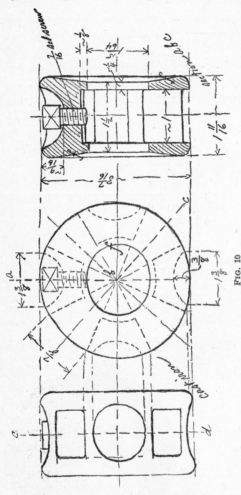

A side view and front view, Fig. 10, give all the outside features. To show everything of the inside in a single section, a so-called conventional section has been taken along the broken line *a b c* of the front view. This enables the draftsman to show both the hemispherical cavities— in one of which the setscrew is placed with its head below the outside circumference, so it cannot catch on the clothing—and the holes with rectangular cross-sections cored in the casting to secure lightness. The section further shows the offset in the middle of the shaft hole, leaving only a comparatively small surface at each side to be finished and fitted to the shaft. It also shows that the end surfaces are not planes but concave surfaces. A section along a line *c d*, equivalent to the dotted lines in the front view, would not

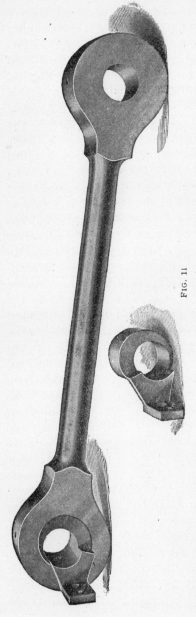

FIG. 11

show these latter features clearly and would therefore not be sufficient.

10. Sketch of Two or More Objects Fitted Together.—When a combination of parts is to be sketched, such as an entire mechanism, it is advantageous in several respects to sketch them as a whole first. The following is gained thereby: a clear idea is acquired of how the various parts fit and work together; many dimensions will have to be taken but once. After having gained all the information possible without taking the mechanism apart, each piece is removed one by one, sketching while doing so any additional features that may present themselves, which may even call for additional figures. Fig. 11, which shows one of a pair of connecting-rods from a printing press, is an illustration. The two parts fitted together are the rod proper, having two eyes, one of which is provided with an eccentric bushing having a bracket of peculiar shape. In taking the view of the combination as a whole, the bushing was observed to have a larger outside diameter in the front than in the back. To find out how far into the eye the larger part extended, the bushing had to be slipped out, when it was seen that the larger diameter was due simply to a slender shoulder following the rounding of the edge of the eye of the rod proper, and a little sketch (*a*), Fig. 12, was jotted down to emphasize this. Otherwise, the two parts sketched together give all the information necessary to draw them separately on the working drawing. The mate of the rod sketched is exactly the same with the exception that the $\frac{3}{8}''$ pin is symmetrically opposite on the other side of the center line, and the bracket (*h*) of the bushing is reversed, as seen on the bushing, shown detached. In a case like this it is sufficient to mark on the sketch "one right, one left," the sketch thus covering four pieces at once. The abbreviation *f. a. o.* found on this sketch means "finished all over."

11. Fragmentary Views: Symmetrical Objects. Many objects present a repetition of parts, in which case, it is sufficient to sketch only parts of such objects. This is particularly the case in objects that are symmetrical with reference to certain lines so that the sketch will also be symmetrical to such lines, which are called axes of symmetry. An **axis of symmetry** is any line so drawn, that if the part of the figure on one side of the line be folded on this line, it will coincide exactly with the other part, point for point and line for line. The use of frag-- mentary sketches must not, however, be carried too far, using the expedient only when it is of real help—when it saves time and it does not make the sketch clearer, to draw the view in full. Thus, it would not help much to show only half of the bolt (Fig. 1), the bushing (Fig. 3), the gripper (Fig. 5), the bracket (Fig. 7), or the collar (Fig. 9), as these pieces, though they are symmetrical to a certain center line, are as easily sketched in full. Cases in which fragmentary sketches may be made are symmetrical machine frames, as shown in Fig. 13 and sketched in Fig. 14, or pulleys and other wheels, as shown in Fig. 15 and sketched in Fig. 16.

12. Center Lines and Proportions. — In starting a sketch, decide on a view that seems to disclose most of the features of the object. Select one of

FIG. 13

the most striking dimensions,—as, for instance, the total length or total height of the piece to be sketched,—and mark

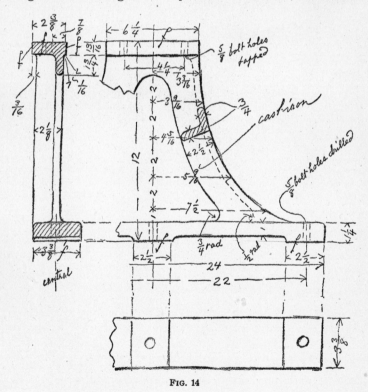

FIG. 14

down a distance on the paper that represents the dimension. Then, until the sketch is completed, this forms the basis to proportion the other dimensions, by comparing them

mentally with it. If the object is symmetrical to certain axes, draw these axes first. Thus, in round pieces like those shown in Figs. 1 and 3, draw the center line. Although measurements are not taken from these imaginary lines, they are of great help in guiding the eye while making the sketch. This is especially true in the case of circles. When more than one view is sketched

FIG. 15

of an object, the center lines at once serve to bring various views in proper relation to one another. Thus, in sketching

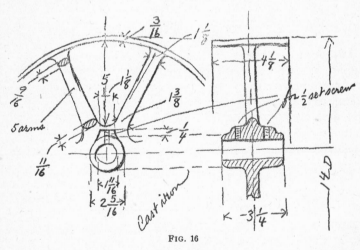

FIG. 16

the object, Figs. 7 and 8, the front view is drawn first, starting with the center line, dividing the figure vertically into symmetrical halves. Next draw the base line, and then the center lines of the bolt holes in the base at equal distances right and left of the main center line; draw the center line of the shaft holes in uprights parallel to and at the proper distance (judging by the eye only, of course) from the base line, and around this skeleton of center lines, draw the outlines of the object. When the front view is finished, start the plan. To do this, prolong the main center line, also the center lines of the holes in the base. Draw a horizontal axis of symmetry parallel to the base and the axis of the shaft, thus obtaining a skeleton of center lines for the plan around which to draw it. Proceed similarly with the side view, carrying over the center line of shaft holes and drawing a new axis of symmetry parallel to the main center line of the first view.

13. Projection Lines.—In sketching various views of an object, use will be made of the principles of geometrical drawing, and projection lines will be drawn from one view to the other. Such lines should be traced on the sketch very faintly, and many of them only mentally, as they will make the sketch confused if used too freely or made too heavy.

14. Shade Lines.—It is not customary, as a rule, to employ shade lines on a working drawing. They are, however, recommended on sketches, as they tend to make the sketch clearer, without entailing much expenditure of time, and no artifice should be spared that will effect this, especially as a sketch may be laid aside a long time before the finished drawing is made.

15. Sections and Cutting Plane Lines.—Sections must be placed in the sketch in proper position toward the lines of section along which they are taken. The proper position alone will indicate in most cases along which line the section is taken, but in so-called conventional sections it is necessary to make the cutting plane line very plain and to note near the sectional view the line of section, as

done, for instance, in Fig. 10. There are two sections in
Fig. 12; one is taken on the center line passing through the
center of both the eccentric hole of the bushing and the
center of the eye of the rod; the other section is really a
conventional section, the section of the eye being taken on
the center line passing through the center of the eye, and
the section of the bushing being taken on the center line
passing through its own center. There is no need of men-
tioning this on the sketch, however, as no one will suppose
that a measurement is taken of the dimension of the eye
along the line passing through the center of the eccentric
bushing.

16. Cross-Sectioning Material. — No distinction is
made on a sketch between materials by means of cross-
section lines—the name of the material should be written
on the sketch.

17. Finish Marks.—Finish marks should be placed in
the sketch wherever lines represent finished surfaces, except
in those cases where it is evident from the nature of the
pieces that the surfaces must be finished, such as surfaces
fitted together. The principle to be followed in making a
sketch is in general: Give all the data necessary, but avoid
unnecessary marks and lines.

MEASUREMENTS

MEASURING INSTRUMENTS

18. The instruments to be used in measuring the dimensions of an object for the purpose of making a sketch and
subsequently a working drawing depend to a certain extent
on the accuracy required. To explain more fully, suppose
one of the eccentric bushings on the connecting-rod for a
printing press, Fig. 11, to be so worn as to need replacing,
but that the press is to be kept running while a new piece is
being made. A very accurate measuring of the dimensions

is then necessary, as the piece must fit exactly. On the other hand, suppose a whole machine is to be rebuilt from an existing pattern, and that for this purpose drawings are to be made which henceforth shall be considered standard. The dimensions need not necessarily be as accurate as in the first case, as the various pieces of the new machine will be fitted together when assembling. In the former case, it may be necessary to employ much more delicate instruments than in the latter case, so that in general it may be said that a draftsman may in the long run make good use of any measuring instrument to be found in the market. For ordinary cases, however, the tools here enumerated and described will be found amply sufficient.

19. The Two-Foot Rule. — The best-known tool for measuring linear dimensions is the two-foot rule, which is

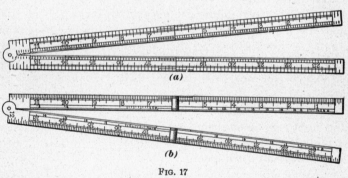

FIG. 17

usually made up of four leaves, hinged together, to allow it to be folded for convenience in carrying, as shown in Fig. 17. The rule is usually made of boxwood, with brass joints and edges. It is divided into inches and fractions of an inch. Divisions smaller, however, than $\frac{1}{16}''$ are rarely marked on them, so that the smallest fraction that can be directly measured is $\frac{1}{16}''$, but with a little practice it is possible to locate the middle and quarter points between the sixteenth-inch marks with a fair degree of accuracy, thus making it possible to measure distances as small as

$\frac{1}{32}''$ and $\frac{1}{64}''$. The two-foot rule is well adapted to comparatively rough work, where accuracy of measurement is
not particularly essential.

20. The Standard Steel Rule.—For more accurate
measurements, steel rules are used. These rules are always
graduated on both edges of each side, and a large choice of
different kinds of graduations is offered by the makers.
For use in sketching, two kinds of rules, both 12 inches
long, will be found very essential. One has divisions of the
inch into 8 parts on one edge of the one side, into 16 parts
on the other edge of the same side, and into 32 and 64 parts
on the two edges, respectively, of the other side. The
other rule has divisions of the inch into 10, 20, 50, and
100 parts on the four edges, respectively.

21. Steel Tapes.—In measuring distances greater than
a few feet, steel tapes are very convenient. They are
made in lengths varying from 2 feet to 100 feet for shop
use. The graduations are not very fine; hence, tapes are
only suitable for approximate measurements. For a special
use of a pocket steel tape, see Art. **33.**

22. The Straightedge.—It is very convenient to have
a straightedge among the tools, although any straight piece
of metal or wood, the blade of a square (see Fig. 18), may
be used instead in an emergency.

23. The Square.—An instrument that comes into frequent use is the square. It is best to have one with an
adjustable blade, called an *adjustable square*, and shown in
Fig. 18. The blade a is held in the stock b by means of a
hook clamp that enters the groove c in the blade, and is
tightened by means of the nut d. The stock can be set at
any point throughout the length of the blade, and also, of
course, flush with the end of it, and thus serves also as a
solid square. A special bevel blade e for testing angles
of 45° and 30° is generally furnished with this square.

The stock is also usually provided with a level at *f* that may
be used in testing either a vertical or a horizontal surface.

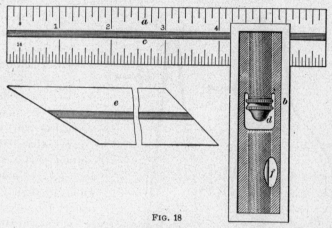

FIG. 18

It should be borne in mind that a square is perfect only
when the blade and stock are exactly at right angles to each
other, and that a fall or any careless use is liable to destroy
its accuracy.

24. Calipers.—Calipers are of almost endless shapes and
sizes. They are used to measure either the diameters or
lengths, from a small
fraction of an inch
to several feet. The
simplest forms of cali-
pers are shown in
Fig. 19. Fig. 19 (*a*)
illustrates *outside
calipers*, used for ta-
king outside meas-
urements of shafts,
wheels, and similar
articles, and Fig. 19 (*b*)
shows a companion
tool, the *inside cali-*

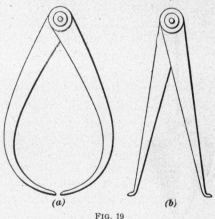

FIG. 19

pers, which, as the name implies, is used to measure the

diameter of holes, or the distance between two objects. Another class of calipers is provided with an adjusting screw, as shown in Fig. 20 (*a*) and (*b*). Calipers are often used to measure the outside diameter of screws, and when so used are made as in Fig. 20 (*a*), except that the contact surfaces *a* and *b* are made wide enough to reach across two or more threads. Similar calipers are used to

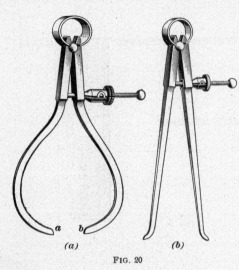

(*a*)   (*b*)

FIG. 20

measure the bottom of screw threads, in which case the points are beveled and thin, like a knife blade.

25.   The Plumb-Bob.—The **plumb-bob** is often very convenient to have among the tools used in sketching, although any small piece of metal, as a nut, a penknife, or other small, heavy object tied to a thread does equally well in most instances, since it does not often happen in sketching that a plumb-line must be established over a certain point; in this latter case, a regular plumb-bob having a sharp point would be required, as shown in Fig. 21.

FIG. 21

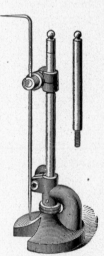

FIG. 22

26. Surface Gauge.—A **surface gauge** consists of a flat base to which is attached a vertical standard that carries an adjustable scriber. Fig. 22 shows a simple form of this instrument. Its use in sketching, as well as that of the other tools described, will be more fully treated in the following pages.

TAKING MEASUREMENTS

27. Writing Measurements on the Sketch.—After the sketch itself is completed,—or when in a combination of objects fitted together, as a whole machine, the sketch has been completed as far as that is possible without taking the combination apart,—the taking of measurements is begun. *Each measurement must be put down on the sketch as soon as it has been taken.* The student should never take several measurements one after another with the intention of writing them down on the sketch together. He is certain to make mistakes, causing himself and others considerable annoyance in using the sketch afterwards.

The ascertaining of dimensions of an object by measuring often calls for considerable ingenuity, and sometimes methods of the draftsman's own devising will be resorted to that are not found described in the following pages, which contain, however, those in most frequent use.

28. Distance Between Two Points on a Plane Surface.—This is the simplest measurement; it is taken by means of the rule, and needs no explanation. Most frequently the points between which the dimension is wanted are located on the edge of a flat surface, that is, in the corner of two flat surfaces meeting as, for instance, in Fig. 14, the top and bottom measurements ($6\frac{1}{4}''$ and $24''$) of the stand.

29. Length of Cylindrical Surfaces.—A measurement equally simple is to find the length of cylindrical surfaces by means of the rule, as, for instance, the lengths ($1\frac{1}{2}''$ and $\frac{5}{16}''$) of the two cylinders in Fig. 4, or the length of the shank of the tap bolt ($1\frac{23}{64}''$) of Fig. 2.

30. Round and Otherwise Undefined Corners: Distance Between Parallel Planes.—Often one of the points, or even both, the distance between which is to be ascertained, is imaginary, as, for instance, when there are round corners. In such cases the adjoining surface must be prolonged so that a sharp corner is established. For instance, the length ($1\frac{11}{16}''$) of the safety collar, Fig. 10, could not be measured directly with the rule, but the collar had to be placed between two flat surfaces, and the distance between the latter measured. This was most conveniently done by laying the collar on a plane surface and using the adjustable square, as shown in Fig. 23.

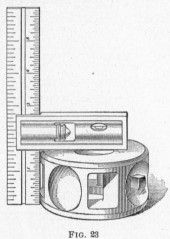

FIG. 23

In the same manner, the square must be used to get the over-all dimension ($1\frac{13}{16}''$) of the bushing, shown in Fig. 4. See Fig. 24. As will readily be observed, this method is really equivalent to taking the shortest, that is, perpendicular, distance between two parallel planes.

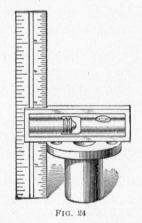

FIG. 24

31. Thickness.—It is not always convenient or possible to measure distances between parallel planes, real or imaginary, by means of the plane surface and adjustable square, as shown in Figs. 23 and 24. In such cases, the outside calipers are used; thus, while the distance across flats of the hexagonal head of the bolt, Fig. 1, may be measured with the plane and square, it is more convenient to use the calipers, while the thicknesses ($\frac{3}{4}''$) of the webs in the cast-iron stand, Figs. 13 and 14, must be measured with the outside calipers, if the measurement is to be accurate, the corners being round. Such dimensions are called *thicknesses*.

32. Distances Between Curved Surfaces: Outside Diameters.—The outside calipers are also used to ascertain dimensions of curved sur-

faces. Thus, the dimension ($1\frac{3}{16}''$) between the top of the piece, Fig. 6, and the bottom is measured with the outside calipers. Logically, all outside diameters are measured with the same instrument. The procedure is as follows: Open the calipers approximately wide enough to let the body to be measured pass freely between

FIG. 25

the points. Then, by gently tapping the calipers against some convenient object, a frame near by, for instance,

FIG. 26

gradually close (or open) the legs until the points just touch the body measured. See Fig. 25. There should be no play, nor should the points pinch too hard. It requires a little practice to get the proper touch by tapping the calipers. The process is easier with spring calipers, having screw adjustment, shown in Fig. 20.

After the calipers are properly adjusted, the distance between the points is measured with the steel rule in the manner shown in Fig. 26.

33. It often happens that very large diameters are to be measured, for which the calipers available are too small, as in the case of pulleys, wheels, and similar objects. Often in such cases one can measure near enough across the side of such objects, as a pulley, for instance, with a long rule or a stick, but equally as often this cannot be done on account of other parts being in the way; for instance, when a pulley is keyed to a shaft, perhaps near to a hanger besides. In most cases the steel tape furnishes excellent means for getting at the diameter, by measuring the circumference of the wheel or pulley and dividing the same by 3.1416. Thus, if the circumference as measured with the tape is 7 ft. $\frac{1}{16}''$, the diameter is 7 ft. $\frac{1}{16}'' \div 3.1416 = 7.0052$ ft. $\div 3.1416 = 2\frac{1}{4}$ ft., very nearly $= 2$ ft. $3''$.

34. Inside Dimensions: Holes.—To measure inside dimensions, such as the diameters of holes, for instance,

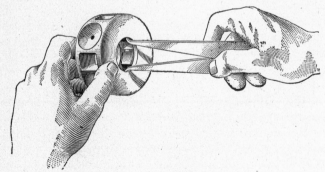

FIG. 27

the inside calipers are used, as in Fig. 27. The procedure is identically the same as with outside calipers, but care must be taken in tapping the instrument not to strike on the points, as these will be easily injured thereby. After the instrument is adjusted, the distance between the points is again measured with the rule, as shown in Fig. 28.

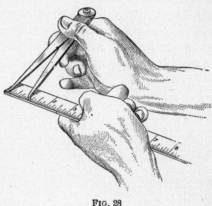

FIG. 28

35. Over-All Dimensions.—When the length of an object is measured in successive steps, as, for instance,. the bushing, Fig. 4, it is best also to measure the whole length, which then serves as a check on the measurements previously taken.

36. Exact and Approximate Dimensions.—In the case of most objects some dimensions must be exact, while others may be approximate. Thus, in Fig. 2, the length ($1\frac{23}{64}''$) of the shank of the bolt must be measured exactly, as the bolt is to be fitted into the eye of a lever that must move freely, without undue play between the shoulder of the head and the piece into which the bolt is screwed. Suppose that the bolt had been broken off at the screw and a new one was to be made; then it is evident that the shank of the old bolt must be very carefully measured so that the new one will exactly fit the length of the lever eye. The other lengths, that is, the extreme height of the head ($\frac{1}{2}''$) and the length of the screw to the top of its rounded end ($1\frac{3}{16}''$) are clearly not so important. It is permissible to round off such unimportant dimensions to the nearest $\frac{1}{32}''$ or even $\frac{1}{16}''$, as the case may be. Thus, suppose the length of the screw, Fig. 2, actually measured $\frac{51}{64}''$, it would be perfectly correct enough to mark this dimension $\frac{13}{16}''$ on the sketch. Other examples are the width and thickness of the base and uprights of the object shown in Figs. 7 and 8. The piece is a casting finished only at the surfaces marked f, f. The actual measurements showed the thickness of the base to be between $\frac{13}{32}''$ and $\frac{15}{32}''$ and the thickness of the upright varied between about the same figures. This was evidently due to the shaking of the pattern in the mold, and the thickness intended was no doubt $\frac{7}{16}''$, so this measurement was marked on the sketch. Likewise, the radii of the fillets joining the uprights and base were "guessed at" more or less (see Art. **43**) to be $\frac{1}{4}''$ and $\frac{1}{8}''$, respectively. In the various sketches a number of such dimensions that have been rounded off, averaged, or more or less arbitrarily fixed are marked with a little wavy line preceding the figures. See Figs. 8, 12, etc.

37. Establishing Centers. — Distances between two centers, as of two shafts, two holes, or distances between a center and a surface, etc., cannot in the majority of cases be measured directly with any of the instruments, and it requires considerable ingenuity and care at times to establish such dimensions. The following are a few examples.

A case very frequently occurring is the establishing of the distance between centers of two holes, as, for instance, in the connecting-rod, Figs. 11 and 12. This dimension ($24\frac{3}{16}''$) is here obtained by measuring the distance between the inside edges of the holes ($21\frac{27}{32}''$), and adding to this measurement half of the diameter of each hole, measured with the calipers, the result being $21\frac{27}{32}'' + \frac{2}{2}'' + \dfrac{2\frac{11}{16}''}{2}$

$= 21\frac{27}{32}'' + 1'' + 1\frac{11}{32}'' = 24\frac{3}{16}''$. Fig. 11 also furnishes another illustration: the distance between the center of the outside circle of the eccentric bushing and the center of the inside circle, that is, the eccentricity of the two circles. To find this, measure the thickness of the bushing at the thinnest part ($\frac{1}{16}''$), add to it half of the diameter of the inner circle, and deduct this sum from half of the diameter of the outside circle; thus, $\dfrac{2\frac{11}{16}''}{2} - (\frac{1}{16}'' + \frac{2}{2}'') = 1\frac{11}{32}''$

$-(\frac{1}{16}'' + 1'') = 1\frac{11}{32}'' - 1\frac{1}{16}'' = \frac{9}{32}''.$

38. If the holes are of the same size, the distance between centers is at once obtained by measuring from the outside edge of one hole to the inside edge of the other, as, for instance, the distance $3\frac{1}{4}''$ between centers of bolt holes in Fig. 8, and $4\frac{1}{4}''$ and $22''$ in Fig. 14. Similarly, the distance between the center of the shaft holes in the object, Fig. 7, and the bottom of the base is obtained by measuring the distance from the bottom of the hole to the bottom of the base and adding to this the radius of the hole. The first dimension is, how-

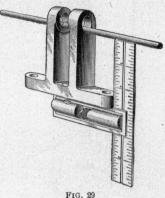

FIG. 29

ever, not directly measurable with a rule, but must be gotten by prolonging the bottom line of the hole by means of some convenient straight piece and the square, as shown

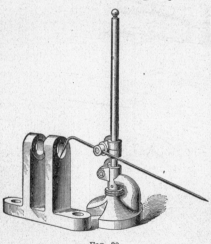

FIG. 30

in Fig. 29. This straight piece must, moreover, be round in section, as its under edge would not otherwise represent the prolongation of the bottom line of the hole. At first sight it might seem as if this dimension might have been taken more easily by measuring the total height of the piece and deducting therefrom the thickness of the metal on top of the hole and the radius of the latter; but this would not give a reliable measurement, as the piece is not finished on top, while the bottom is, and as the dimension sought is an essential one, it must be accurate. An easier way to get the measurement, however, is by the use of the surface gauge. The gauge is adjusted so that the point of the scriber lightly touches the bottom of the hole; the scriber is then removed and the distance from the plane to the point measured. See Figs. 30 and 31.

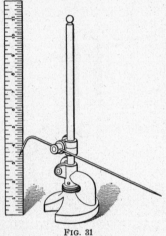

FIG. 31

Another example of finding the distance of a center from a plane surface is shown in Fig. 32. The adjustable square is used to find the distance from the top of the frame of the machine, which is finished, to the top of the collar below. To this is added half of the diam-

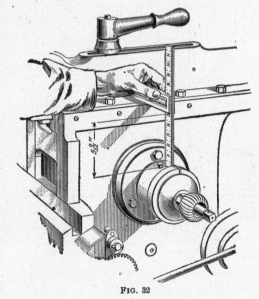

FIG. 32

eter of the collar, ascertained by means of the outside calipers.

A further example is given in Fig. 33. It was required to measure the horizontal distance of the center of the shaft from the vertical finished front of the machine. The square could not be used in the same manner as in Fig. 32, as the sliding carriage, already in its lowest position, was in the way. The dimension had thus to be transferred higher up, as it were. The plumb-bob was conveniently suspended, so that the plumb-line just touched the left side of the disk.

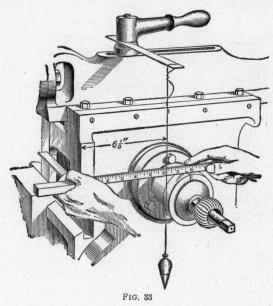

FIG. 33

Next, the distance between this line and the front of the machine was measured and one-half of the diameter of the disk added thereto. Before this method could be employed, however, it had to be ascertained whether the machine so stood on the floor that the front surface of the frame were vertical. It was found not to be the case, and had to be wedged up on one side to make it so.

39. Centers of Gear-Wheels: Pitch of Gears.—The distance between centers of two gear-wheels in mesh must be measured with particular accuracy, as it furnishes the only clue to accurately ascertain the pitch of the gears. If the shafts are accessible, either in front or back of the gears,

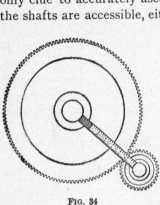

FIG. 34

the distance between centers is easily established by measuring the distance between the shafts by means of inside calipers if the distance is short, or by means of two steel rules slid one upon the other, if the distance is greater. See Fig. 34. To this measurement the radii of the shafts are added. If the shafts are flush with the wheels, so that the distance between centers cannot be measured in the above way, and if there are no hubs to make use of, the distance may be obtained by measuring across the wheels themselves and deducting their outside radii. This method will be absolutely exact only, however, if the number of teeth in both wheels is even, because, if the number is odd, the outside diameter cannot be measured accurately with the calipers ; there is a tooth on one end of the diameter and a space on the opposite end, the measurement being between the point of the tooth on the one end of a diameter and the point of the tooth next to the space at the other end of the diameter. The difference between the dimensions so obtained is, however, but very slight in ordinary cases.

40. Having by some means ascertained the distance between centers, the diametral pitch* is found by dividing the sum of the teeth of both wheels by double the distance from center to center, and the circular pitch† by multiplying

---

* The diametral pitch is a number indicating the ratio between the number of teeth and the pitch diameter; thus, 4 (diametral) pitch means that there are four teeth to each inch of the diameter, so that a wheel that has this pitch and has a pitch diameter of 5 inches has 5 × 4 = 20 teeth, or a wheel that has 4 pitch and 20 teeth has a pitch diameter of 5 inches.

† The circular pitch is the linear measure on the pitch circle from a point on one tooth to the corresponding point on the next tooth.

double the distance from center to center by 3.1416 and dividing the product by the sum of the teeth of both wheels, or by formulas:

$$\text{diametral pitch} = \frac{N + n}{2c},$$

$$\text{circular pitch} = \frac{6.2832c}{N + n},$$

in which N = number of teeth of large wheel;
           n = number of teeth of small wheel;
           c = distance from center to center.

By calculating both pitches it is generally recognized by what system they are constructed. Thus, if the calculation yields, for instance, a whole number, or a whole number and a half, or a whole number and a quarter, for the diametral pitch, but an awkward decimal number for the circular pitch, it is fair to assume that the gears are cut to the diametral pitch indicated by that number. If the calculation yields an awkward decimal number for the diametral pitch, but a whole number, or a whole number and simple fraction for the circular pitch, it is fair to assume that the gears are cut to circular pitch.

Thus, the distance between the gears, Figs. 35 and 36, is by measurement $11\frac{37}{64}''$ ($= 11.578''+$) from center to center. There are 15 teeth in the pinion, or small gear, and 124 teeth in the large gear. The diametral pitch is thus

$$\frac{124 + 15}{2 \times 11.578} = \frac{139}{23.156} = 6.003,$$

or 6, very nearly.

The circular pitch is

$$\frac{6.2832 \times 11.578''}{124 + 15} = .5233'',$$

that is, between $\frac{33}{64}''$ and $\frac{17}{32}''$.

FIG. 35

It is thus very evident that the gears are cut to 6 diametral pitch. As a proof, using 6 for the diametral pitch, the distance from center to center is:

Pitch radius of large wheel + pitch radius of pinion

$$= \frac{1}{2}\left(\frac{124}{6} + \frac{15}{6}\right) = \frac{139}{12} = 11\frac{7}{12}'' = 11\frac{37\frac{1}{3}}{64}'', \text{ as against } 11\frac{37''}{64}$$

from actual measurement, the difference being only $\frac{1}{3}$ of $\frac{1}{64}''$, or $\frac{1}{192}''$.

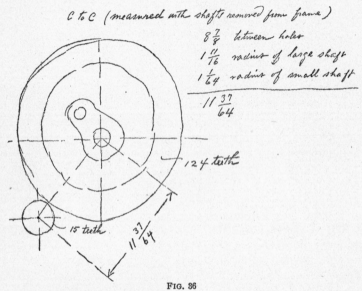

C to C (measured with shafts removed from frame)

$8\frac{7}{8}$ *between holes*

$1\frac{11}{16}$ *radius of large shaft*

$1\frac{1}{64}$ *radius of small shaft*

$11\frac{37}{64}$

124 teeth

15 teeth

$11\frac{37}{64}$

FIG. 36

In taking dimensions of gear-wheels, it is generally more exact to measure with a rule having inches divided into 100 parts.

41. The method of finding the pitch from the distances between centers is the only exact one, but cannot always be employed; in many cases, the circular pitch must be measured directly at the point where the two wheels are in mesh, guessing more or less at the location of the pitch line; this will be quite close, however, since the teeth touch at the pitch line when passing through the line connecting the centers of the wheels. This method must be employed invariably with miter and other bevel gears; it should always be employed as a check.

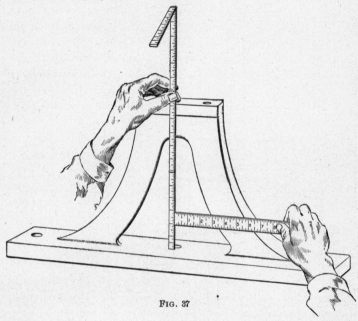

FIG. 37

42. Curved Outlines: Fillets.—Curved outlines, such as occur in machinery frames, sometimes give considerable trouble in sketching. Fortunately, the dimensions are in such cases seldom required to be exact, and the measurements can be rounded off. The frame, Fig. 13, is an example. To get the curved outline of the stand, the two-foot rule was held verti-

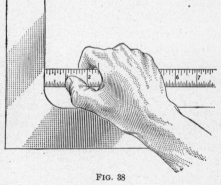

FIG. 38

cally in the center and horizontal measurements taken at various points of the rule, as illustrated in Fig. 37.

43. Sharp corners are avoided in machine frames whenever possible, and rounded off by fillets. It is generally

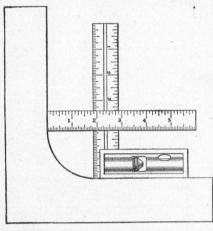

sufficient to measure
the radius of such fil-
lets approximately.
Small ones may be
judged entirely by
eyesight, placing the
rule against the sur-
face of the object
where the curve begins
and reading off a
length equal to the
distance of the rule
from the other surface.
See Fig. 38. Large
fillets are best meas-
ured by means of the

FIG. 39

rule and square, placing, as before, the rule against one
surface of the object where the curve begins and the square
on the other surface, sliding it against the rule until both
indicate the same distance, as illustrated in Fig. 39.

There are cases, however, in which it is essential to get a
curved outline very exactly. In such cases it is best, if
possible, to trace the outline by
placing the object on the
sketching pad and run the pencil point along the curves, as
was done with the curved
piece, Figs. 5 and 6. Evidently
this method cannot always be
resorted to, as, for instance,
when the object is large or
when the curve is so located
on the object that it cannot
be traced. The cam shown

FIG. 40

in Fig. 40 is an example. In such cases nothing short of a
templet will suffice, made of either stiff paper or even tin

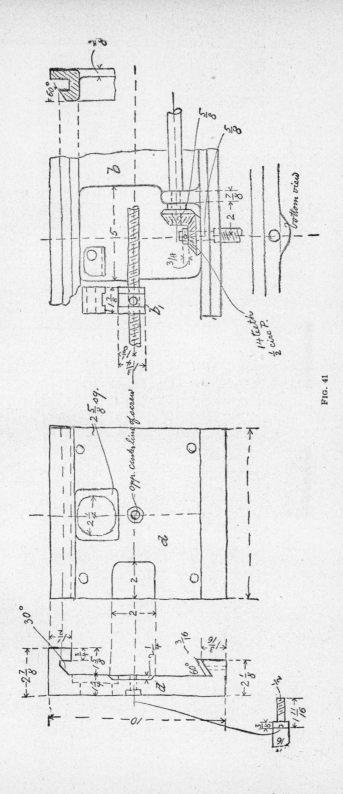

FIG. 41

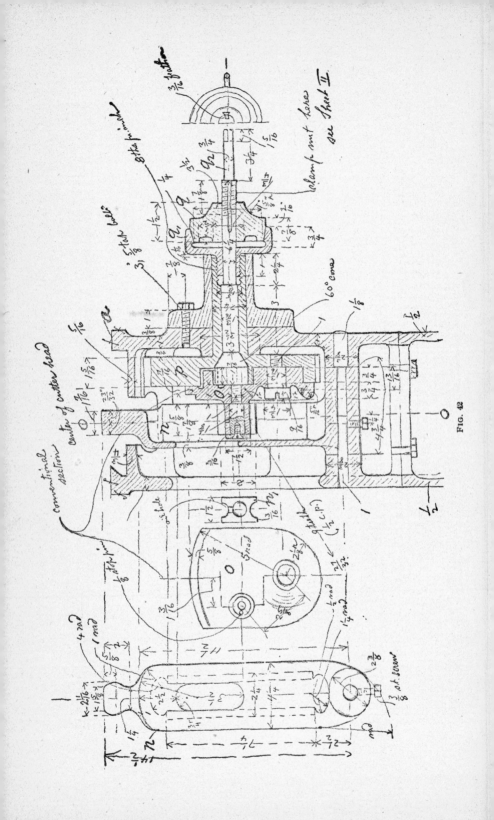

FIG. 42

plate. The sheet is placed over the curve and by gentle taps with the hand or a peen hammer the outline is transferred.

SKETCHING COMPLETE MACHINES

NOTE.—The student is requested to read the following pages with great care, and he is invited to ask questions concerning anything he does not understand. The sketches are exact reproductions of the original sketches, which were made by an experienced draftsman. While the student would not be expected to make sketches of such a complicated machine as this until he had had considerable experience, yet he can derive great benefit from a careful study of these sketches and their description.

44. In order to further illustrate what has been said in the foregoing articles, a complete set of sketches as actually taken from a machine are here added. The machine is a shaping machine, or, as it is called, a **crank-shaper**, illustrated in Figs. 43 and 44. The function of this machine is to cut into or plane the surfaces of any work fastened to the table seen in front; the cutting operation is performed by a tool held by a reciprocating slide, while the work is moved at right angles to the direction of motion of the tool (or vertically) a certain amount called the *feed* after every stroke, either automatically or by hand.

The five accompanying illustrations are large folders, and to distinguish between these and the other cuts, they have been designated as plates and numbered according to the Roman notation.

45. In accordance with the principle laid down in Art. **3,** the machine was first sketched in its entirety, in four views: a front view (Plate I), a plan (Plate II), a right-side view (Plate III), and a partial left-side view (Plate IV). Each of these views requires a whole sheet of the sketching paper; then various details were sketched and also a sectional elevation of the frame (Figs. 41 and 42 and Plate V).

The side view was started and finished first; next the front view, and lastly the plan. After these views were completed, the various measurements were taken, those being taken first which could be ascertained without removing any of the parts. Most of the outside dimensions, either of the frame or of the parts fastened to it, were obtained at this time; likewise, the distances between shaft centers, by the methods shown in Figs. 32 and 33.

After obtaining as many dimensions as possible without dismantling the machine, and especially such dimensions as are common to pieces fitted together, one part after another was taken off to get at other dimensions. The dismantling must be done very cautiously, so as not to miss a single point of importance. Wherever necessary, separate sketches should be made of parts that would be represented on too small a scale in the main view to be clearly seen. In such cases it is advisable to draw a line from these separate details to the main view, indicating the places where they belong, as shown on Plates I–V, and Figs. 41 and 42.

46. It should be remembered that the various dimensions are rarely found more than once in the sketches, and that dimensions of one and the same part may often be found in entirely different places, perhaps in connection with the part to which it is to be fitted. It is therefore necessary that the draftsman clearly understand the construction and function of the machine before he attempts to lay out a drawing from the sketches.

The reference letters used in the following description are to be found on the sketches, Plates I to V and Figs. 41 and 42, and the sketches should be studied in conjunction with the text illustrations, as the student, by means of the latter, will get a better understanding of the shape and location of the parts.

47. The fundamental part of the machine, as seen in Figs. 43 and 44, is the *frame*, or *column*, *a* (Plates I and III), provided on its face with vertical rails a_1, along which the *cross-rails b* may be made to move up or down, by means of the vertical screw visible below it. This screw may be turned by the pair of bevel gears, shown in Fig. 45, one of which is keyed to the shaft having a crank at one end. The *saddle d* is moved along the cross-rail *b* by means of a

FIG. 43

nut on the feed-screw; see Figs. 44 and 45, the latter showing the nut detached from the saddle. When the feed-screw is turned by hand or automatically by the mechanism to be described farther on, the saddle may be made to move either to the left or right, according to the direction in which the screw is turning.

FIG. 44

48. The *table e* is fastened to the face of the saddle and is provided with T slots along its vertical side, for the attachment of the work to this side, if necessary. On its

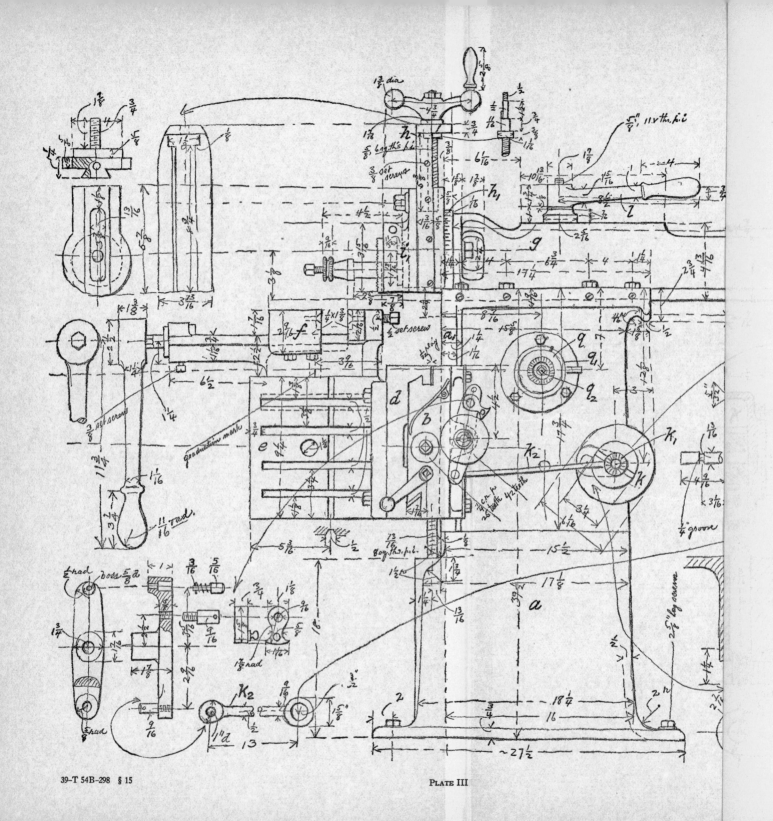

Plate III

top side it supports the *vise f* (Plates I, II, III), provided
with one stationary and one movable jaw. The front jaw
may be moved in and out by turning the screw (Plate II) to
adjust the distance between the jaws for different sizes of
work, and to hold it securely. The vise is swiveled on the
table, and may be held in any position by a clamp screw
underneath. Graduations on the table are intended to
register with a mark on the lower edge of the vise. By

Fig. 45

these means the vise may be quickly adjusted into any
angular position with reference to the path of the cutting
tool. By loosening the clamp screw that holds the vise to
the table, the vise may be detached and fastened to the side
of the table by inserting the clamp bolt through the hole in
the center; see Plate III and Fig. 44.

49. A cutting tool is inserted in the tool post projecting
from the *tool block i*. The latter, together with the *shaper*

head h, is fastened to the *ram g* and can be adjusted. The ram moves forwards and backwards in a longitudinal direction, between beveled guides, carrying the tool over the work. It should be noted that the tool block *i* is not rigidly attached to the shaper head *h*, but that it is able to swing

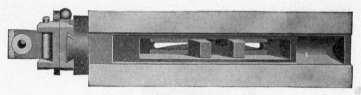

FIG. 46

on a pin in its upper end. This may be better understood by studying Fig. 46, a bottom view of the ram, in which the tool block is seen swung out in a position perpendicular to the face of the shaper head. By being swiveled in this manner, the tool is relieved from any unnecessary pressure against the work during the backward motion of the ram. This is not the only way in which the tool block may be moved relative to the ram. As indicated in the upper right-hand corner of Plate I, in the detail view of the shaper head *h*, the base plate *i*, of the tool block is able to swing in a plane at right angles to the ram around a central screw passing into the shaper head. The curved slot in the upper part of the plate indicates the extent of this angular motion. The purpose of this adjustment is to enable the tool to cut at the proper angle. Whenever such adjustment is to be made, the bolt, projecting through the curved slot, is loosened that the tool block may be swung into the desired position. The whole shaper head is also capable of moving up or down along the beveled guide in the front end of the ram (see Plate II). The handle, visible above the latter in Figs. 43 and 44, is attached to a screw that engages with the ram head. This screw supports the shaper head *h*, and the latter may therefore be lowered or raised by turning the screw in the proper direction (see Plate III). The purpose of this adjustment is to bring the tool down to the work and to regulate the depth to which the tool will cut.

50. The various adjustments mentioned are not sufficient for all purposes; provision must also be made for cases in which the tool has to cut along a plane that is at an angle with the horizontal plane of the machine. In this case the forward motion of the tool after each cut must be in a direction parallel with the plane along which the tool is cutting. For this purpose the head h of the ram (see Plates II and III), to which the shaper head is attached, may be swung around a stationary bolt in the ram until the desired angle is obtained. Various angles are marked off on the movable ram head, which, in conjunction with an index on the ram itself, will indicate the angular inclination. The nut engaging with the bolt just mentioned is seen in the recess in the front end of the ram (Plate III).

FIG. 47

51. The reciprocating motion is imparted to the ram by means of the oscillating lever n, Fig 42, shown detached in Fig. 47 and in position in Fig. 49. The upper end of this lever engages with a fork g_1 (Plate IV and Fig. 46) fastened in a slot in the upper part of the ram, while its lower end is fulcrumed on a rod the end of which is seen in Fig. 49. The point where the stroke of the ram begins and ends, relative to the work, may be determined by the position of the fork in the ram. It may be shifted along the slot, seen in Fig. 46, and held in any desired position by means of the handle l engaging with a screw in the fork (see Plate III, Figs. 43 and 44). It should be noticed that the length of the stroke is unaffected by any position the

FIG. 48

fork may occupy. To alter this length, other means are required to be pointed out farther on.

If the jib *m* (Plates II and IV), which is fastened to the frame by the four bolts, visible in Fig. 44, is detached, the

FIG. 49

ram may be removed from the frame, when the inside of the frame with its mechanism may be examined. This examination may be further facilitated by detaching the plate a_2 with its door (Plate IV and Fig. 43), with the result shown in Figs. 49 and 50.

52. The means by which motion is given to the lever *n* is most clearly shown in Fig. 51, where (*a*) is a front elevation of the mechanism and (*b*) a sectional elevation taken on the vertical center line of (*a*). The operation is as follows:

Sliding along a slot in the lever *n* is a block n_1 that is swiveled on a pin o_2 in the plate *o*, called the *crank*, also shown in Figs. 48 and 52. The rear side of the crank is provided with a toothed segment and a boss, which engage with the pinion p_1 and the recess, respectively, on the large gear *p*, seen inside the frame in Fig. 50, but shown more

FIG. 50

fully in Fig. 51. The crank *o* is fastened to the gear *p* by means of the stud o_1. The peculiar shape of the crank made it difficult to get the center-to-center distance between crankpin and stud center, the hole for the stud being depressed below the surface of the crank proper, while the crankpin projects above it. The distance was found by pressing the edge of a steel rule or other flat straight piece against the inside of the stud hole, as shown in

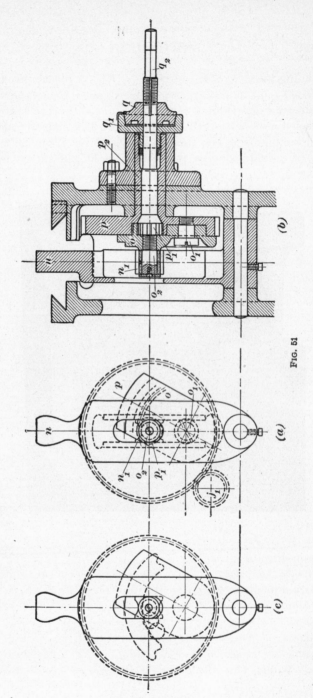

Fig. 51

Fig. 52, and calipering carefully between the edge of the hole and the pin. To this distance is added one-half the diameters of pin and hole. For the present it will be assumed that the pinion p_1 is in one piece with the gear p. When, therefore, the gear p is revolving, the crank will revolve with it, and also the block n_1, giving an oscillating motion to the lever n. The extent of this motion will depend on the distance between the centers of the block n and the gear p. Motion is imparted to the gear p by means

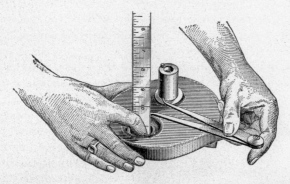

FIG. 52

of the pinion j_1, Fig. 51 (a), on the driving shaft j_2 (Plates IV and V, Figs. 49 and 50), which also carries the cone pulley j (Plates II and IV). The latter may be driven by a belt from a countershaft conveniently situated above the shaper.

53. Automatic Cross-Feed.—The previous description refers to the main functions of the machine; attention will now be called to the possible modifications and extensions of these various functions. When the work is to be moved in a horizontal direction while undergoing a planing process, it is generally desirable that this motion shall be performed automatically. In that case the screw shown in the cross-rail in Fig. 44, with a handle attached, must be given a fraction of a turn during the return stroke of the ram. This is the purpose of the two gears, seen in Fig. 44, at the right-hand side of the cross-rail. The smaller gear is pinned to the screw, while the larger revolves loosely on a stud on the cross-rail. On the same stud is a rocking lever, seen in Fig. 44 and on Plate III. The upper end of this lever has a pawl, which, when the cross-feed is to be made by hand, is held out of mesh by a little spring-actuated pin. When the feed is required to be automatic, the pawl is let down either to the left or right of its supporting stud, depending on whether the gear is to be driven to the right or left, respectively. The lower end of the lever has a pin inserted in one eye of the connecting-rod k_2, whose other eye fits over the shoulder of the hollow nut k_1 on the cross-feed disk k. This disk has a dovetail slot, seen more clearly in Fig. 44, in which is a block having a screw with a washer and the hollow nut k_1. By means of the latter the dovetail block can be clamped in any position in the slot of the disk. It

follows that when k revolves it will impart an oscillating motion to the rocking lever, and that the extent of this motion will depend on the distance between the center of the nut k_1, and that of the disk k. The disk is fastened to a stud that revolves in the boss, seen in Figs. 44

FIG. 53

and 53, and the detail sketch on Plate III. It receives its motion from the little pinion, partly visible in Fig. 45, which engages with the gear seen on the inside of the disk k (Plate III). Fig. 53 represents the disk moved out of gear with the pinion to better show the inside of the disk. This pinion consists of teeth cut directly in the end of the driving shaft j_2 (Plate IV).

54. Adjustment of the Stroke.—The adjustment of the ram stroke will now be explained in detail. On the right-hand side of the frame and above the feed-disk k is a collar, fastened to the frame, as seen in Figs. 44

and 54. Outside of this collar there is a revolving pulley q_1, Plate III, with a clamp disk q, Fig. 51 (*b*) and Fig. 44. This disk carries a little pointer that indicates, by means of marks on the pulley, the length of the stroke. By loosening the spherical nut outside the disk q, it is possible to adjust the latter relative to the pulley q_1 until the pointer indicates the desired stroke. How this adjustment affects the stroke will be explained by means of Fig. 51 (*a*). The clamp

FIG. 54

disk q is feathered to the shaft q_2, and will therefore turn with the latter, but can be moved in and out longitudinally.

It has already been explained that the pinion p_1 engages with the segmental gear on the crank o and that the latter may swing around the stud o_1. Fig. 51 (*a*) is a front elevation of these parts, in which the center of the crankpin o_2 is shown in line with the center of the pinion p_1. If adjusted in this position, the effect will be that while the gear p is revolving with the pinion and the crank, the pin will simply revolve around its own center, letting the block n_1, lever n, and the ram remain stationary. To impart motion to the latter, the shaft q_2 with its pinion is turned by means of a crank that may be placed on the end of the shaft q_2 and the crank o moved to the left until the pin o_2 occupies any position between the central and the extreme left-hand position, indicated by means of dotted lines in Fig. 51 (*c*). After the crank has been adjusted, the spherical nut is screwed up against the clamp disk q; this draws the conical surface of the clamp disk, as well as the conical surface on the back of the pinion p_1, down on their seats, making a solid frictional connection between the parts. As the hollow shaft p_2 supports all these parts, the whole mechanism will revolve with the gear p.

55. Some explanations will here be added to facilitate the understanding of the various sketches, each plate being considered in succession.

Plate I. — The main view is a front elevation of the assembled machine, some parts being shown in section and some broken away so as to expose hidden parts. The left half of the shaper head h has been removed in order to show the circular head of the ram. Likewise, part of the right-hand side of the vise is broken off to obtain a free view of the upper part of the frame, it being understood that both halves of the vise are symmetrical. The lower side of the table is shown in section better to show the **T** slots and central hole through which to insert the clamp screw, when the vise is fastened to the side of the table. In all cases where parts are sketched separate from the places where they belong, connecting lines indicate their true positions. For instance, the little screw sketched on the right-hand side has a line connecting it with the hole in the tool block. The long piece in the upper left-hand corner is a side view of the gib that holds the ram in place, and a line is seen leading from this piece to the place where the front end of the gib is seen in the main view.

Plate II. — The graduated circle shown above the main view is a constructive detail enabling the student to space the graduations on the ram in a correct manner. The set-screw shown to the right and below the ram is one of four screws that serve to adjust the gib with reference to the ram. These screws may also be seen in Fig. 44.

Plate III. — The two views in the lower right-hand corner represent a sectional plan view and end view, respectively, of the boss that supports the end of the driving shaft j_2 and the stud for the cross-feed disk k. Above these views is found a sectional view of the cross-feed disk with its dove-tail block and hollow nut k_1. In the lower left-hand corner is the connecting-rod k_2 with some details for the rocking lever.

Plate IV. — In the upper right-hand corner is a plan view of the table e on which are indicated the graduations by which the vise may be adjusted. In the upper left-hand corner is a rear view of the frame with the ram in position. At the bottom of the plate is a longitudinal section of the ram with the fork g_1, also various sections taken across the ram at the places indicated by the vertical lines. The detail in the lower right-hand corner is the screw in the top of the fork.

Fig. 41.—The views taken from left to right are: An end view of the saddle, a rear elevation of the same, and, lastly, a front elevation of the central part of the cross-rail. There is also shown part of the screw that supports the cross-rail and the bevel gears by which it is raised and lowered; also, details of the nut engaging the cross-feed screw, a sectional detail of the upper part of the rail, and a partial bottom view of the rail.

Fig. 42.—The views on this sheet should be easily understood in conjunction with Fig. 51, and require no additional information.

Plate V.—The main view is a sectional side elevation of the frame taken along line $o\,o$, Fig. 42, with the lever and crank removed.   Sections are also taken along lines $x\,x, y\,y$, and $z\,z$, and shown at various places on the sheet.   Section $x\,x$ gives a plan view of the driving pinion j_1, together with the driving shaft j_2 and the supporting boss.   Above is found a detail view of the crank and below a plan view of one corner of the base.

CONCLUSION

56. The student is advised to practice sketching at every opportunity. He may sketch any convenient object, as, for example, a monkeywrench, a table, a vise, etc. The kitchen stove, or a wagon will present considerable difficulty. No matter what the object may be that is sketched, it must always be kept in mind that every sketch must be so made and dimensioned that a working or finished drawing can be made from it without the necessity of seeing the

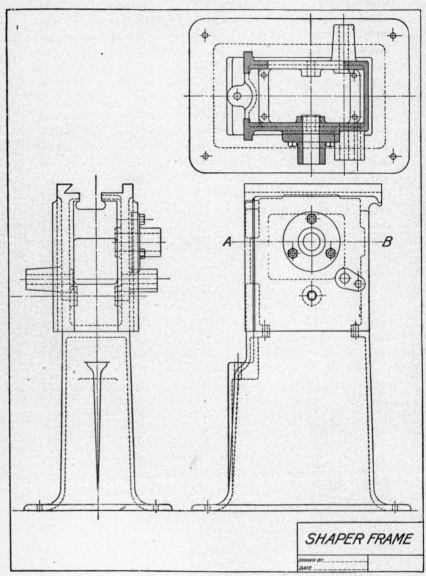

A   B

SHAPER FRAME

DRAWN BY
DATE

FIG. 55

object again. Hence, the student is advised not only to make sketches of convenient objects, but also make at least pencil drawings from these sketches. The making of the drawing will reveal any omissions or defects in the sketches, and will afford him the best kind of practice.

After the student has attained a certain degree of proficiency and gained confidence in himself, he is advised to go to some machine shop or other establishment where mechanical work is being done and sketch some of the smaller objects to be found there. Then, when he gets employment as a draftsmen, he will find the work comparatively easy and his advancement will be more rapid.

PRACTICAL PROJECTION

INTRODUCTION

1. Orthographic Projection.—When the mechanic is required to make any article whose form or dimensions are not previously known, it is evident that a description of the work in question should be furnished him. This description may be, and often is, given by verbal instruction; but in order to enable the worker to understand definitely what is wanted, the form of the object, its dimensions, and the quality of the material to be used should be stated. Instruction given in this way is, however, seldom satisfactory either to the workman or to his employer, since it is difficult in such cases to place the responsibility for any errors that may occur.

Written instruction, therefore, would seem to be preferable; but, since most objects would require an extended description, a shorter and more convenient method of conveying the desired information is to be sought. A **drawing** of the object is therefore made.

These drawings are generally made by a process termed *orthographic projection*, or, as it is usually called, **projection drawing.** Every detail of the object is correctly represented in this drawing, so that the workman knowing how to "read the drawing" may obtain his measurements therefrom for the construction of the object itself. He is also enabled by an examination of the drawing to understand exactly how the object will appear when completed. Hence, we have the following definition:

§ 16

Orthographic projection *is the process of making correct representations of objects by means of drawings.*

2. A Working Drawing Generally Necessary.—
Before a pattern for any article can be made, a working
drawing is needed. No pattern, however simple or plain, can
be produced until we have something definite to work from.

The metal worker does not go to the trouble of preparing
a drawing on paper for every piece of work he is called on
to make, since many objects are so plain that a brief verbal
or written description of their dimensions gives the mechanic
all the information he needs to enable him to lay out his
work.

If, for example, a tinsmith is called on to make a box out
of IX tin, 4 inches long, 3 inches wide, and 1 inch deep, he
immediately proceeds with the steel square to lay off the
given sizes directly on the metal; but if the same mechanic
is required to make a round pan having flaring sides or some
article of a form not readily carried in the mind, there is
one thing he must do before he can proceed with the work
or even lay out the pattern—he must make a **working
drawing** of the object.

3. What Constitutes a Working Drawing.—There
are several ways in which this drawing may be made,
depending altogether on how complicated the object is.   In
the case of the pan referred to, it may be desirable, by an
application of certain principles, to omit the operation of
making a drawing consisting of several views and proceed
as with the box to "lay it out" directly on the metal.   In
this case, however, it will be found that the operation
differs from that of making the box referred to, since it is
first necessary to mark out the sizes and outlines as they
will appear when the pan is completed.   These sizes may or
may not form a part of the pattern, but they are required
as preliminary lines from which to "lay off," or "strike
out," the pattern.

Marking out these sizes or dimensions of an object is
really making a working drawing.   This drawing may be

full size—in which case it is referred to as a **detail draw-ing**—or it may be drawn to a scale, either larger or smaller than the object itself.

4. Where the Drawing Is Made.—In the case of plain articles, the necessary drawings may be made directly on the metal; in the majority of cases, however, the work is of a more or less complex nature, making it highly impor-tant that a full-sized properly made detail drawing be used. This is not always provided, and the mechanic frequently has to make his own detail from a small freehand sketch or possibly from a drawing made to a small scale. In the latter case, an enlarged drawing must generally be made before the work of laying out the pattern can proceed. This neces-sitates operations with drafting board and drawing imple-ments—with which the student is already familiar. The proficiency that has been acquired may now be put into practical use in the operations to follow.

It is the purpose of this section to present methods by which working drawings may be *made* and *read*. These methods are presented in a practical way, that the principles laid down may be readily understood by the student.

GENERAL PRINCIPLES

5. Various Kinds of Drawings.—The most common representations of objects are those used for purposes of illustration merely and known as **perspective drawings**. They are of little value to the mechanic to serve as working drawings, since they are not drawn to a scale in the same way as a projection drawing, and to obtain measurements therefrom is an operation both complicated and indirect. A *photograph* is an ideal perspective picture, but no one would think of using a photograph as a working drawing. The photograph and the perspective drawing represent the object " as we see it," or as it appears to the eye of the observer, while the working drawing—the projection drawing—repre-sents the object *as it actually is*, or will be when made.

A photograph, however, shows only such objects as really exist, while a projection drawing often shows objects that exist only in the imagination of the draftsman or a person capable of understanding, or "reading," the drawing. By means of such drawings the imagination is aided in picturing the object as already constructed—or, as we would say, it enables the mechanic to see the object "in his mind's eye."

6. What Is Shown in a Drawing.—The perspective drawing always shows more than one side of an object—generally three sides—while the working drawing seldom shows more than one side, that being the side towards the observer. The position of such other portions of the object as are not located on the side shown in the drawing may, however, be indicated in a projection drawing by dotted lines. No lines should be used in a working drawing that do not represent actual edges, or outlines, in the object itself. We sometimes find certain edges or outlines of an object represented in a drawing by heavy lines. These heavy lines are called **shade lines;** but since they are not essential features of the working drawing, no description of them is necessary in this section. There is also an elaborate system of representing the effect of light and shade on curved and receding surfaces by means of lines properly disposed over the surfaces shown in the drawing. Since these lines are for effect only, and their meaning is apparent to the observer, the principles governing their use are not made a part of the subject matter of this section.

7. Position of Observer. — Another point of difference between the perspective and the projection drawing is that, in taking the view of which the perspective drawing is a representation, the eye of the observer remains in a fixed position, and in the same relation to the drawing as the camera is to the photograph; while in that view of the object of which the projection drawing is a representation, the eye of the observer is always supposed to be directly over or opposite that point in the drawing which is being noted.

This may be illustrated by the student for himself in a very simple way. Place a sheet of paper on the drawing board and draw a horizontal line, say 6 inches long; now lay an ordinary 2-foot pocket rule against this line, in the manner shown in Fig. 1, and proceed to mark off the line

FIG. 1

to correspond with the divisions on the rule. He will find that he is obliged to get his eye directly over each mark on the rule, and to "sight" carefully down on to the rule before making each mark, very much as he would "sight" or look along a piece of work to see whether it is straight or not. It will be noticed also that he is making *one* eye do all the work in this "sighting," and, further, it will be observed that in making the markings he is moving his head as he progresses towards the end of the line. He is obliged to do this to keep his eye exactly over each point on the line as it is marked.

8. Line of Sight.—The line first drawn on the paper is not the only one made use of in reproducing the markings on the rule. The student has unconsciously made use of another line, or, more properly, a set of lines, that are an important feature of projection drawing. These lines are those made use of in doing the "sighting" necessary for the marks; they are purely imaginary lines and are not represented in the illustration. They are very properly called **lines of sight.** The lines of sight in a projection drawing are *always perpendicular to the drawing.* They extend from a point in the eye of the observer to a point on the drawing that is directly opposite, as indicated by the point of the draftsman's pencil in Fig. 1.

These lines of sight—which, as stated, are only imaginary lines and are not represented in a working drawing—constitute one of the most important features of the projection drawing; for on these lines we are enabled to obtain the views from the object, and, by means of other lines, called **projectors,** bearing a certain relation to the lines of sight (as will be explained later), we can reproduce the views thus obtained on the drawing.

9. Lines of Sight Always Parallel. — When it is desired to make a drawing of any object, the lines of sight must be used in the same manner as in marking the divisions on the line in Fig. 1; that is, care must be taken to keep the lines of sight in any one view parallel to one another. We may take different views of the same object, or, to express it otherwise, we may take positions on different sides of the object, in order to obtain views therefrom; but in any view thus taken the above statement must be carefully observed and the lines of sight kept exactly parallel to one another.

10. Several Views Necessary. — We have already noted that a projection drawing seldom shows but one side of an object. Since there are no objects that present all their dimensions on any one side, it necessarily follows that, in order to convey a correct idea of the form of an object, it is necessary to make a drawing—or a *projection*—of as many sides as will enable the correct shape and dimensions to be shown. We may make these drawings from as many points of view as may be desired; but for certain reasons,

to which attention will be called later, it is generally preferable to view all objects from six sides, which correspond to
the six sides of a cube.

11. Before we proceed with the explanation of orthographic projection, it is important that the student should
be informed about what are known as the *angles of projection*. That is to say, he must know something about the
positions supposed to be assumed by the object when the
different views are taken. Draftsmen generally recognize
for projection drawing two principal angles in which the
objects are placed, and the drawings made in these two
angles are called, respectively, *first-angle projections* and
third-angle projections.

These different positions of the object will be understood
by the student from an examination of Fig. 2, in which four
angles are formed by the intersection of the horizontal
plane $A B C D$ with the vertical plane $E F G H$.   Then, of the
four right angles included between the planes, the angle BPG
is called the *first* angle, the angle GPC is known as the
second angle, the angle CPF is the *third* angle, and the
angle FPB is the *fourth* angle.   In the view shown at (*a*)
these two planes are assumed to be opaque and the object to
be transparent.   The lines of sight are projected from the eye
of the observer to the plane of projection, *through the object.*
In the view at (*b*) the planes are assumed to be transparent
and the lines of sight pass from the object to the eye of the
observer, *through the plane.* The effect of these different
positions of the object is merely to change the relative positions of the different views when made on the drawing board.

The drawings made in this section are first-angle projections.   Third-angle projections are made by processes
similar to those here explained and the different positions of
the views will be pointed out to the student at the proper
time.

12. Plans and Elevations.—It being assumed that
the object is in some fixed position, the various views take
their names from the different positions of the observer in

his view of the object. Thus, a view taken from above, or looking down on the object, is called a **plan**; so also is a

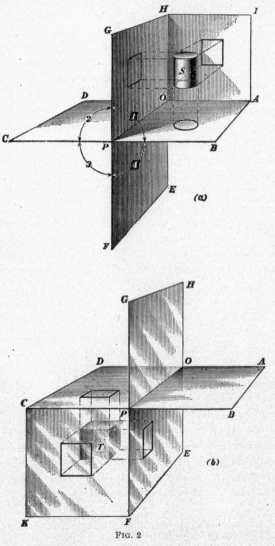

FIG. 2

view from beneath, or looking up at the object; thus we have the terms *top plan* and *bottom plan*. The two views thus obtained are frequently designated by terms that vary with the class of objects represented and not infrequently derive their names from some portion of the object itself. Thus, a top plan of a house is a view of the roof taken from above and is called a *roof plan;* while a *ceiling plan* is, as its name indicates, a view of another part of the house taken from the opposite direction. In the case of small objects generally, such views are termed *top plan* or *bottom plan*, as the case may be. These views, in certain cases, should be marked on the drawing, in order to guard against error. Here it should be noted that while the position of the object is not changed in making either the top or the bottom plan, yet the position of the observer is. When the two plans thus made are compared, it is found that the corresponding points of the drawings are changed in their relation to each other in the same manner as the hands of two persons that are standing exactly in front of and facing each other—the right hand of the one being opposite to the left hand of the other.

A view taken from the side of an object is called an **elevation.** That side of an object shown in any elevation gives its name to that drawing; thus, a view of the front of an object is called a *front elevation.* So, also, we have the terms *rear elevation* and *side elevation.* In some cases it may be more convenient to designate the elevations by the points of the compass; for example, the *north elevation* of a building is a projection of that part of the building which faces north, or, to state it as we have done before, that part of the building seen when looked at from the north.

13. **Section Drawings.**—Cases frequently occur in which the views or dimensions desired to be given on a working drawing cannot be shown in either plans or elevations. Under such circumstances, recourse is often had to a class of drawings termed **sections.** A section drawing is a projection of an object assumed to have been cut in two in a certain direction, usually at right angles to the lines of sight. Those parts of the object between the observer and the place where the cut is made are assumed to have been removed, so as to present an entirely new surface. This surface is not seen in the object itself, since the cutting is entirely imaginary—done simply for the purpose of showing some interior construction.

The cut just referred to may be made in a *horizontal*, a *vertical*, or an *oblique* direction, according to the way in which it is desired to show the section. Portions of surfaces that have been cut in this way are usually represented by certain conventional methods, indicating the character or composition of the material. A custom frequently adopted, and which will be followed in the drawings for this section, consists in designating surfaces exposed by the cut by a series of closely drawn parallel lines. Such lines are usually drawn at an oblique angle, as compared with the other portions of the drawing, and are called *cross-section* lines or *cross-hatching*.

14. A Set of Plans.—It is a common practice, when speaking of a set of drawings consisting of various plans, elevations, sections, etc.—as for a house or for some other object—to refer to them as a "set of plans." This is a collective phrase for the drawings and its use in this way is perfectly proper; when used in this sense, however, it is not understood as applying simply to a plan view as explained in Art. **12.** Drawings for large objects are frequently of a size such that the different views are more conveniently made on separate sheets. Architectural drawings are usually separated in this way, and it is often necessary for the one that is to read such drawings to arrange the sheets in a particular manner, in order that the relation between the views may be understood. This arrangement of the views will be considered later.

15. Foreshortened Views.—The lines in a projection drawing—or, as we shall term it hereafter, a *projection*—are either of the same length as the corresponding edges or out-lines of the object itself, or they are *foreshortened*. No lines are represented longer than they actually exist on the object, except in cases where the drawing is made to an enlarged scale. All lines that are used to represent the edges or outlines of an object, and that are at right angles to the lines of sight in any view, are represented in that view by their true length. Lines that represent other edges or outlines, and are not at right angles to the lines of sight, are consequently represented shorter than they exist on the object, and are then said to be **foreshortened**.

16. Geometrical Forms.—The simplest geometrical form that we can imagine is a *point;* next we have a *line,* defined as the shortest distance between two points; then a *surface*, which is a flat, or plane, figure bounded by lines; and, finally, a *solid*, which in turn is bounded by different surfaces.

17. The Combination of Geometrical Forms.—Since the mechanic deals with objects of various forms that may be said to represent geometrical solids, we shall endeavor to convey an idea of the way in which the representation of these objects may be simplified by resolving them into their elements, or the parts that combine to produce these forms. We thus have to deal with points, lines, surfaces, and solids; of these four things, one only—the solid—can be represented by any actual thing or be such as to enable us to handle it, for there is no object that does not possess *length, breadth*, and *thickness* to a greater or less extent. It consequently follows that the other three forms are entirely imaginary. The student that can most readily conceive or imagine their existence in this way will most readily comprehend the principles involved in projection drawing and pattern drafting.

18. A Test of the Student's Imagination.—The following illustration will show how a solid may be resolved into the simplest of its elements and still retain its definite and characteristic form. We will suppose a sheet-metal box to be made in the form of a cube, each edge being 1 inch long. The six square pieces of sheet metal that make the sides of this box are to be lightly soldered together, "edge and edge." This box represents a geometrical solid, although it is by no means a solid considered in a physical, or practical, sense. It is, in fact, popularly spoken of as being "hollow"; but we could very readily convert it into a solid by filling it with molten solder. It represents, however, as it is, a geometrical solid, and as such we will consider the parts of which it is made up, without paying any attention in this elementary part of the subject to the material of which it is composed. We are now dealing with *forms* only, and until these principles are fixed in the student's mind no attention will be paid to other details.

19. We first look for the surfaces of this solid, of which we find six. The student may have some difficulty in understanding that the surfaces of this cube, which he can apparently distinguish by the sense of touch, exist only in an imaginary way. We refer him, therefore, to our definitions for the explanation of this seeming paradox. A surface, we have been told, has length and breadth, while a solid has these and also a third property—thickness. Now, as we have said before, we cannot consider the material of which the cube is composed, but if we handle it we will be obliged to refer to the metal of which the sides of the cube are made. These metal sides have thickness; it may be only a few thousandths of an inch, but still it *is* thickness, and consequently does not come within our definition of a surface. A surface may be compared to a shadow, which can be distinguished by its outlines or shape, but, as every one knows, is absolutely without thickness. It is in this sense that we refer to the sides of the cube as its *surfaces*. We find also that each of these six surfaces is bounded, or defined, by four edges or outlines, the lines in turn being terminated at the corners of the cube by points, of which there are eight. It will now be seen that these eight points, situated at the extremities of the lines, or edges, of the cube, perfectly define the shape and size of the geometrical solid.

If we could imagine the metal sides of the cube to disappear entirely, leaving only the points at the corners, we would still have as perfect a representation of the size and shape of the cube in our minds as if it had an actual existence and could be seen by the eye. For these imaginary points could then very easily be imagined as being connected by lines, and we could then "see" the surfaces, and finally the solid, existing in the same imaginary way. It will thus be comparatively easy for us to transfer a representation of this solid to our drawing, since we can use the points as the markings on the rule were used in connection with the lines of sight in a previous illustration.

20. The Imagination a Valuable Assistant to the Draftsman. — An object, or solid, of any conceivable shape may thus be resolved into its elementary parts or points. The drawing of the object, then, will consist simply of locating the positions of these points on the drawing. We may have drawings to make that will require the location of a hundred or more of these points, depending entirely on the form or shape of the object we are dealing with, but the principles are in all cases the same.

If the student, after resolving an object in this imaginary way, will carefully study or imagine the proper location of these points in their relation to the object itself, defining their positions on the drawing one at a time, much that may appear complicated at first sight will resolve itself into very simple and comparatively elementary work. Complicated work is usually nothing more or less than the aggregation of a number of simple operations that appear complicated only because they are combined. *There is no field of work to which the latter statement is more applicable than to that of the draftsman.*

It is in the "imaginary" way thus described that the student is directed to picture to himself each figure as presented to him for the making of the drawings on the plates. This part of the study is, as will be noticed, almost entirely the work of the imagination; but it should be practiced by the student for the sake of the assistance it will be to him later on.

The operations of projection drawing follow one another in a natural sequence, which we will proceed to trace out in a series of drawing plates. As the student follows these operations, keeping in mind the foregoing principles, he will have no difficulty in making or reading any drawing.

PLATES

21. Seven plates are to be drawn by the student in accordance with the directions given in this section. They are to be of the same size as those drawn for *Geometrical Drawing*, and the same general instructions regarding the preparation of the plates are to be observed; they must be drawn and sent to us for correction in the same manner.

The letter heading for each problem, which has heretofore been placed on the drawing, will be omitted, and the stu-dent is required only to designate each plate with the letter heading, or title, that is printed in heavy-faced type, both in this section and on the reduced copies of the plate. For this purpose the *block-letter* alphabet is used.

22. The dimension lines and figures shown in the first three problems of the drawing plate, title: Projections I, are

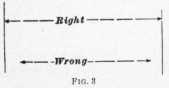

FIG. 3

to be especially noticed by the student. They are ordinarily used in all working draw-ings, and preference is invari-ably given to a dimension figure, rather than to the scale to which a drawing is made. Dimension figures are not to be placed on the plates, since the object in requiring the student to draw these projections is rather to enable him to gain an idea of their principles than to be able to make a finished working drawing.

Dimension and extension lines when used should be light broken lines. Care should be exercised to make the arrow-heads as neatly as possible and of a uniform size—not too flar-ing. They are made with a steel writing pen and their points should touch the extension lines, as illustrated in Fig. 3.

DRAWING PLATE, TITLE: PROJECTIONS I

23. General Instructions.—This plate is divided into four equal spaces, and each of these divisions, with the exception of the upper left-hand space, is again divided, by means of a central vertical line, into two equal parts. Use light pencil lines, as they are not to be inked in and are intended only to facilitate the location of the problems. These lines are not shown on the printed copies of the plates. Before attempting to draw any of the problems on the plate, the explanations accompanying each problem should first be carefully read and compared with the reduced copy of the plate and also with the illustrations in this section. The principles of projection drawing will thus be better understood by the student and their application readily made when more difficult drawings are undertaken.

The fundamental laws of projection are contained in the first four problems, and if these are thoroughly mastered by the student, the application of the laws to the remaining problems will be comparatively easy.

24. Why Different Views Are Drawn.—The names of the different views have already been noted; in this plate it is shown how they are distinguished from one another in a drawing. The relation of the different views to one another will also be explained.

Some objects in certain positions may have all their dimensions represented in two views—a plan and an elevation—but generally three views should be drawn. There are, indeed, many cases where views from each of the six sides, as well as sections and views taken from oblique positions, are necessary. It has already been observed that lines are represented in their true length only when at right angles to the lines of sight; consequently, since the position of the object in any set of views is not changed, it is necessary to change the position of the observer in such a manner as to bring the lines of sight where they will be at right angles to the lines in the object, thus enabling the latter to be shown in their true length on the drawing.

The student will readily perceive that in drafting-room work it is of the highest importance that the lines which combine to make up the surfaces of any object should be shown in their *true length*, or at least be presented in such positions that their true lengths may be easily found. Without these true lengths, no measurements can be obtained from which to lay out patterns, a pattern being merely a representation of the surfaces of some solid. It is necessary, therefore, to be prepared to take views of any object from any position; for there are many different forms, or shapes, of solids, and it is necessary to be able to show in its true length any line in the object that may be needed for a pattern.

25. The Base Line.—We shall first consider objects in positions that may be shown in two views. Draw a horizontal line through the central portion of the upper left-hand space on the drawing, as at *m–n* on the plate. In the portion of the space below this line are to be drawn the top plans of each of the two simplest forms, viz., the point and the line. The space above this line is to contain the elevations of the same forms. The line thus drawn is called a **base line** and defines the boundary of the surfaces on which we are to "sight," or, as we shall say hereafter, on which we are to *project* the lines of sight. It is necessary to call the imagination into use again and imagine the paper to be bent up at a right angle on this line.

26. Planes of Projection. — The drawing paper is imagined to be the surface that intercepts the lines of sight; and in the case of a plan, as seen from instruction already given, must be a horizontal surface, while in the case of an elevation, it is imagined to be a vertical surface. The different portions of the drawing on which the projections are made are called **planes of projection,** and are also distinguished by other names that designate the position they are supposed to occupy in intercepting the lines of sight. That portion of the drawing on which the elevation is drawn is called the **vertical plane** of projection; it is represented

on this plate by the space above the base line; the portion
below the base line is devoted to the plan and is called the
horizontal plane of projection. We shall, for the sake of
brevity, refer to these surfaces by the use of the letters
V P and **H P**, respectively. Copy these letters into the upper
and the lower left-hand portion of their respective spaces
on the drawing, using for that purpose a block letter one-
half the size of the title letter and leaving a distance of
¼ inch from the border lines of the spaces.

27. Foot of the Line of Sight.—Before proceeding
with the drawing of this plate, it is desired to call the attention of the student to the distinction to be observed between
the *imaginative* and the *practical* features of this subject.
The imaginative feature is employed when a conception of
an object is formed by the student in accordance with the
instruction in previous articles, and also when the lines of
sight are applied in the imaginary way, as in the "sighting"
illustrated in Fig. 1. The application of the practical
feature in this instance is made when the position of each
division of the rule is indicated on the drawing by a pencil
mark or dot. The practical part of the work is always
accomplished by the aid of pencil and drawing instruments.

The two features are closely associated, since we cannot
have a practical representation of any object without first
having an idea, or an imaginative conception, either of the
object itself or of the means of projection. The practical
feature of the work was introduced in the illustration (Fig. 1)
when a mark or dot was made on the paper, thereby indicating the position of the point at which the line of sight was
intercepted by the plane of projection.

That point on any plane or drawing where a line of sight
is intercepted is called the **foot** of the line of sight. When
the foot of every line of sight that can be used on the elementary points of any object is thus represented on the
drawing by dots, and connecting lines are drawn between
such dots, the drawing is completed, and the object is said
to be "projected."

28. Projectors.—If but one view of an object were required, the use of the lines of sight as previously explained (representing the imaginative feature) and the drawing of the dots and lines referred to in the previous article (representing the practical feature) would be all that is necessary for the student to understand before proceeding with the work on the drawing board.

Since it has been shown that several views are required, another important practical feature must necessarily be explained. This relates to the connection usually established between the different views of a drawing and the lines that are drawn in a certain manner between corresponding points in each view. These lines are usually not represented in a finished drawing, since they are in the nature of construction lines. They are essential, however, to the work of making the drawing, and it is very important that the student should thoroughly understand the principles by which they are employed. These lines are called **projectors** and may be defined as the *trace* of a line of sight, or the representation of the foot of a line of sight moving in a certain direction. Projectors are used in two ways, which are distinguished from each other for the present by the terms *primary* and *secondary*.

29. Primary Projectors.—This use of projectors is illustrated in Fig. 4, which shows the drawing bent up at a right angle along the base line *m–n*. The point *A* is projected to **H P** by the vertical line of sight *C B*; it is also projected to **V P** by the horizontal line of sight *D E*; *B* and *E* are dots at the foot of each line of sight.

It is assumed that the first position of the observer is at *C*; he then moves, in the direction of the arrow, along the dotted line to *D*. If, in so doing, he continues to sight through the point *A*, it is apparent that a line will be traced from *B* to *F* on **H P** and from *F* to *E* on **V P**. The upright portion of the drawing **V P** is now imagined to be bent backwards until laid flat on the drawing board, and it is evident that *E F B* is represented on the flat surface of the two planes of projection by the straight line $E' F B$. It may therefore be drawn as a straight line by the aid of the triangle and **T** square, the position of the point A in each view being determined by the points B and E' at the extremities

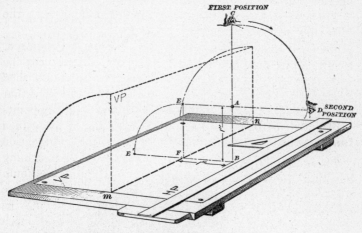

FIG. 4

of the line.   These points (or dots, for points, being entirely imaginary, could not, of course, be actually represented) * B and E' are the projections of the point A—the line drawn between them $(B F E')$ is called a *projector*.   When

---

* Attention has been called to the fact that points, lines, and surfaces are entirely imaginary geometrical forms.   This is true in the sense that the student must consider such forms in the imaginative study of this subject.   When their representation on the drawing paper is considered, however, something that can actually be seen by the eye is required.   Therefore, when a point is referred to in this section as pertaining to the drawing, it is to be represented by a neat dot in the proper place on the paper.   In like manner, a line should be represented by a fine pencil mark drawn between two points marking its extremities.   When the line is to serve a special purpose, as explained in this section, it is inked in in a particular manner characteristic of its use, in order that the drawing may be more easily read.   A surface, therefore, would be represented by a portion of the drawing bounded by the proper lines and descriptive of the form of surface represented.   Remember that accurate work cannot be done unless the pencil points are in good condition.   The student should provide himself with a smooth file or piece of fine sandpaper and frequently sharpen the chisel point of the leads in both pencil and compasses, in order that fine sharp lines may be readily drawn.

projectors are used as in this illustration—that is, between two planes that may actually be bent up as shown in Fig. 4— they are said to be used in a *primary* manner.

The *secondary* use of the projector will be shown in connection with Problem 3, Case III.

The practical use of the projector is clearly shown in the following problems. It is a most important factor in the projection, and, as will be seen from instruction soon to follow, is often the first line to be used in a drawing.

PROBLEM 1

30. **To project the plan and elevation of an imaginary point.**

There are two cases of this problem, representing different positions of the point. Definite instructions are given for drawing the first projection and the student is expected to draw the second projection without further directions.

Case I.—*When the point is located 1 inch from each of the two surfaces* **V P** *and* **H P**.

This position is illustrated in Fig. 4, referred to in Art. **29.**

CONSTRUCTION.—Fix a point B (see plate) 1 inch below the base line on the drawing. This point should be $\frac{5}{8}$ inch from the left-hand side of the drawing and is the plan view of the point given in the problem. Bring the **T** square and triangle into position and draw the projector vertically upwards and across the base line. Fix a point at.E' on the projector 1 inch above the base line. A projection drawing is thus made, showing two views—a plan and an elevation —of the required point, the position of which is thus definitely established.

Fig. 4 is an illustration of the imaginative feature and the projection drawing just made is a representation of the practical feature of the work—the part actually made by the draftsman. The intimate connection between the two features may be seen if the drawing just made is compared

with the illustration in Fig. 4. Similar results are found
to have been accomplished in both cases, the method last
employed being the only one practicable for actual use.
When inking in this drawing, make small round dots to
represent the positions of the points, and always ink in
projectors as light dot-and-dash lines, as shown on the
plate. These dot-and-dash lines should be inked in in a
uniform manner, as on the plate, the dashes being about
$\frac{1}{4}$ inch in length and spaced about $\frac{1}{16}$ inch apart, with a
light dot between each dash. Measure the distances by the
eye and preserve a uniform shade for all projectors, thus
giving the drawing a neat appearance. The base line should
be represented by a heavy dotted line, as shown at *m–n* in
the perspective illustration of Fig. 4.

*When making the preliminary drawings, do not attempt
to draw dotted lines with the pencil, since this is liable to
affect the accuracy of the work.* Keep the chisel point of
the pencil sharp and draw as fine a line as can be distinctly
seen. The contrast between the different lines on the drawing may then be clearly indicated when the work is inked in.

Case II.—*When the point is located $1\frac{1}{2}$ inches from* **V P**
and $\frac{1}{2}$ inch from **H P.**

The student will fix the location of the point in the plan
and elevation on the drawing without further instructions,
bearing in mind the fact that distances from **V P** are measured on the plan and distances from **H P** are shown in the
elevation. Reference to Fig. 4 explains this statement.
Case II should be placed on the drawing about $\frac{1}{2}$ inch to the
right of the preceding figure.

PROBLEM 2

**31. To project the plan and elevation of an imag-
inary line, the line being in a right position.**

The term *right* position is used in connection with projection drawing as distinguished from the terms *inclined*,
or *oblique*, position. The line, therefore, can be either in a

horizontal position or in a vertical position and still be designated as in a *right* position. There are three figures for this problem, representing three cases where the line is in a right position and yet represented differently on the drawing. The different positions, the various distances, and the length of the lines for the three cases of this problem are clearly illustrated in the perspective drawings shown in Figs. 5, 6, and 7. Instructions are given for the drawing of Case I on the plate, but the student is expected to be able to make the drawings for Cases II and III without further directions than those contained in the illustrations. Be careful to preserve a distance of $\frac{1}{2}$ inch between the drawings, so that the plate may present a neat appearance when completed.

Case I.—*When the line is parallel to both* **H P** *and* **V P.**

Explanation.—This position of the line is illustrated in Fig. 5, and, as apparent from that figure, the drawing is

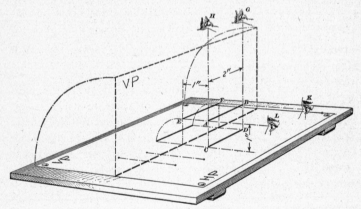

Fig. 5

merely an extension of Problem 1. Each end of the line is treated as a point, projected first to the plan and afterwards to the elevation in precisely the same manner as was the point in Problem 1, the only difference being that there are two points instead of one, for we cannot have a line without establishing at least two points.

This problem also illustrates another principle of projection already referred to, viz., all lines at right angles to the lines of sight in any view are shown in that view in their true length; or, in other words, the lines that are to be made on the drawing to represent the plan and elevation of AB, Fig. 5, will be of the same length as AB is indicated in the figure, viz., 2 inches. The angles HAB and LAB are right angles, although shown in perspective in the figure; and, since the lines of sight in any view are always parallel to each other, the angles GBA and KBA must also be right angles; consequently, as the line AB is at right angles to the lines of sight in both views, it must be shown in its true length in both the plan and the elevation on the drawing.

CONSTRUCTION.—To make this drawing on the plate, draw a horizontal line of the given length and the proper distance (i. e., 1 inch) below the base line. This will be the plan of the line AB. From each end of this line (CD in Fig. 5 and on the plate) draw projectors to the elevation; or, to use the term by which such operations are designated, project the ends of the line CD to the elevation. After measuring off the proper height above the base line, draw the horizontal line EF, which is the elevation of the line AB.

NOTE.—When a point is projected from one view to another, its projector (a straight line) is drawn from the first view to the view projected, and always at right angles to the base line.

Case II.—*Where the line is in a horizontal position and at right angles to* **V P**.

EXPLANATION.—Fig. 6 illustrates this case. It will be noticed that the plan view of the line does not differ very much from the plan of the line given in Case I, merely that it is represented by a vertical line on the drawing in the plan in place of a horizontal line, as in Case I. The line AB is at right angles to the vertical lines of sight GD and HC in both cases. The line AB in this figure is in such a position that the horizontal line of sight KE passes through both points B and A. The projection of these points, therefore, on the elevation is the single point E at the foot of the line of sight KE. A single line of sight may pass through an unlimited number of points in any view, but the foot of such line of sight is always represented in that view by *one* point on the drawing. The student who is to read that drawing must picture to himself, or imagine, the position of these points as they are supposed to exist in the object of which any drawing is a representation. It is further to assist his imagination that other views are drawn, and by means of which the position of the different points may be definitely located. Thus, in this case, if we were

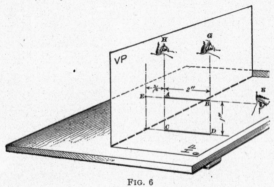

FIG. 6

to consider the elevation alone, without paying any attention to the plan, we would say that the point E represented merely some other point (imaginary, of course) that could be situated anywhere on the line of sight KE. A glance at the plan, however, shows not only where the location is, but how many points are represented. In this case there are two points represented by E, one directly in line with the other. The plan also shows how far apart these points are, and from the two views it can be further seen that the line is in a right position perpendicular to **VP**. If it were not, the two points would not be in the same line of sight, and would, consequently, require two positions on the elevation, whereas they are designated by the one position E, **Fig. 6.**

CONSTRUCTION.—Since the drawings for this case have been shown in the preceding explanation to be similar to those of Case I, no definite instructions need be given. The two drawings differ in position only and are drawn as shown on the plate, the plan being first constructed.

Case III.—*Where the line is in a vertical position.*

This is shown in Fig. 7, each feature of which has already been explained in connection with Figs. 5 and 6. The

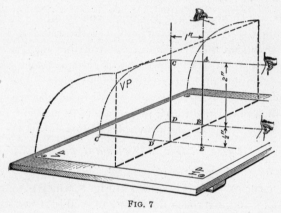

FIG. 7

drawing may, therefore, be made by the student in accordance with the dimensions given in the illustration.

32. Proof of a Projection Drawing.—The various cases of the foregoing problem represent lines in different positions, and, as in the case of the point in Problem 1, the student will see that these projections definitely represent the position of each line; further, that for each position indicated, but one line can be placed, or can occupy that position. It is recommended that the student prove this assertion as follows: Copy the projections of this problem on another piece of paper and bend the paper at right angles along the base line, as shown in the illustrations; take a piece of small wire of the given length, to represent the lines, and proceed to hold it, in turn, over the drawing for each case, at the same time "sighting," or using the

lines of sight, as illustrated. It will be seen that, in order
to make the foot of each separate line of sight come to the
proper place on the drawing, the wire must be held in the
position indicated in the statement of the case.

PROBLEM 3

**33. To draw the projections of an imaginary line
in a rightly inclined position.**

There are three cases of this problem, in all of which the
given line is *rightly inclined;* that is, the angle of inclination is such that the true length of the line may be shown
in either a plan, a front elevation, or in some elevation that
shall be at right angles to the front elevation. The different cases of this problem are presented in perspective views,
from which the projection drawings are to be made by the student. They illustrate the principles of foreshortened views.

Case I.—*Where the line is horizontal, but inclined to* **V P**
at an angle of 45°.

EXPLANATION.—This is shown in Fig. 8, which gives all the
dimensions and distances necessary to enable the student to

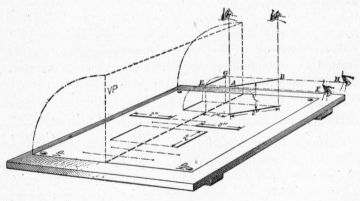

FIG. 8

draw the projections on the plate. The student will note the
position of each point and carefully observe the instructions

for making the drawings.   Bear in mind that, although the drawing is only that of a single line, careful study must be given to it, for the principles on which these simple projections are made are the same as for any other projection drawing.   These principles are shown in a more comprehensive way in simple problems than if an object of complex form were presented, requiring a confusing number of points to define its outline.   In Cases I and II of this problem, the plan is first to be drawn and the elevation projected therefrom.

CONSTRUCTION.—Since the line in Case I is in a horizontal position and therefore at right angles to the vertical lines of sight, it will be shown in its full length on the plan.   The line is stated to be inclined to **V P** at an angle of 45°; draw the plan, therefore, at that angle to the base line and at such distance below the base line as indicated in Fig. 8 and shown at *A B* on the plate.   Project the points *A* and *B* to the elevation, and at the given height above the base line draw a horizontal line between the projectors.   This is the elevation of the line shown in the plan, and since its entire length is contained between the horizontal lines of sight *F E* and *H G*, Fig. 8, the line cannot be shown on the elevation as being any longer than the perpendicular distance between the projectors.   This distance being less than the actual length of the line, the elevation is, in this case, called a *foreshortened* view of the line.   It represents, however, the entire line, and reference to the plan is necessary in order to find its true length.

Case II.—*Where the line is parallel to* **V P** *but inclined to* **H P** *at an angle of 60°.*

CONSTRUCTION.—Fig. 9 shows that the plan is to be represented by the horizontal line *F H*.   It also gives the length of the line in the plan, which is a foreshortened view. Therefore, draw *F H* 1 inch long and 1 inch below the base line.   Draw the projectors and fix a point at *J* on the projector drawn from *F*, at the proper distance above the base line.   This will be one end of the line in the elevation.

With the compasses set to 2 inches (the length of *A B*) and using the point *J*, fixed on the projector drawn from *F*, as a center, describe an arc intersecting the other projector. The point that represents the other end of the line is located at this intersection, and the line may then be drawn. Now bring the **T** square into position and prove by the

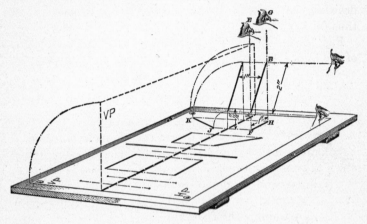

FIG. 9

triangle that the line *J K* is at an angle of 60° with the base line. It will be seen that it would have been possible, after fixing the position of a point at either end, to have drawn the line at once with the 60° triangle. Attention is called to both methods in order to show the student the connection between them.

Case III.—*Where the line is rightly inclined to* **V P** *at an angle of 60° and is also inclined to* **H P**.

EXPLANATION.—In Cases I and II, the line has been in such positions as to enable its full length to have been shown in one of the views drawn on the plate. In this case, a position is illustrated in which the line is shown foreshortened in both of these views. It will therefore require another view to be projected in order that the line may be shown in its true length. Since it is known that the line is rightly inclined, the additional view required will be at right

angles to the base line.   As another view is to be drawn, so
another base line will be required.   This base line, being
merely the lower boundary of a surface supposed to be in an
upright position to receive the lines of sight and at right
angles to the surface of the elevation previously drawn, will,
consequently, be at right angles with the base line in a
drawing that shows only two views—such drawings as have
thus far been made.

Fig. 10 contains the given dimensions, etc. for this position
of the line.   This perspective figure shows the interception

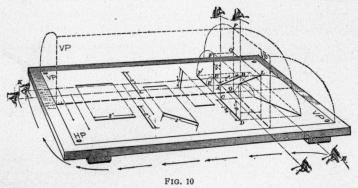

FIG. 10

of the lines of sight from still another direction than has
been shown in the preceding illustrations.   In the same
manner a view may be obtained from any side of an object
or at any angle other than a right angle.   The method of
accomplishing these results by the use of the **T** square and
triangle on the flat surface of the drawing board will now
be shown, and the illustration of the bent-up surfaces will
not be continued beyond this problem.   Such illustrations
are, however, always implied in a projection drawing, for
that part of the work is the imaginative feature previously
mentioned, to which the attention of the student will be
directed throughout this instruction.

Since the angle of inclination to the elevation is the same
in this case as in the plan of Case II, the length shown on
the elevation of this projection will be the same as in the
plan of that case.   In this drawing, the line is, however, in a

different position as related to the plan, and from Fig. 10 it will be seen that it must be represented by a vertical line in that view on the drawing.

CONSTRUCTION.—Extend the ᴏase line on the plate to the center of the next space, from which point draw a vertical line downwards to the division line; these lines are to be inked in the same as the base line in the first space. In the smaller space thus enclosed on the drawing is to be drawn the plan for this problem, the front elevation occupying the same relative position as before, directly above the plan, while in the space at the right the side elevation will be projected. First, draw the elevation as at $E'F'$ on the plate, fixing the point E' at the specified distance above the base line. As the foreshortened length in the plan is given in Fig. 10 as $1\frac{3}{4}$ inches, draw the line CD of that length, as shown on the plate, keeping the point C at its proper distance below the base line, as indicated in Fig. 10. The view to represent this line in its true length may next be drawn. It is known that this view must be one in which the line itself is represented at right angles to the lines of sight. There is a choice of two views for this projection—either to the right or to the left side. Having already utilized the space to the left on the plate, the side elevation is, in this case, projected to the right. The method employed in Case II might here be used to project the side elevation, but since it is customary, when a number of elevations are projected from the same plan, to facilitate the operation by drawing between such views lines that are termed *secondary projectors*, an explanation of their use is here presented.

34. Secondary Use of the Projector. — The term *secondary* is not applied in the case of projectors as indicating an unimportant or infrequent application of these lines. The name is used rather to distinguish operations in which similar principles as applied to the imaginative features are differently represented on the drawing in the application of the practical features of the work. In fact, both uses of these lines are required in most drawings. It is therefore essential that the student should become familiar with the various means employed in producing them on the drawing.

35. It is evident, from an inspection of Fig. 10, that the eye of the observer at E in moving around along the broken line in the direction of the arrows to take position at K would trace a line from F, through O, to L. The part of this line ($F O$) that shows on the front elevation is parallel to the base line of that surface; and, also, that part of the line ($O L$) shown on the side elevation is parallel to the base line of the side elevation. It is seen that the definition of the projector, as previously given, applies equally to the lines $F O$ and $O L$. If the two planes of projection represented by the two upright surfaces could be bent in the same relation to each other as were the plan and the elevation in Fig. 4—i. e., on the line $P Q$, Fig. 10—the use of the projectors in these views would be no different from that already described. It is customary, however, in first-angle projection, to assume that such upright surfaces are always bent downwards and away from the plan; to accomplish this result, the secondary use of the projector is employed. Suppose, now, that the upright surfaces, represented in Fig. 10, were bent backwards until laid flat on the drawing board. Evidently, there would be an appearance presented similar to that shown in Fig. 11, and an open space would be shown

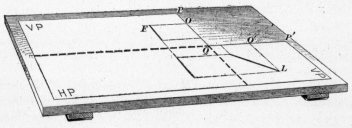

FIG. 11

on the drawing board included between the angle $P Q P'$. The paper on which the drawing is made is not of an irregular shape, thus to be bent up at will: further, the operations performed in projection drawing are such that they can be accomplished only on the flat surface of the drawing board.

36. It is found that similar results may be obtained in two ways, both being easily affected by the aid of the drawing instruments. The first is known as the *angular* method, and is thus accomplished: If the projectors $F\ O$ and $O'\ L$, Fig. 11, or any other corresponding set of projectors, parallel to their respective base lines, are extended until they intersect each other, it is found that *all the intersections are on a diagonal line terminating exactly at the intersection of the base lines.* It is also found that *this diagonal line exactly bisects the outer angle formed by the base lines.* Applying these principles, therefore, to the drawing, bisect the outer angle formed by the base lines on the plate and produce the bisector indefinitely towards the right-hand side of the space. The outer angle formed by the base lines in this case being an angle of 270°, the bisector may be drawn with the 45° triangle, since a line thus drawn will be at an angle of 135° with both base lines.

37. Fig. 12 is a reproduction of the projection drawing from the plate, showing the bisector drawn as previously

FIG. 12

directed. Draw $F'\ x$ and $E'\ y$ parallel to the base line in the front elevation; from their intersections with the bisector at x and y, draw $x\ L$ and $y\ R$ parallel to the base line in the side elevation. Project the points C and D from the plan to the side elevation by the use of primary projectors, as previously described. The side elevation of the line $A\ B$ of Fig. 10, then, is a line drawn between points of intersection of the primary with the secondary projectors, as shown by $R\ L$, Fig. 12. The lines $F'\ x$, $x\ L$, and $E'\ y$, $y\ R$ are called *secondary* projectors, and are used,

as in this case, when projecting points between views that
are related to one another in the manner shown.   Projectors are used in a similar way when, for reasons that will be
shown later, the base lines are at an angle other than a
right angle.   In all cases, the outer angle is bisected as
shown in Fig. 12, and the secondary projectors are drawn
parallel to their respective base lines.

*Note that the front elevation, shown in Fig. 12, is a fore-
shortened view, and corresponds in length with the perpendicular distance between the secondary projectors in the
side elevation.*

38. Reading a Drawing.—The ability to read a drawing consists of the intelligent comparison of the different
views and is well illustrated in the projections just drawn.
The different views—or the different *projections*, as they
are called—must never be considered as drawings apart
from one another.   Each projection is shown to be necessary in order to enable the position of some point or element
of the object to be established in the reader's imagination.

PROBLEM 4

**39. To draw the projections of an imaginary line
in an obliquely inclined position.**

The projections of this problem are to be drawn by the
student in the next space on the plate, following the instructions here given.

CONSTRUCTION.—Draw the base lines as in the last space
used for Problem 3, but place the lines ¾ inch higher on the
plate and extend them ½ inch farther to the right in the
space.   These base lines will be used in the construction of
the projections as before, but will not be inked in on this
drawing; they are construction lines only—to be erased from
the plate after the drawing is completed.   It has been
shown that base lines are necessary for determining the
position of the different points on a drawing and are

essential in establishing the first few points in any projection; but as the drawing progresses and other lines are produced, any right line in a view—i. e., a line at right angles to the lines of sight—may be used as a base from which to establish the position of points in a drawing.

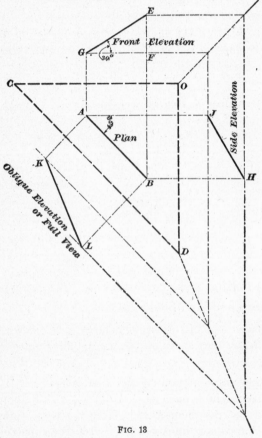

FIG. 13

Represent a foreshortened view of this line in the plan by a line 1½ inches long, drawn at an angle of 45° with the base line of the front elevation, as shown at *A B*, Fig. 13; draw the front elevation (also a foreshortened view) at an angle of 30° with the base line. Draw the line *A B* in the plan and $G\,E$ in the front elevation in such positions that the end of either line nearest to the base line shall be $\frac{1}{2}$ inch from that line. Next draw the side elevation as explained in Problem 3, Case III, and it will be seen, when the side elevation is completed, that $H\,J$ is also a foreshortened view, not representing the true length of the line.

An elevation will now be projected in which the line may be shown in its true length. This will be an elevation whose surface is parallel to the line. Draw the base line of this surface $\frac{1}{2}$ inch from the line $A\,B$ on the plan and parallel to that line, as at $C\,D$, Fig. 13. This figure is an illustration of the projection drawing, showing all the lines used in its construction, certain of which, as already explained, are not to appear in the completed drawing on the plate. Note that the oblique elevation $K\,L$ is projected in the same manner as the side elevation was drawn, the only difference being that the outer angle $O\,D\,C$, formed by the base lines, is greater than a right angle, but is treated in the same way. This completes the problem, and in finishing the figure on the plate, the student will ink in only the different views and the primary projectors, erasing all other construction lines.

40. Finding True Lengths by Triangles. — It is possible to find the true lengths of lines from a plan and any elevation showing such lines obliquely inclined by a shorter method than that given in Problem 4. This is accomplished by the use of the right-angled triangle. If such a triangle is constructed, with its

FIG. 14

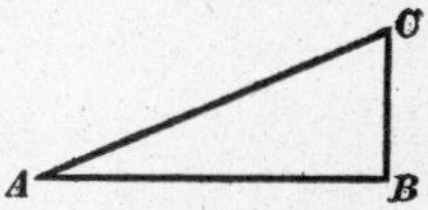

base equal to the length of the line shown in the plan and its altitude equal to the vertical height shown in the elevation, *the hypotenuse will be equal to the true length of the line.* This is shown in Fig. 14, in which $A\,B$ is made the same length as $A\,B$, Fig. 13, and $B\,C$, Fig. 14, is equal to the vertical height shown in the elevation, i. e., $E\,F$, Fig. 13. Since $A\,B\,C$ is a right angle, the hypotenuse $A\,C$, Fig. 14, is equal to the true length of the line. This statement is of the greatest importance to the draftsman and should be proved by the student. Construct a triangle on a separate piece of paper and set off the lengths from the drawing with the dividers; afterwards compare the length of the hypotenuse with the length of the line shown in the oblique elevation, or full view. This is an illustration of a principle of much use in later problems, and one on which certain important principles of patterncutting depend.

41. All Projections Depend on Similar Principles.—There is no conceivable position of a line that may not be shown or its true length not be ascertained by the application of the principles contained in the foregoing simple problems. Lines have been used to illustrate these problems drawn at such angles as were conveniently made with the **T** square and the 45° or 60° triangles, but any angle or any position could as well have been represented, since the principles are in any and all cases the same. We will now proceed with the representation of flat, or plane, surfaces.

42. Planes, or Plane Surfaces.—All drawings made to represent surfaces are composed of lines that bound, or limit, their borders, or sides. These drawings, therefore, will differ from those of the foregoing problems only in the fact that they are the representation of lines shown in their relation to one another. There are, however, certain principles relating to flat, or plane, surfaces that must be borne in mind, since they influence this relation of the different lines in a drawing.

43. That the student may have a thorough knowledge of the principles employed in the representation of surfaces, it is essential that he first have a clear conception of what a plane is. A plane surface, as has been stated, has only an imaginary existence, being bounded, or enclosed, by imaginary lines; this surface may be in any conceivable position, but is always a flat surface. If viewed from a certain direction—viz., as if "on edge"—it would be represented by a single straight line. If the student can imagine a plane surface indefinitely extended in every direction beyond the boundary lines of the figure, he will have a very good conception of a plane; any number of points or lines, the positions of which are anywhere on this surface thus extended, are said to be " in the same plane " in relation to one another.

44. To illustrate: Suppose two flat-top tables of the same height are on the floor of a room perfectly level and of indefinite extent. Here is a practical representation of two planes, both of them in a horizontal position; one plane is represented by the floor, while the other plane is parallel to the first and "passes through " the tops of the tables. The surfaces represented by the tops of the tables are said to be " in the same plane." The tables may be placed some distance apart, yet the straight edge of a ruler laid across their tops would exactly coincide with the upper surfaces of both tables and would remain in contact at all points for every position of the ruler.

The plane surface represented by the top of one table is said to be " in the same plane " as the corresponding surface of the other table. The same could be said with reference to any other surfaces answering the same test. Any number of flat surfaces are said to be in, or to "lie in," the same plane with one another, and the same is true of any lines or points used to define any surface or position in that plane.

The planes in the foregoing illustration of the floor and tables are horizontal planes, but may be imagined in any position, vertical or inclined, needed for the projections of a drawing.

45. How the Position of a Plane Is Determined. Since any two points determine the position of a line, so any three points not in the same straight line determine the position of a plane. To illustrate: Take a square piece of cardboard, thick enough to remain flat, and push pins of equal length through each of the four corners so that they will resemble the legs of a chair. The object will stand firmly when placed on a level surface with the points of the pins down, for the reason that all the points represented by the ends of the pins are in the same plane. If one of the pins is withdrawn and a shorter one inserted in its place, the cardboard will not be stable when placed as before, and can be "rocked," for the point at the extremity of the short pin is not in the same plane with the other three. Two planes are thus defined—one determined by points at the extremities of the three long pins and the other by points at the ends of the short and the two adjacent pins. Both of these planes may be imagined as extended indefinitely, one plane being inclined to and intersecting the other.

Again, a flat sheet of metal may be supposed to represent a plane surface. All points that may be located on this sheet are in the same plane; but if a sheet that is "buckled" is chosen, it is possible to locate some points on the surface of that sheet higher or lower than others, and the points would then be in different planes. The connection between the plane and the plane surface, then, is such that, to be defined as a plane surface, every point on that surface must be in the same plane.

46. In drawing different views for the illustration of the plane surface, we shall first use the octagon, requiring the projection of eight points and the intermediate lines. The use of the word "imaginary" in connection with the statement of the problem will henceforth be discontinued, since it has been clearly shown that all surfaces, as well as other geometrical elements, depend for their existence on the imaginative feature referred to in previous articles. It will be understood, therefore, when any geometrical element is mentioned, that the practical feature is to be employed—the imaginative, of course, being implied.

PROBLEM 5

47. **To project three views of an octagonal surface, representing it in a horizontal position.**

The three views consist of a plan, front, and side elevation. A perspective view of the surface in the required position is shown in Fig. 15.

EXPLANATION.—All lines used to define this surface in the plan are at right angles to the vertical lines of sight; and since the lines will thus be drawn in their full length in that view, the surface will there be shown in its full dimensions.

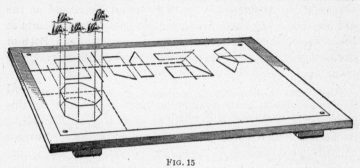

FIG. 15

This principle also applies to any view of a plane surface in which all its lines are at right angles to the lines of sight. The plan of the surface, then, will be a true octagon, and may be drawn on the plate with lines tangent to a circle 1½ inches in diameter, using the **T** square and 45° triangle for that purpose.

CONSTRUCTION.—Draw the base line for the front elevation 3 inches above the lower border of the drawing, and draw the vertical base line (for the side elevation) 2¾ inches from the left-hand border. Describe the circle previously mentioned in such a position that the nearest edges of the octagon will be ½ inch from each base line; the figure may then be completed in the plan. In this and the remaining problems to be drawn on this plate, the right views are to be drawn ½ inch from the base line in all cases. In both elevations, the lines of sight in crossing the surface pass also

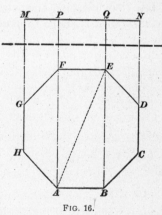

FIG. 16.

through the points in that portion of the surface farthest from the observer; and as the eye of the observer travels from points opposite to M and N, Fig. 16, in tracing the front elevation, the foot of every line of sight would be projected on a single line on **V P**. The elevation of the surface, therefore, is represented on the drawing by the single straight line $M N$, Fig. 16. Project the front and the side elevations in their proper places, completing the problem.

NOTE.—The single line that constitutes each elevation of this problem represents the eight lines of the octagonal surface shown on the plan. This is shown in Fig. 16, which is a copy of the plan and front elevation on the plate, lettered for convenience of reference. Two of the lines in the plan, $A B$ and $F E$, Fig. 16, are shown in their full length by that portion of the line $M N$ included between the points P and Q; since $F E$ is directly in line with $A B$ in the elevation, as already explained, it is shown by the same line $P Q$ used to define $A B$. The line $H A$ is shown foreshortened at $M P$; and as $G F$ is directly behind $H A$, $M P$ represents $G F$ also; $Q N$ bears the same relation to $B C$ and $E D$. The line $G H$ is represented in the elevation by the point M; N, in like manner, represents $D C$. Thus, the line $M N$ represents a certain view of the eight lines $A B, B C$, etc. to $H A$, and also a view of the surface defined by those lines.

The above is very important and should be carefully read, as it shows the application of principles to Problem 5.

PROBLEM 6

48. To project the views of an octagonal surface that is in a rightly inclined position.

NOTE.—No perspective figure is shown for this problem, and the projections will be made on the plate from the following directions. The same figure is used for this problem as for Problem 5. These drawings are really a continuation of that problem; and since a full view of the surface is shown in the plan of Problem 5, projectors will be drawn from that view, in order to define the plan of this problem.

CONSTRUCTION.—Draw the horizontal base line in the next space on the drawing and at the same distance from the lower edge as the corresponding base line was drawn in the space for Problem 5; draw the vertical base line $1\frac{3}{4}$ inches from the left side of the space.

The front elevation of this problem will first be drawn. Draw a line inclined to the horizontal base line at an angle of 60° and equal in length to the line shown in the front elevation of Problem 5; the lower end of this line should be ½ inch above the base line, as previously explained. It should be drawn in such a position on the plate that vertical projectors from the ends of the line will pass through the central portion of the horizontal base line. Mark the position of the points indicated by the projectors, as at *M, P, Q,* and *N*, Fig. 16, and from these points draw four vertical projectors to the plan. Intersect these with horizontal projectors drawn from the plan in Problem 5; draw the connecting lines between corresponding points thus projected; this produces a figure that is the plan of the octagonal surface in the rightly inclined position indicated by the front elevation.

Project the side elevation by the use of secondary projectors, as previously explained. Reference to the copy of this plate will be of assistance to the student during the projection of these views. The completed drawings are there shown and the method of projecting between different views is indicated by projectors partially extended towards the left of the plan of this problem.

49. Basis of Projection.—The plan and side elevation of this surface are foreshortened views. There are, however, two lines in each view shown in their true length; this may be proved by a comparison of the figures with the plan of Problem 5; the other lines in each case are foreshortened.

It does not necessarily follow, however, that any of the lines in a rightly inclined view are shown in their true length. Had the angle of inclination been along the line *A E*, Fig. 16, every line would have been foreshortened; again, in the case of surfaces having curved or irregular outlines, the least angle of inclination in any direction would preclude the possibility of representing, in a foreshortened view, any portion of the outline in its true length.

It will thus be seen that the point is the only geometrical element not subject to change, or variation, in any view. It may therefore be relied on as a basis of projection. The outline of any surface in the different views is determined by *first fixing the location of points at the extremities of the boundary lines of such surface*, afterwards drawing the connecting lines, as in this problem.

PROBLEM 7

50. To project a full view of a surface from a given plan and elevation showing that surface in a rightly inclined position.

A full view of any surface may be projected by assuming a view to be taken at right angles to a line in which the entire surface is represented, for in such a view the lines of sight are at right angles to the outlines of the surface.

CONSTRUCTION.—In the next adjoining space to the right on the plate, copy the plan and the front elevation of Problem 6, placing the projections so that they will occupy the same relative position in the space. To obtain a full view of the surface in this problem, a view must now be assumed at right angles to the line in the elevation; in other words, the elevation must be considered as a plan and a new front elevation projected therefrom. The plan copied from Problem 6 is used as a base plan, secondary projectors being drawn from thence in the manner shown on the plate and described in the following article. The projectors in this case are drawn by the arc method, sometimes more conveniently employed than the angular method previously described.

51. Arc Method of Drawing Secondary Projectors.—Draw a base line, for the projection of the full view, from the intersection of the base lines previously drawn and parallel to the line that represents the surface of the octagon, as *A B* (see plate). At the point of intersection of the base lines (*B*) erect a perpendicular to the oblique base line *A B*, as *B C*, producing it indefinitely towards the right. The positions of all points in the plan

are now to be located on this line in the same relative position as they would occupy if projected horizontally to the
vertical base line in the drawing. The points are accordingly projected horizontally to the vertical base line $B\,D$;
thence, by using the compasses and describing arcs from a
center B, located at the intersection of the base lines, they
are projected to the line $B\,C$. The projectors are then continued beyond $B\,C$, but parallel to $A\,B$; they are there
intersected by primary projectors drawn from corresponding
points in the elevation, as shown. Locate the various positions of the corresponding points at the intersections of these
projectors and produce the full view of the octagon by
drawing the connecting lines.

It will thus be seen that the drawing of secondary projectors by this method involves *first*, projection to the
nearest base line; *second*, the describing of arcs from the
center shown; and *third*, the continuation of the projectors
parallel to the base line of the desired view. If the drawing has been carefully made, it will be found that the surface thus defined is an exact counterpart of the plan in
Problem 5, and that the full view projected in this problem
is in the same relation to the elevation as the plan in Problem 5 is to the elevation of that problem.

**52. Views Necessary for the Projection of the
Full View.**—When it is desired to project a full view of
any surface that is represented in a drawing in an inclined
position, it is necessary to have one view that will show all
the points of that surface as contained in one line. A projection must also be drawn at right angles to that view, in
order that such dimensions of the surface as are at right
angles to those in the first view may be shown in their true
length.

**53. Full Views Sometimes Obtained Without Pro-
jection Methods.**—A comparison of the views in the
projections of the last problem will prove that the vertical
primary projectors included within the surface of the octagon shown in the plan are of the same length as the secondary

projectors in the view last projected. This knowledge may be used to some advantage in producing a full view without using all the projectors employed in this problem.

Thus, draw a horizontal center line through the plan, as *E F* (see drawing on the plate for Problem 7) and draw primary projectors from the elevation to the full view in the regular way; at a convenient distance draw a line at right angles to, and crossing, these projectors, as *G H*. This line will be the center line for the full view, the points of which may then be located with the dividers in the following manner: Set the dividers to the length *a e* in the plan and set off a corresponding distance at *a' e'* in the full view; in like manner make *b' f'* equal to *b f*, etc., as shown on the plate. Complete the outline of the full view, then, by drawing connecting lines as heretofore.

This method is generally followed in pattern drafting, since it requires less time than to draw full projections as in the construction of the problem, and there is less liability of error.

54. If the student that does not clearly understand the principles by which these projections are made will cut a piece of cardboard to the same size and shape as the plan of Problem 5 and hold it in such positions that the foot of the lines of sight falls on the points designated on the drawings for the different views, he will at once see the correct position of the surface as represented in each view.

55. Surfaces Bounded by Curved Lines.—Surfaces that are defined by curved lines do not present any points from which to make projections. In making such projections, the same principles are employed, however; but it is first necessary to establish a number of points at various positions on the curved lines. The points thus established are then projected in the same way as in the foregoing problems. When, for purposes of projection, points are located on the outline of a curved surface in any view, it should be observed that they are so placed that, when the points thus located are projected to a line that represents an edge view of that surface, each end of that line is defined by the projection of a point.

***

56. **To project views of a plane surface defined by a curved line, the surface being in a rightly inclined position; also, to project a point located on that surface.**

NOTE.—Before making the projections of this problem, the lines to remain on the drawing for Problem 5 should be inked in, and, to avoid confusion, all other lines not to be inked in on that figure should be erased; the circle drawn for Problem 5 may then be redrawn for this problem.

CONSTRUCTION.—The surface for the projections of this problem is that of the circle to which the sides of the octagon in Problem 5 are tangent. After describing the circle, the next step is to locate points on its circumference. Do this by first drawing a vertical and a horizontal diameter, and then drawing, with the 45° triangle, two other diameters at right angles to each other, thus locating eight points at equal distances on the circumference. Those points indicated by the horizontal diameter will, when projected to the elevation, define the ends of the line in that view.

Also, locate a point at the center of the circle. The plan and elevation of the surface thus projected is shown in Fig. 17, the points being denoted by numerals. Project these points to the elevation of Problem 5, using lines easily erased, since they are not to appear in that problem when the plate is finished. In the last space on the plate draw horizontal and vertical base lines in the same corresponding position as in the space for Problem 6. The line that represents the front elevation of the circular plane surface is then drawn in the same position as in the elevation in Problem 6; with the dividers, locate points thereon in the same position as the points projected from the circle to the front elevation in Problem 5, as shown in Fig. 17. Project these points vertically to the plan and intersect these projectors with horizontal pro-

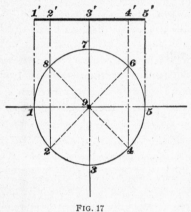

FIG. 17

jectors drawn from the circle in Problem 5.

When projecting points across a drawing—as from the space occupied by Problem 5 to the drawing for this problem — it is not necessary to draw lines the entire distance. By carefully placing the edge of the T square on each point in turn, corresponding lines may be drawn across the plan in this problem. This saves erasing unnecessary lines, but care must be taken, when making projections in this way, to observe that points thus located are at the intersections of projectors drawn from points in corresponding positions in each of the views. Find the location of each point thus projected and through these points trace the curve that represents the foreshortened view of the circle, using the irregular curve for this purpose. Thus a plan and a front elevation of the circular plane surface is drawn, in which the surface is represented in a rightly inclined position.

Project the side elevation by the angular method of secondary projectors, as previously explained, and designate the point in both views by a small dot at the center of the surface. Finally project the full view by the arc method, as in Problem 7. In this problem a good test of accuracy is afforded if, after the nine points have been projected to the full view, a circle with a radius of $\frac{3}{4}$ inch, described from the central point, passes through the other eight points.

57. Importance of Accuracy.—Next to a knowledge of the principles of projection, neatness and accuracy are the prime requisites in a drawing. The student should

PROJECTIONS-II.

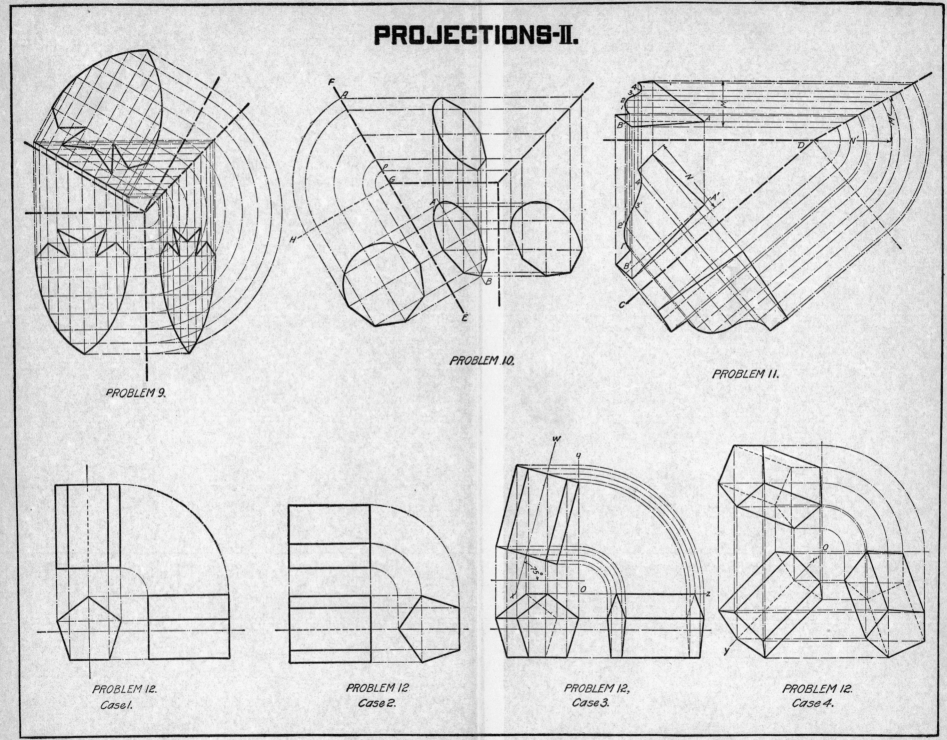

PROBLEM 9.

PROBLEM 10.

PROBLEM 11.

PROBLEM 12.
Case 1.

PROBLEM 12
Case 2.

PROBLEM 12,
Case 3.

PROBLEM 12.
Case 4.

carefully observe that, when the points determined by the intersection of lines are used as centers for arcs or circles, the needle point of the compasses should be placed exactly on that position; again, drawing three or more lines that shall intersect at the same point is very commonly required in projection drawing and in pattern drafting; this is not an easy thing to do accurately unless carefully practiced by the student. It is needless to state that unless the work is accurately done it is of no value.

When putting in the figures for the dimensions on drawings, care should be observed that they are placed on those views in which the lines and surfaces are shown in their true length. Do not designate a foreshortened view of a line or surface by a dimension figure, when another view is given in which the true length is shown. Again, do not repeat the same dimension on different views of the same drawing; thus, in Problem 2, Case I, the length of the line is given as 2 inches in the plan, and it is obviously unnecessary to give the same dimension in the front elevation.

The student may ink in all the problems on the plates, but the letters used to describe the different positions and lines are not placed on the drawing. The date, name, and class letter and number are inscribed as in the plates of *Geometrical Drawing.*

_____

DRAWING PLATE, TITLE: PROJECTIONS II

58. The problems for this and the succeeding plates should be practiced on other paper and then copied on the drawing that is to be sent in for correction. The student can thus judge better as to the relative position the figures should occupy and the completed plates will present a neat appearance. In making the projections on this and the succeeding plates, the views may be assumed to be ¼ inch from their respective base lines, as this will enable the projections to be kept in closer proximity. The base lines are not to be inked in on this or the following plates. Divide this plate by a central horizontal line; the part of the

drawing above this line is divided into three, and the part
below the line into four, equal spaces.

---

59. **To project a side elevation and a full view
of a rightly inclined plane surface defined by an
irregular outline.**

This is a problem in which the student has an opportunity to use, in a practical way, the
knowledge of projection thus far
gained. The surface to be projected
is shown in a rightly inclined position
in Fig. 18, which is a foreshortened
view of the surface. This figure is to
be copied, in the size indicated by the
dimension figures, into such a position
in the upper left-hand space on the
drawing that the projections when
completed will occupy about the center of the space.

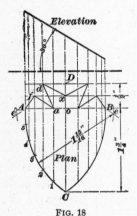

FIG. 18

CONSTRUCTION.—First draw the
horizontal line $A B$ 1¾ inches long and
bisect it at o by the vertical line $C D$. Make $o D$ ½ inch
long and bisect it at x, as shown, making $o C$ 1¾ inches
long. Set the compasses at a radius of $1\frac{15}{16}$ inches, and
with A and C, respectively, as centers, describe arcs intersecting at e; with the same radius and with B and C as
centers, describe arcs similarly intersecting at e'. From
these centers (e and e') describe the arcs $A C$ and $B C$,
thus producing the curved outline of the lower portion of
the plan. Next, divide these arcs, by spacing, into six
equal parts, thus locating the points 1, 2, 3, 4, and 5;
from these points draw vertical lines, as shown in Fig. 18.
Complete the upper outline of the surface as represented in
the figure; thus, locate a at the intersection of the vertical
from 1 with a horizontal from A; d, at the intersection of

the vertical from *2* with a horizontal from *D*; *f,* in like manner, at the intersection of a vertical from *3* with a horizontal from *x*.

The points at the extremities of these lines and those located on the curved outline are now to be treated as in former problems and the projections made in the usual way.

CAUTION.—When making the projections for this problem, the student must observe the precautions given in regard to the taking of the same corresponding points in each view. Project the side elevation first; it may be desirable for the student to ink in that figure, in order to avoid the confusion arising from a number of lines crossing one another on the drawing. Use the angular method for the secondary projectors in projecting the side elevation and the arc method for the full view. Since it is often necessary, when developing patterns, to draw several views over one another in this way, the student should accustom himself to drawings that have a complicated appearance from this cause, and should learn to follow each set of projectors as readily as though they were in separate drawings. During the construction of this projection, it will be noticed that the base line for the full view, in order to be drawn from the intersection of the other base lines, will fall below the front elevation of the surface. This is unimportant, however, since its purpose is the same, and the result is merely that of a slight appearance of crowding on the drawing.

PROBLEM 10

60. **To project views of a plane surface in an obliquely inclined position.**

EXPLANATION.—A full view of the surface to be projected in this problem is shown in Fig. 19, the dimension figures giving the size in which it is to be drawn by the student. The upper portion of this surface is defined by a semicircle, the lower by one-half of an octagon. The purpose in selecting a surface of this outline is to give the student some practice in the projection of both straight and curved outline surfaces.

It has been shown that, before an inclined view of a surface was projected, a right view—i. e., a right plan and elevation, as in Problem 5—has first been drawn. These views alone are pro-

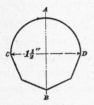

FIG. 19

jected in drawings of simple or plain objects, it being obviously unnecessary to show any object in a working drawing in a position not commonly occupied. But owing to the different shapes of objects, variously outlined surfaces are presented in a diversity of positions, and it is essential that the student should be capable of projecting any surface into any conceivable position and of drawing a full view from such a projection.

CONSTRUCTION.—The method of drawing oblique views of surfaces is shown in detail at (a), (b), and (c), Fig. 20, the

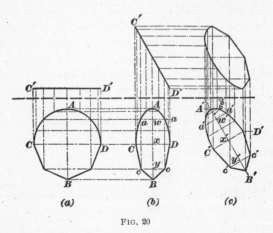

(a)   (b)   (c)

FIG. 20

projections at (c) being the ones required for the plan and elevation of this problem. Lay a separate piece of paper over the drawing of Problem 9 on the plate, and reproduce thereon the projections shown at (a) and (b), Fig. 20, in accordance with principles already explained. Next, draw

the plan and elevation at (c) in their proper places on the
plate. The drawing shown at (a) may be seen to be similar
to that of Problem 5 of the preceding plate; (b) is projected
directly from (a), in the same manner as Problem 6, the
angle of inclination being 60°. The plan of this surface in
(b) is then copied at (c) in such a position that the center
line A B makes an angle of 60° with the base line of V P.
This is accomplished by first drawing the center line A' B'
at the given angle in (c), noting thereon the position of the
points w', x', and y'; draw perpendiculars through these
points, and make w' a' in (c) equal to w a in (b), x' D' equal
to x D, etc. The outline of the plan at (c), therefore, is
exactly the same as it is shown in (b), the only difference
between the two views being the fact that the line A' B' in (c)
is inclined to V P, while in (b) it is perpendicular to that plane.

Let us consider what changes have here been represented.
Cut a piece of cardboard to the outline and size shown in
Fig. 19 and compare it with the different positions in the
drawings just made. It will be seen that the cardboard
must be held in a horizontal position to coincide with the
drawing at (a); to represent the drawing at (b), the point C
must be raised until the line C D is at the angle of 60°
with H P. The plan at (b) is, therefore, a foreshortened
view of the surface, although its elevation may still be represented by the single line C' D'. Now turn the cardboard
to the position indicated in (c), that is, so that the line A' B'
makes an angle of 60° with V P.

It will be seen that the line C D in its relation to H P is
not affected by this change, its angle with H P remaining as
before; *therefore, the vertical distances to be shown in the
elevation of (c) will be the same as in the elevation of (b),*
and may be projected directly to (c) from (b), as shown in
Fig. 20. Draw horizontal projectors from the elevation
at (b) to the elevation in (c), intersecting them, in the manner shown, by primary projectors drawn vertically upwards
from the points in the plan at (c). Trace the outline of the
surface thus indicated through the intersections of projectors drawn from corresponding points in each view. The

projections shown at (c) being completed on the plate, the paper on which (a) and (b) were drawn may now be removed and the side elevation required for the problem projected by the angular method previously described. Three views are thus shown, in all of which the surface is represented as inclined at an oblique angle to the lines of sight; all these views, therefore, are foreshortened. Oblique views may always be drawn in this manner; that is, a right view is first drawn; next, a rightly inclined view is projected, the desired angle being represented in the elevation. The plan thus produced is then redrawn for the oblique view and its elevation projected as in this problem.

61. Position of Full Views: How Determined.
To project a full view of this surface it is first necessary to determine whether any of the lines or distances in any of the views are shown in their true length, but without having recourse to the projections made on the separate paper, since projection methods are to be used. This may be done by comparing the relative position of any two points in the outline of the surface, as located in the plan and elevation. If it is found that a line drawn between any two of these points in the elevation will be parallel to the base line (and therefore at right angles to the vertical lines of sight), that line will be shown, of course, in its true length on the plan. Any other lines parallel to it will also be shown in their true length. It is found on examination that points in the elevation corresponding to the positions represented by A and B, Fig. 19, are located on the same horizontal projector; therefore, a line drawn between these points as they are located on the plan will be represented in its true length in that view; and a view projected from these points in the plan by primary projectors drawn at right angles to this line, intersected by secondary projectors from the front elevation (by a modification of the method used in Problem 7), will be a full view of the surface.

Draw the oblique base line in the proper position, i. e., parallel to that line shown in full length in the plan (A B on the plate), as above explained, and at such distance away from the plan as directed in the instructions for drawing this plate, producing the line indefinitely towards the upper portion of the drawing, as shown on the plate at EF. In this case, the line thus drawn defines the inclination of the surface, since the angle is the same in both plan and elevation, viz., 60°. The full view is projected as follows: Draw the line GH at right angles to the base line EF and from the intersection of EF with the horizontal base line. By the arc method, draw secondary projectors from the elevation, as shown; intersect these projectors by primary projectors drawn from the plan at right angles to EF, thus producing the full view of the surface. It will be found that this full view is an exact counterpart of the surface shown in Fig. 19, and should correspond to the preliminary drawing in the plan at (a) on the separate paper. Note that the portion of EF included between p and q corresponds in length to that of the rightly inclined front elevation at (b), Fig. 20. This may be seen by comparing that portion of the line with the view on the preliminary drawing.*

The student should now be able to recognize any view of a surface in any position; that is, he should be able to tell whether a view represents such a surface in a right position, a rightly inclined position, or an obliquely inclined position; and by the application of the principles illustrated in the foregoing problems and the exercise of a little judgment, he should be able to project any surface into any desired position. Or, being given a surface in a position indicated by a properly projected plan and elevation, he should be able to produce the full view and designate the angle of inclination.

The following problem will serve as a test of his progress. The principles involved have already been presented and the method of application will be readily understood. The

---

* It should be noted that this is the case only when the angle of inclination is the same in both views.

angle of inclination in the plan is not the same as is shown in the elevation; both angles are to be determined by projection methods.

---

62. **To project the full view of an irregularly outlined surface obliquely inclined.**

The projections of this problem are to occupy the upper right-hand space of the drawing plate. The plan and front elevation are shown in Fig. 21 and are reproduced full size on the sheet opposite this page.* The outline represented is frequently used as a "stay," or profile, to which moldings are formed in cornice work. Since the view shown is known to be obliquely inclined, its dimensions are foreshortened, and their true lengths are to be found by projection methods, as follows:

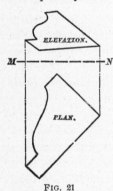

FIG. 21

CONSTRUCTION.—The student should detach the sheet opposite this page and paste the plan and elevation in such a position in the third space on the plate that the base line $M N$, Fig. 21, will be $2\frac{1}{2}$ inches below the top border line and exactly horizontal. Locate a number of points on the curved outline in the elevation, by equally spacing that portion of the figure with the dividers, as shown at *1, 2, 3,* and *4* in the drawing for this problem on the plate, and project these points to the plan. To ascertain the angle of inclination in the plan, draw a horizontal line through the widest portion of the figure in the elevation, locating, if possible, one end of the line at an angle of the surface—as the line $A B$. Project this line to the plan at $A' B'$, as explained in Art. **61**; parallel to this line erect the oblique base line $C D$.

---

* This sheet is not inserted in the bound volume containing this Paper.

The angle formed by these lines (A' B' and C D) with the horizontal base line is the angle of inclination of the surface to **V P**, or that angle shown in the plan.   The angle of inclination to **H P**, or that shown in the elevation, is most easily found by constructing a right-angled triangle whose base and altitude are equal to certain distances found in the plan and elevation; that is, the base is equal to the extreme width of the figure in the plan, taken at right angles to the line of inclination in that view (shown by the dimension N).   The altitude is the vertical height shown in the elevation at M. Construct this right-angled triangle on the horizontal base line extended, as shown at N' M', and locate one end of the base at D, the intersection of the base lines.   Extend the hypotenuse indefinitely towards the right of the drawing. Next, intersect primary projectors drawn from the plan to the oblique view by secondary projectors drawn from the elevation by the arc method, as shown on the plate.   The full view of the surface is then traced through the intersections of these projectors, completing the problem.

63.   Projection of Solids.—We now come to the projection of solids, which, as before noted, are merely various combinations of surfaces.   Projections of surfaces in a variety of positions having already been made, we shall encounter no new principles in the projection of solids, the surfaces of which are projected in the same manner as has been shown in preceding problems.

Since lines intersect in a point, so surfaces intersect in a line, and in drawing projections of solids it is necessary only to find the true projections in any view, or set of views, of those lines that represent the correct intersections of the adjacent surfaces; this is a comparatively easy thing for the student to do, if he will use proper care and diligence in the application of the principles of the preceding problems.

64.   Projection of the Cube Illustrated.—Every solid consists of a number of surfaces, each of which is differently shown when the solid is projected to the various views.

This is due to the fact that the observer is assumed to occupy a different position in each view of the solid thus projected. In certain positions some solids show one or more of their surfaces directly behind another surface of the same size and shape. This would be the case if the projections of the cube, referred to in Art. **18,** were drawn as shown in Fig. 22. When the cube is in a right position—that is, with two surfaces horizontal, and that surface nearest the observer in a side view in such position that the lines defining that surface will be at right angles to the lines of sight, as indicated in Fig. 22—it is evident that the surface parallel to and behind

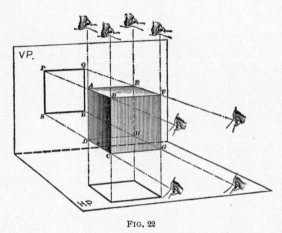

FIG. 22

the front surface will be projected by the same lines of sight as the front surface. Therefore, in such a case, a projection of the front surface of the cube is equivalent to a projection of the entire cube. Each projection of the cube in the plan, front, and side elevations is a square, the sides of which are 1 inch long, while the views are arranged, as shown in Fig. 23, in such a way as to appear related to one another.

65. In "reading" the projections shown in Fig. 23, we merely compare the surfaces of the cube as they are shown in the different projections. Thus, the surface *A B C D*, Fig. 22, is represented in the plan of Fig. 23

by the line *A B*, and in the front elevation by the line *B C*, while a full view of that surface is shown in the side elevation; so, in like manner, the position of each surface of the cube may be determined.   Note that, in each full view, two surfaces are represented; thus, in the front elevation of Fig. 22, the surfaces *B F G C* and *A E H D* are projected on **V P** as one surface at *P Q R S*.   It is thus shown that surfaces in their relation to one another, when combined in one view, as in the projection of a solid, partake of the same principle that has been

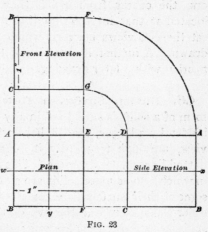

FIG. 23

shown in its application to points and lines, viz., *surfaces whose outlines are contained in the same lines of sight in any view are projected in that view as one surface.*

The difference in position of the several views due to the use of first- and third-angle projection may easily be illustrated in connection with Fig. 23.   Here the cube is represented as having been projected in the first angle.   If the student will now turn the book " upside down," he will see the three views of the cube in the relative positions they would occupy were the drawing made by the third-angle method.   It will be seen that the effect is merely that of rendering the plan uppermost on the drawing.   The front elevation then is seen below the plan, while the side elevation, as in first-angle projection, is at the side of the plan. In the case of a simple solid like the cube, the use of different angles of projection has but slight effect, but when a more complicated solid is represented on the drawing, it becomes necessary for the one that would " read " the drawing to know which angle has been used by the draftsman.

39—24

Note that in Fig. 23 the secondary projectors are described from E as a center, the lines of the cube being used as base lines, as mentioned in Art. **39.** When this short method is adopted in the case of secondary project-ors, the center from which they are described must be located at that intersection of the primary projectors near-est the two views between which secondary projectors are drawn. A further illustration of this will be given in con-nection with a later drawing.

66. Hidden Surfaces: How Indicated.—When the form of a solid is such that in any view a smaller surface is hidden by a larger, the smaller surface is not shown in that view, although frequently its outline may be defined by dotted lines on the drawing. This applies also to projections in which two or more solids are shown in positions such that some of their surfaces are completely or partially hidden by other surfaces nearer the eye of the observer. Only such surfaces as receive the lines of sight directly from the eye of the observer are shown in a view by full lines, although, as mentioned above, the outline of such other surfaces as it may be desirable to show in a drawing may be indicated by dotted lines.

67. Facility in Reading Drawings Acquired Only by Practice.—The reading of working drawings is, there-fore, a comparatively easy matter, if the student will resolve each portion of the object represented into its respective surfaces and look for the various outlines as they are shown in the different projections. If this is found a difficult task, the surfaces may be further resolved into lines and points, whose respective positions may then be located in each view shown. It is not to be expected that the position of every surface in a complicated drawing will be seen by the beginner at a single glance—an expert seldom acquires such profi-ciency—but as "practice makes perfect," the student may easily accustom himself, by careful study of the various positions of the surfaces composing the solids that are projected in the following problems, to the more or less complicated projections found in the various mechanical and architectural journals, in shop drawings, or in such other projection drawings as are within his reach.

68. The Center Line.—It has been found convenient, when making projections of objects, to make use of a line that is imagined to pass through the central portion of the solid as it is shown in any plan and elevation.   Such a line is called a *center line*, and in many projections it is inked in when the drawing is finished, since it frequently affords a convenient means of indicating certain positions of the figure, besides assisting in the location of the several surfaces of the solid in the different views.   This line, however, is central only in its relation to the object of which the drawing is a representation, and not in relation to the planes of projection.   This may be better understood by considering the center line as the projection of an imaginary surface (or plane) that passes through the central portion of the figure. It is generally represented in those views only in which that imaginary surface can be shown in one line, or, as we have said before, as if "on edge."   Thus, in the right view projected in Fig. 23, the lines $w\,x$ and $y\,z$ are center lines, represented on the drawing by the broken-and-double-dotted lines shown in Fig. 23.   The practical use of the center line will be illustrated in the succeeding problems by the projection of solids into various positions.

PROBLEM 12

69. To draw the projection of a given solid, several positions being indicated.

The solid for the projections of this problem is shown in perspective in Fig. 24.   It is, as the figure shows, a pentagonal prism; that is, a solid whose ends are pentagons and parallel to each other and whose sides are parallelograms. The dimensions are given in Fig. 24; three projections are to be drawn, each showing the solid in a different position; each projection will be complete in a set of views consisting of a plan and front and side elevations. Each set of projections is to occupy one of the remaining spaces on the plate, the prism being shown in the positions indicated by the following cases:

Fig. 24

Case I.—*In an upright position, the side nearest the observer being parallel to* **V P.**

The projections showing this position of the prism may be readily drawn by the student from the explanations and instructions already given. The plan, which is a pentagon with ¾-inch sides, should be drawn first, according to instructions given in *Geometrical Drawing.* Draw the center lines as in Fig. 23 and ink them in, completing the drawing as shown on the plate. All lines that represent the intersection of surfaces—i. e., the edges of the prism—and that intercept the lines of sight directly from the eye of the observer are to be represented by full lines on the drawing. All hidden edges are to be shown by dotted lines.

Case II.—*In a horizontal position, the upper side being parallel to* **H P,** *and the ends of the prism parallel to* **V P** *in the side elevation.*

In this case, which differs from Case I only in the position of the prism, the side elevation should be drawn first. It may here be mentioned that, in drawing different views of objects in right positions, the question as to which view is drawn first is merely a matter of convenience, depending on the form of the object represented. Thus, in Case I the plan is drawn first; in this instance it is, however, more convenient to draw the side elevation first. In this drawing it is only in the plan and the side elevation that the center line can be shown, since an edge view of the plane represented would not be given in the front elevation.

Case III.—*In a rightly inclined position, the angle of inclination of the center line (and consequently of the prism) to* **H P** *being* 75°.

EXPLANATION.—The sides of the prism are in the same relative position to **V P** in the front elevation as in Case I. (See the plate.)   The projection of solids to inclined positions is accomplished in the same manner as the projection of surfaces to similar positions in preceding problems. Practical use may be made of the center line in this drawing; this line may be shown in the front elevation, but cannot be continued to the plan from that view, since it is clear that its true position may not be shown there in one line.

CONSTRUCTION.—First draw the line $w\,x$ in that part of the space devoted to the front elevation and at an angle of 75° to the base line.   The line $w\,x$ is the center line of the front elevation.   Next, copy the front elevation of Case I in the same relative position on this line, thus producing the rightly inclined front elevation.   Draw primary projectors vertically downwards from all points of this front elevation, and intersect them with horizontal primary projectors drawn from the plan of Case I, in the same manner as the plan of Problem 6 on the preceding plate was produced.   Next, draw the outline of the plan by connecting the intersections of projectors that have been drawn from corresponding points in each of the two views.   Project the side elevation by means of secondary projectors described from the intersection of the upper and right-hand primary projectors, that is, at O on the plate (see Art. **65**).   When drawing secondary projectors for solids whose surfaces do not extend to the outer primary projectors in the adjacent views, note that the primary projector must be produced as at $O\,y$ and $O\,z$.

Case IV.—*In an obliquely inclined position, with the center line at an angle of 45° to* **V P** *and 15° to* **H P**, *the upper side being in such a position that a full view will be shown of its upper and lower edges.*

EXPLANATION.—As in Problem 10, where a surface was projected to an obliquely inclined position, so in this problem some preliminary work must be done on another piece of paper. These preliminary projections are shown in Fig. 25, of which (*a*) is the right plan and elevation and (*b*) is the rightly inclined drawing.

CONSTRUCTION.—On a separate piece of paper construct the projections shown at (*a*), Fig. 25; copy the elevation produced at (*a*) in such a position at (*b*) that the angle of the center line *w x* is 15° to **H P**, as required by the conditions of the problem. Next, project the plan in (*b*) from the plan of (*a*), in connection with the elevation of (*b*), as indicated by the primary projectors drawn from these views. Redraw the plan of (*b*) at (*c*) and give its center line *y z*

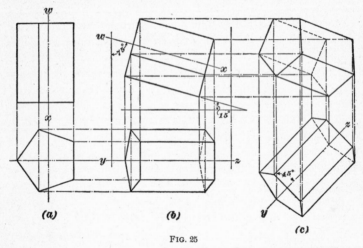

FIG. 25

the required angle of 45° to **V P**. Next, produce the elevation in (*c*) by drawing primary projectors from the elevation in (*b*) and intersecting them by primary projectors drawn from corresponding points in the plan in (*c*). These operations are precisely similar to those used in producing the obliquely inclined views of the surface in Problem 10; and if the extra piece of paper is laid over the drawing in such a manner as to leave the lower right-hand space exposed, the

drawings shown in Fig. 25 at (c) may be projected directly
to their proper position, thus producing the plan and front
elevation required. The side elevation is then projected by
means of secondary projectors described from the center O,
as shown on the plate. It is thus shown that oblique views
of solids are projected by the same methods as those used in
the case of surfaces.

NOTE.—The appearance of this plate will be improved if the base
line of the front elevation of this case is placed ⅜ inch higher than in
the preceding cases.

70. The Axial Line.—In views such as are projected
in this drawing—i. e., obliquely inclined views—the center
line, as the representation of the central plane of the figure,
can be shown only in the plan; that is, in the position of
the solid shown in this case. The position of the solid might
be such that the center line would be shown in one of the
elevations, or possibly not in any right view. However, it
is sometimes represented in drawings merely as a central
line, and not as the representation of a central plane; it may
in such cases be projected to the other views by means of
points located at convenient distances on the line. It is then
called an *axial line*, or *line of axis*, and represents the position of the axis of the solid. It is not projected in the cases
of the preceding problem, since the figure is not of such a
form as to demand the location of an axial line. The axial
line is similar in its use to the center line and is represented
on drawings by the same kind of a broken-and-dotted line.

In order to avoid confusion, the center and axial lines are
usually indicated by small lettering placed conveniently
near one end of the lines; thus, "center line" or "axial line."

DRAWING PLATE, TITLE: PROJECTIONS III

71. Three problems are to be drawn on this plate, each
of which will require two sets of projections. Like the projections of Problem 12, they consist of a plan and front and
side elevations. Each set of projections occupies one space
on the drawing, and the plate is divided into six equal spaces

by a single horizontal and two vertical lines.   The different cases of each problem are drawn in the same vertical division; thus, Case I of Problem 13 occupies the upper left-hand space and Case II of the same problem is directly under it. Cases I and II of the other two problems on the plate are to be placed in the same way in the remaining spaces.

PROBLEM 13

72. To draw the projections of a cylinder.

The method of projection used in the case of surfaces having curved outlines has been shown in a preceding problem.   Two such surfaces are presented in the ends of the cylinder shown in perspective in Fig. 26, and the fig-

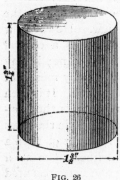

FIG. 26

ure also gives the dimensions of the solid as it is to be drawn on the plate. Since, with the exception of those at the intersection of the ends, there are no edges formed by the curved sides of the cylinder, there will be no full lines on the drawing except those required to show the ends in their different positions and the outline of the sides. A front elevation of the cylinder in the right position indicated by Fig. 26 is therefore a parallelogram, the length of whose horizontal sides is equal to the diameter of the circular surfaces at the ends of the cylinder—the vertical sides equal in length to the height of the cylinder.   Its entire dimensions and its form are indicated in a plan and front elevation, and there is no need of making any further drawings to enable the mechanic to understand the shape of the solid thus represented.

Case I.—*When the cylinder is rightly inclined.*

EXPLANATION.—In this drawing the cylinder is inclined at an angle of 60° to **H P**.   Rightly inclined views of solids are often drawn by a method somewhat shorter than that shown in preceding problems. By this method, temporary views are drawn in convenient positions on the paper and rightly inclined views are projected, as shown in this case. Less space is required for the drawing and a saving of time is effected; the principles involved, as will be seen from the following construction, are identical with those of the preceding problem.

CONSTRUCTION.—First draw the center line in the elevation at the given angle—as A B in the drawing on the plate. Describe the circle shown at (*m*), which represents a full view of the end of the cylinder; next, draw the front elevation C D E F on the center line A B according to the given dimensions. Describe a circle similar to (*m*) at (*n*); this is a temporary view of the end of the cylinder and corresponds to the plan of the prism at (*a*), Fig. 25. Locate a convenient number of points at equal distances on the outline of each full view thus drawn at (*m*) and (*n*). Project the points of (*m*) to the elevation C D E F, and thence draw primary projectors vertically downwards; intersect these primary projectors by other primary projectors drawn horizontally from similar points located on the outline of the full view at (*n*). Trace the outline of the plan thus produced through points of intersection corresponding to those on the full views. The temporary full views (*m*) and (*n*) may then be erased from the plate. Project the side elevation by means of secondary projectors described by the arc method, thus completing the drawing.

Case II.—*When the cylinder is obliquely inclined.*

EXPLANATION.—The method of projecting the drawings required for this case is similar to that already given for oblique views of surfaces and solids, and has been fully explained in Art. **60,** and also in connection with Case IV of Problem 12. A right view is first drawn [as the elevation and full view (*m*) of the preceding case]; next, a rightly inclined view. The rightly inclined plan thus drawn is then recopied at the given angle, thus producing the plan of the oblique view; from this plan, in connection with the rightly inclined elevation, the obliquely inclined elevation is projected. The rightly inclined plan and elevation having been drawn in Case I of this problem, the plan there shown may be redrawn for the plan of this case.

CONSTRUCTION.—On a separate piece of paper reproduce the plan and front elevation of Case I and fasten this paper by thumbtacks to the drawing board, towards the left of the space used for this case. Next, redraw the plan of Case I in its proper place on the plate for this case, and in such a position that the line *G H* of Case I forms an angle of 60° with the base line of the front elevation, as shown at *G' H'* on the plate. Then produce the front elevation by drawing primary projectors upwards from the plan and intersecting them by similar projectors drawn horizontally from the rightly inclined elevation on the attached sheet, which may then be removed. Trace curves through the points thus projected and draw the tangential lines, as previously described and as shown at *C' D' F' E'* on the plate. Project the side elevation as in preceding problems, taking special care to project from similar points in each view.

PROBLEM 14

73.   To draw the projections of a hexagonal pyramid.

A *pyramid* is a solid whose base is a polygon and whose sides are triangles uniting at a common point called the

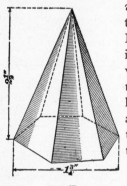

vertex. The pyramid for the projections of this problem is shown in Fig. 27, where its dimensions are clearly indicated. Since these drawings are very easy and are constructed in a manner similar to those of preceding problems, definite instructions are omitted, and the student is expected to be able to complete the drawings by the aid of the brief explanations that follow.

FIG. 27

Case I.—*When the pyramid is in a right position.*

EXPLANATION.—The plan of this projection is most conveniently drawn first, a circle 1¾ inches in diameter being described from O as a center, as shown on the plate. The edges of the pyramid are then drawn: a horizontal diameter and two diameters at angles of 60° with the first represent the upright edges; chords of the arcs thus designated are then drawn, and the plan of the pyramid is complete. Next draw the center lines $A\,B$ and $C\,D$; set off the height of the pyramid on the line $A\,B$ and complete the front elevation by the aid of primary projectors, as shown on the plate, the side elevation being projected as in former problems.

Case II.—*When the pyramid is in an obliquely inclined position.*

EXPLANATION.—The angles of inclination in the projections of this case are 60° to **H P** and 45° to **V P**. Preliminary

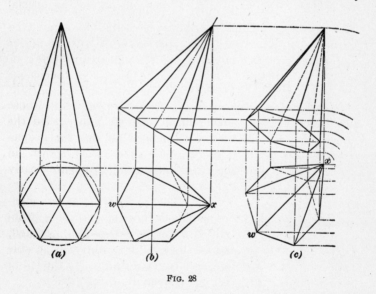

FIG. 28

drawings are required on separate paper, as shown in Fig. 28, first, as at (*a*), showing a right view of the pyramid; and second, as at (*b*), showing a rightly inclined view, the angle of inclination (of the center line) being 60° to **H P**. The plan produced at (*b*) is then copied on the plate in such a position that its axial line will make the required angle, viz., 45° to **V P**, as shown by the line *w x* at (*c*), Fig. 28. The front elevation is then projected as in Case II of the preceding problem, that is, by vertical primary projectors drawn from the plan in (*c*), intersected by horizontal primary projectors drawn from the elevation in (*b*). The projection of the side elevation by the arc method of secondary projectors is also similar to the preceding projections, as will be seen from an inspection of the plate.

PROBLEM 15

74. To draw the projections of a cone.

The *cone* is a solid that may be produced by the revolution of a right-angled triangle around one of its sides as an axis. Its base, therefore, is a circle, and its curved surface tapers uniformly towards a point at the top called the vertex, or *apex*. Like the cylinder, its entire form and dimensions are presented in a plan and a single elevation showing a right view of the cone. The cone for the projections of this problem is shown in perspective in Fig. 29, which gives the dimensions that the cone is to present on the plate. The methods used are precisely similar to those used in the case of the hexagonal pyramid in the preceding problem.

Case I.—*In a rightly inclined position.*

EXPLANATION.—In order to produce the rightly inclined front elevation, a construction similar to that used in Case I of Problem 13 is here used. The drawing differs from that projection only in the form of the solid. The angle of inclination in this case is 50° to **H P**.

CONSTRUCTION.—Draw the center line *A B* (see the plate) at the given angle, that is, 50° to the horizontal. Next, construct the triangle representing the elevation of the cone and describe the circle at (*m*)—a temporary full view of the base.   Describe a similar circle at (*n*), also a full view of the base, and locate a convenient number of points on the outline of each full view—in this case eight—as shown at *a*, *b*, *c*, etc., on the plate.   Project the rightly inclined plan in a manner precisely similar to that used in the view of the cylinder in Case I of Problem 13.   Erase the temporary views (*m*) and (*n*), and project the side elevation as in preceding projections.

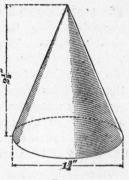

FIG. 29

Case II.—*In an obliquely inclined position.*

EXPLANATION.—The angle of inclination to **H P** is the same as in the drawing last made, and the plan of that projection may be recopied for the plan of this case, but it is to be drawn on the plate in such a position that the center line *w x* will make an angle of 45° to **V P**.   The plan and front elevation of the preceding case must be redrawn on separate paper and temporarily fastened over the drawing towards the left of the space required for this case, in order that the projection of the front elevation may be drawn.   As this process is similar to that used in preceding constructions, no further explanation will be given.   Complete the projections in the plan, front, and side elevations as shown on the plate.

NOTE.—When inclined views are drawn of solids having curved surfaces (as the cylinder and the cone), the circular ends should first be projected.   The outline of the curved surface is then represented as tangent to the base, or bases, of the solid, and without regard to the intersection of such outline with any given point on the base outline.

75.   Self-Reliance.—The student that has intelligently completed the projections of the foregoing problems and has made frequent use of the imaginative feature of this subject, as previously explained and directed, should now possess a very complete knowledge of the methods of projection used in representing plain solids in various positions.

The projection of irregularly outlined figures has not been presented, since the methods are identical with those already shown. The student should acquire a degree of self-reliance in this work; for if he is to depend on having the projection of every conceivable form described for him, the principles governing those projections will become a secondary matter, whereas the practical draftsman requires, above all else, the faculty of recognizing the principles by which to define and project the various forms occurring in the course of his work.

NOTE.—The student should understand that the percentage of marking adopted for these plates is based on the degree of accuracy in which the projections are drawn to the angles of inclination, as well as on the quality of neatness attained in the finish of the drawings.

DRAWING PLATE, TITLE: SECTIONS I

76. Use of Section Drawings.—A section drawing, as previously explained, is a projection of a portion of a solid, in a view where the solid is intersected by a plane. This plane—sometimes called a *cutting plane*—may pass through the solid in any direction; that portion of the solid between the plane and the observer is assumed to have been removed. Section drawings are useful in many ways, for by such means the construction of interior parts of objects may be shown. It is desirable in many cases to show some particular form that a solid of peculiar shape possesses at a place where it cannot be presented in an exterior view, and in such cases sections are projected. The section is considered simply as a surface that would appear on the cutting plane in any view of the object projected. The outline of this surface, therefore, will depend on the form of the object, the number of surfaces intersected by the plane, and the angle of inclination of the cutting plane.

To project the views of a solid in which a new surface is thus presented, it is necessary to consider the various surfaces that originally composed the solid. The first view drawn is always that in which the cutting plane is represented as *on edge*. The intersections of the original surfaces of the solid with the cutting plane are thus shown; and by using methods of projection already presented, any view of the section may then be drawn. Those portions of the solid assumed to have been removed are not shown in a section drawing, although their position is sometimes indicated by dotted lines.

77. Sections of the Sphere.—The solid that presents the most simple illustrations of sections is the *sphere*, or *globe*. This solid, also called a *ball*, is such as would be generated by the revolution of a circle around its diameter as an axis.

The cylinder, cone, and sphere are sometimes called the "three round bodies," or the *solids of revolution*. It will be shown later that their imaginary formation by such revolution may be taken advantage of by practical short methods of projection, the principles of which are based on this knowledge.

A full view of any section of a sphere is a circle. If the cutting plane passes through the center of the sphere, the full view of the section is a circle whose diameter is the same as the diameter of the sphere—or the *great circle* of the sphere, as it is called. If the cutting plane intersects the sphere in any other way, the section is still a circle, but of smaller diameter, and is measured from a view in which the cutting plane is shown on edge.

78. Sections of the Cube.—Fig. 30 is a projection drawing of the cube referred to in former illustrations and shows a vertical section. It will be noticed that the view of the section in the elevation is the same as the view in the front elevation in Fig. 23. This is always the case in sections

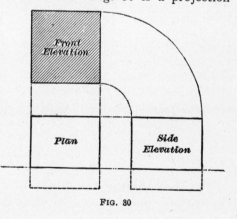

FIG. 30

of regular prisms where the cutting plane is parallel to the ends of the prism. Fig. 31 represents a diagonal section of the cube, the measurements of which will be apparent to the student from an inspection of the drawing. Fig. 32 is an oblique section, in which but three sides of the cube are intersected by the cutting plane; in this figure, the full view of the sectional surface is projected. Fig. 33 represents a section taken at a still different angle and position of the cube. *When a cutting plane passes through a solid having parallel sides, in any direction that causes it to intersect both of those parallel sides, those sides are shown in any*

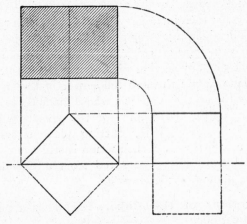

FIG. 31

view by parallel lines. Note that in the sectional views of Fig. 33 the opposite edges of the surfaces are defined by parallel lines; thus, since $A B$ and $C D$ are parallel to each other in the plan of the cube in Fig. 33, so $A' B'$ and $C' D'$ are in the same relation to each other in the side elevation; also, $A'' B''$ and $C'' D''$ in the full view of the section. The same is also true of $A C$ and $B D$, as may be seen from a comparison of the views.

79. How the Cutting Plane Is Represented.—When the cutting plane is shown on edge in a view, it is usually indicated by the same kind of a broken-and-double-dotted line used for the center line and the axial line. The use of this line for these three purposes is somewhat puzzling to the beginner; but as the student is now able to read projection drawings, he can readily determine which purpose the line is intended to serve. It is customary, however, as already mentioned, when center and axial lines are used, to ·mark them as such by neat lettering. A section line in a complicated drawing is usually designated by a letter placed

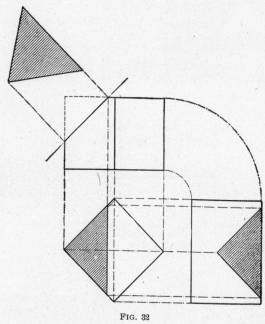

Fig. 32

at each end of the line, to which reference is made in the following manner: If, in the view where the cutting plane appears as a line, it is lettered A–B, the full view of the section is designated as a "section on the line A–B."

80. The problems for this plate, of which there are four, consist of the projection of the section drawings indicated in the accompanying illustrations. They are to be reproduced on the plate by the student to the dimensions

given on each figure. The cutting plane is indicated by the
line *A–B*, and the views shown may be understood by a careful study of the figures on the plate illustrating each problem.
The direction of a certain line in each plan is changed in these
views, and the cross-section is accordingly represented as
foreshortened in the front and side elevations.   A view is
also to be projected in which a full view of the sectional

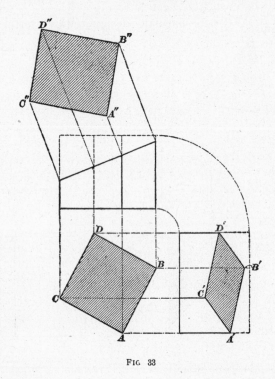

Fɪɢ 33

surface will be seen.   The plate is to be divided into four
equal spaces by horizontal and vertical lines. Problem 16
is to occupy the upper left-hand space.

The student is recommended not to refer to the reduced
copy of the plate more frequently than is necessary to enable
him to fix the location of the views on the drawing; he should
learn to depend on his own knowledge of projection.

PROBLEM 16

81. To project sectional views of an octagonal prism, the cutting plane crossing the solid at an oblique angle and leaving a portion of the upper surface intact.

EXPLANATION.—The position of the prism and the angle of the cutting plane is shown in Fig. 34. This figure is to be drawn, as at (*a*) in the left-hand portion of the space, to the size required by the dimension figures. The plan is then copied to the right, as at (*b*), but in a relatively different position, as will be seen by the arrangement of the letters and the direction of the line *C D*. Thus, the edge *a*, which in the plan of (*a*) is on the extreme left of the figure, occupies a position nearer the lower part of the drawing in the plan at (*b*). This shifting of position of the plan may be effected by describing circles circumscribing the octagons and drawing the diameter *C D* at an angle of 30° to **V P,** as shown in the plan at (*a*). This diameter is then drawn in a vertical position in the second plan (*b*), after which the arc *D a*, as measured on the first, may be set off with the dividers on the second, plan. The projections of the front and side elevations are then made in the regular way. The projection of the full view is accomplished by drawing projectors at right angles to the cutting plane *A B*. At a convenient distance, as shown at (*c*), draw the center line *a″ j‴*, and from this line set off with the dividers the distances from the line *a e* as found in the first plan. As similar positions have corresponding letters in the different views on the plate, the student will have no difficulty in recognizing the method of transfer, it being the same as that mentioned in Art. **53.** Observe that the sides of the section *b′ c′* and

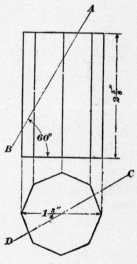

FIG. 34

g′ o′, and *b″ c″* and *g″ o″*, are parallel in every view shown, since the sides *b c* and *g o* (*f*) are parallel, as shown in the plan of the solid. The same is true of *h g* and *c o* (*d*), as seen at *h″ g″* and *c″ o″* in (*c*) (see Art. 78).

The student will finish the drawing on the plate in as complete a manner as in the drawing of the cube in Fig. 30, but omitting all reference letters. The surface of all sections in each view is to be cross-hatched, as in Figs. 30–33.

<hr/>

PROBLEM 17

82. To project sectional views of a hexagonal pyramid.

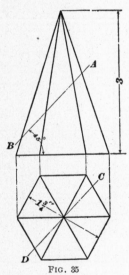

FIG. 35

The dimensions and position of the pyramid and the angle of the cutting plane are indicated in Fig. 35. Any section of a pyramid taken at right angles to the axis of the solid is a polygon having an outline similar to the base of the pyramid. The polygon representing the section of any pyramid thus intersected varies in size as the cutting plane passes through the pyramid at a point on the axis nearer the base or the vertex of the pyramid. If the cutting plane passes through the vertex and the base, or through two sides and the base of the pyramid, the section is a triangle. Any other section is a polygon having sides unequal in length, but equal in number to the sides of the polygon forming the base of the pyramid.

EXPLANATION.—The projections of this solid and its sections do not differ materially from those of the preceding problem. The change of position in the two plans is accomplished by means of the circumscribing circle, the diameter in the first plan being drawn at an angle of 45° and the arc *C a* being measured in a similar manner. This drawing may be more accurately made if the edges of the pyramid are continued by dotted lines to the vertex *O* in the front elevations, as shown on the plate. A comparison of the reference letters in the different views on the plate will assist the student in the work of drawing these projections, as each line shown is similarly lettered in all views.

PROBLEM 18

83. To project sectional views of a cylinder.

The cylinder possesses some points of similarity to the regular prism with respect to its section, viz., a section parallel to its ends has the same outline as the ends, while a section parallel to its axis is a parallelogram. An oblique section of the cylinder is, however, as will be observed during the projection of this problem, an ellipse; and it will further be noted that a certain view of an ellipse is a circle.

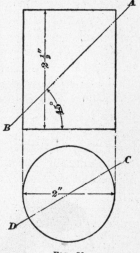

FIG. 36

EXPLANATION.—The position of the cylinder and the angle of the cutting plane is shown in Fig. 36. Make the edge *a–a'* of the elevation at (*a*) $\frac{5}{16}$ inch long. The plan of the cylinder is first divided into an equal number of spaces (in this case 12), the points being lettered *a*, *b*, *c*, etc., as shown on the plate. These points are then assumed to represent edges, as in the case of the octagonal prism, and are projected to the elevation, their respective positions there being indicated by similar letters; thus, the edge *a–a'* in the elevation represents the edge *a* as shown on the plan. The change of position in the second plan is effected by drawing the vertical diameter *l f*, which is shown as *C D* in the first plan at an angle

of 30° to **V P**.   The position of all points is then noted in a
manner similar to the two preceding problems and the projections are completed as heretofore.   After tracing the
curve of the ellipses through the points located in the different views, the sections are indicated by cross-section lines,
as before directed.

PROBLEM 19

**84. To project views of an irregularly formed
solid; also, to project a sectional view from a given
cutting plane.**

EXPLANATION.—This solid, shown in perspective in Fig. 37,
may be described as a transition piece, that, is, a form used
to connect openings or outlines unlike in shape.   Such
solids are frequently used in the sheet-metal trades,
particularly in boiler and pipework.   The dimensions of
this solid are better shown in the projection at Fig. 38.
Its upper base is a circle $1\frac{1}{2}$ inches in diameter, while the
lower base is an oval, which
may be drawn by the method
shown in *Geometrical Drawing*. The end circle of the
lower base is described with
a radius of 1 inch from a center located at *B*, Fig. 38, the

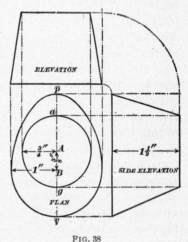

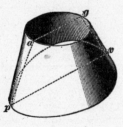

FIG. 37   FIG. 38

distance between the centers of the upper and lower bases,
as measured on the plan between *A* and *B*, Fig. 38, being
$\frac{3}{8}$ inch.   The vertical height of the solid is $1\frac{1}{2}$ inches.

The plan and front and side elevations are drawn as shown on the plate, and since the methods of projection are no different from preceding problems representing regular solids, definite instructions for this work are omitted. Particular attention is directed to the method of finding the outline of the section, as its application to various processes of patterncutting is of great importance. The direction of the cutting plane is shown in the side elevation at (*a*) by the line *A B* on the plate. The plan and elevation is to be redrawn on the plate in the position shown thereon at (*b*), and the full view of the section is projected towards the upper part of the drawing. As it is desired to show a section through a certain portion of this solid, it is first necessary to locate a number of points on the line that represents the cutting plane. Since the solid presents no edges that intersect this plane, a number of lines are to be assumed as drawn on the curved surface of the solid.

CONSTRUCTION.—First draw a horizontal line through the central portion of the plan, as *m n* in the drawing on the plate; this divides the figure into symmetrical halves. Next, by spacing, divide the outline of each base into the same number of equal parts, as at *a*, *b*, *c*, etc. on the upper base and *p*, *q*, *r*, etc. on the lower base. Project the points thus located to the elevation and draw connecting lines in both views, as shown. Across the elevation draw the line *C D*, representing the cutting plane, and project the intersections of this line at *1*, *2*, *3*, etc. to the plan, producing each line thus drawn until it meets the horizontal line *m n*. The full view of the sectional surface may now be drawn as follows: Draw projectors vertically upwards from the points *1*, *2*, *3*, etc. in the elevation, and at a convenient height from that view draw the horizontal line *m' n'*. The width of the surface, as measured on each line, may now be set off with the dividers, as directed in Art. **53**; thus, take the space *x y* from the plan and transfer it to corresponding positions at *x' y' x'* on the same line in the full view. Transfer, in like manner, the length of each vertical dotted line shown in the plan to the full view and trace an irregular curve through the points thus located, completing the projection. This curve may also be traced through the plan and there indicated by short cross-hatching, while the full view of the sectional surface is designated, as heretofore, by cross-section lines in the manner shown on the plate.

85. Practical Method of Representing Certain Sections.—In working drawings, particularly those made for

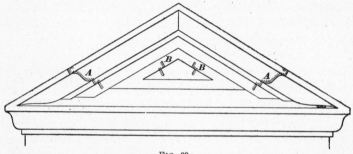

FIG. 39

the execution of sheet-metal work, a section drawing is often made directly over another view, and the lines indicating the section are distinguished by short cross-hatching, as shown on the plate in the plan of the preceding problem. Short portions of sectional views are also frequently shown in this way on working drawings, in order to indicate the

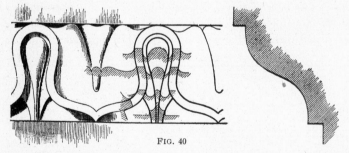

FIG. 40

form, or profile, of moldings, the different planes of adjacent surfaces, or the different levels at which certain notations

are made.   Thus, in Fig. 39, which shows a gable finish,
the section at *A* is the profile, or "stay," of the molding,
while the section at *B* indicates that the panel shown is a
sunk panel.

In detail drawings (mere projections drawn full size) for
decorative sheet-metal work, sections are frequently shown
at different portions of the drawing, as in Fig. 40, an
inspection of which will enable the student fully to comprehend the character of the various parts without the aid of
another view.   Sections, therefore, properly understood and
used, may be employed by the draftsman in many ways,
and are frequently a means of shortening the
labor of drawing intricate projections.

The lines representing the sides of the
octagonal shaft in Fig. 41 are broken in the
lower part of the figure, this being a means
of indicating that the full length is not shown
in the drawing.   Reference to the dimension
figures gives the reason, it being obviously
unnecessary to make a drawing extending
the full length of a simple form.

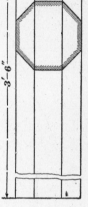

FIG. 41

DRAWING PLATE, TITLE:
SECTIONS II

86.   Conic Sections.—The divisions on
this plate are the same as on the preceding
plate.   The two problems to be constructed
are those relating to sections of the cone.   Besides their
use in many calculations of the arts and higher sciences,
conic sections are of great value to the architectural and
mechanical draftsman, for the curves thus developed possess great beauty and symmetry, and when used in
moldings present pleasing architectural effects of light and
shade.

The full view of the section of a regular cone made by a
cutting plane parallel to its base is a *circle;* if the cutting
plane passes through the vertex and the base of the cone,
the section is a *triangle;* if the cutting plane is at an

oblique angle to the base, which angle is less than the angle made by the elements of the cone with the base, the section is an *ellipse;* if the cutting plane is parallel to any line drawn on the convex surface of the cone from the base to the vertex—that is, parallel to any element of the cone—the section is a *parabola;* if the cutting plane is at any angle (but not passing through the vertex of the cone) greater than the angle which the elements of the cone make with the base, the section is an *hyperbola.*

87. Elements of the Cone.—In the construction of Problem 19, where it was desired to project a section of a solid whose curved surface presented no edges, it was found necessary to assume lines on that surface in order to establish points of intersection with the cutting plane. This process must be followed with all solids whose surfaces are curved, and in the case of the cone the lines thus assumed have a further use, as will appear later. The manner in which these lines are located on the surface of the regular cone is of special importance and is as follows: The outline of the base in the plan is first divided by spacing it into a number of equal parts (16 in the plan of Fig. 42). The points thus located are then projected to a view in which the cone is represented as in the elevation of Fig. 42—that is, a right view—and lines are then drawn from these points to the vertex. They are also shown on the plan in the same relation, each line being represented as a radius of the circle at the base of the cone. These lines are called the *elements* of the cone.

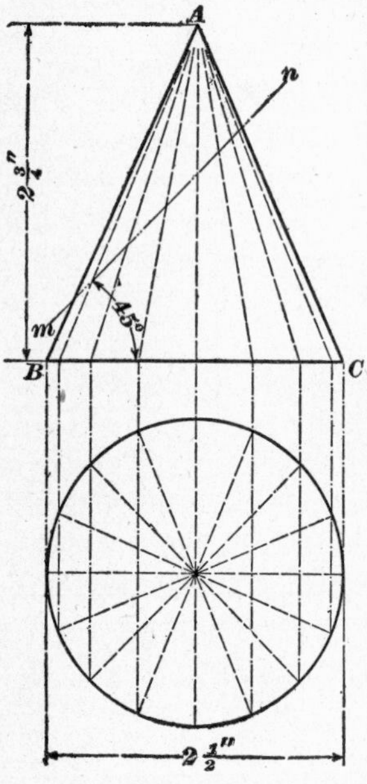

FIG. 42

In such a view of a cone as presented in the elevation of Fig. 42, only two of these elements (viz., *A B* and *A C*) can be shown in their true length—all the others are foreshortened. This must be borne in mind by the student, for it is evident that only on such lines as are shown in their true length can measurements be obtained for any points of intersection. Those points that are located on foreshortened elements are determined in a particular way, as will appear during the construction of the following problem.

The plan and front and side elevations and the full view of the section for each problem and case are to be drawn on this plate in the same corresponding relation as on the preceding plate.

PROBLEM 20

88. To project sectional views of a cone.

The three cases of this problem should be carefully studied by the student, for on the application of the principles here shown depend nearly all operations of pattern drafting that relate to so-called flaring work. A clear conception of the methods used will be found indispensable to the draftsman that desires to become proficient in his work. An effort should be made on the part of the student to trace each operation to its fundamental principle, when it will be discovered that the drawing practically resolves itself into a continuation of problems relating to the true lengths of foreshortened lines. Since such problems have occupied his attention during the drawing of the earlier plates, he should have no difficulty in following the constructions here given.

Case I.—*When the cutting plane is oblique to the base and intersects all the elements of the cone.*

The position of the cone, its dimensions, and the angle of the cutting plane are shown in Fig. 42.

CONSTRUCTION.—Draw a right plan and elevation and represent the cutting plane *m n* (see plate) by a line drawn at an angle of 45° with *B C*, cutting *A B* ½ inch from *B*. Divide the circle that represents the outline of the base of the cone into any convenient number of equal parts (in this case 16). Draw lines from these points (*b, 1, 2, 3*, etc.) to the center; next, project these lines—or *elements*, as they are called—to the elevation. Project the intersections of the elements in the elevation with the cutting plane *m n* to the corresponding elements in the plan and trace a curve through the points thus obtained.

Attention is called to the fact that, although the distances between the points found in this manner are unequal, yet

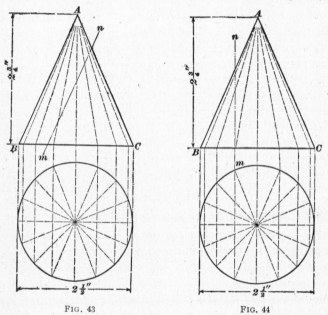

FIG. 43   FIG. 44

the foreshortened view of the sectional surface thus shown in the plan is a true ellipse, as is also the full view of the section next to be drawn. Project a side elevation to the right (see Art. **61**), also showing a foreshortened view of the section—an ellipse of a different curvature.

Case II.—*When the cutting plane is parallel to one of the elements, the section being in this case a* **parabola.**

EXPLANATION.—Fig. 43 is a right plan and elevation, giving the dimensions of the cone. The cutting plane *m n* is in this case parallel to the side *A B* of the cone and cuts *B C* ⅝ inch from *B*. The method of drawing these projections is precisely similar to that in the preceding case and since corresponding points are similarly designated in the different views shown on the plate, the student should experience no difficulty in completing the drawing.

Case III.—*When the cutting plane is perpendicular to the base of the cone, the section being an* **hyperbola.**

EXPLANATION.—To produce that section of the cone known as the hyperbola, the cutting plane may form with the base any angle included between a right angle and the angle formed by an element with the base (as the angle *A B C*, Fig. 44). The dimensions and position of the cone and the cutting plane are shown in Fig. 44, and since the method of projection is the same as in the two preceding cases, the student may complete the views without further instruction. In this case, the projection of a separate full view may be omitted, the latter being shown in the side elevation.

PROBLEM 21

89.   **To project sectional views of a scalene cone.**

EXPLANATION.—This solid, which is of varied form and of frequent occurrence in the metal trades, is an irregular geometrical figure. It is a cone whose axis is inclined to its circular base. All the elements of a regular cone are of equal length, but the elements of a scalene cone are necessarily of variable length, for, since its axis is inclined towards a portion of the base, the elements in that part of the surface must be shorter. It is to be noted in this case that the axis of the cone shown in Fig. 45 does not pass through the center of the circle that represents the base of the solid.

CONSTRUCTION.—To reproduce this drawing on the plate, draw first the horizontal line *b a* in the plan 3⅝ inches long, as called for by the dimension figures in Fig. 45; next,

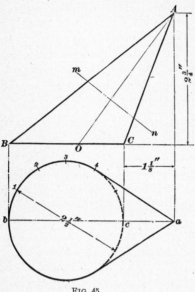

describe the circle $b3c$ 2½ inches in diameter from a center located on the line ba, its circumference passing through the point b. Project the elevation according to the dimensions given in Fig. 45. The axial line is next drawn; bisect the angle BAC and draw the bisector AO; represent the cutting plane mn by a line drawn perpendicular to AO and cutting AC ⅝ inch from C.

FIG. 45

The method of projection for the various views of this solid is the same as in former cases; that is, divide the outline of the base in the plan into a convenient number of spaces (12 in this problem), and from points thus located draw the elements to the apex a (see plate). Next, project these elements to the elevation and finally project their intersections with the cutting plane to the different views, as shown in the drawings on the plate. Note that the full view of the section, which in this problem is taken at right angles to the axis of the solid, is an ellipse. If the cone were in an upright position—that is, with its base at right angles to the axis (as that part of the cone above the cutting plane in Fig. 45)—the solid would be termed an "elliptical" cone. This, strictly, is not a geometrical solid, but its characteristics in projection drawing are somewhat similar to the regular cone, although the elements in each quarter of the base are always of unequal length.

The student should now be able to project any sections that may be desired.

DRAWING PLATE, TITLE: INTERSECTIONS I

90. The Miter Line.—To represent properly the intersections of the surfaces of solids—or to "draw the miter line," as it is commonly called—is the final process of projection. It has already been remarked that plane surfaces intersect in a line ; the representation of the intersection of plane surfaces is therefore a very simple process, the draftsman merely having to define each surface by the application of the regular projection methods already explained. The intersection of curved surfaces is apparently more complicated, but only because it is necessary to locate a greater number of points than are required for the intersection of plane surfaces. The location of points for the representation of the intersection of curved surfaces is done in a manner somewhat similar to that already shown in connection with the projection of plane surfaces having curved outlines. There is, however, this important difference to be observed: in the case of the surfaces mentioned, their projection is accomplished by means of *points* located on their outlines; while in the case of the intersection of curved surfaces, it is necessary to locate *lines* in such positions on each surface that they will lie in the same plane, although drawn on different surfaces. It is possible to locate a number of these lines in such positions on the drawing that through their points of intersection a curve may be traced that will be the correct line of intersection of the surfaces.

91. Relation of the Miter Line to the Pattern.—No drawing of an object in which intersected solids are represented is complete unless the line of intersection is accurately produced. This is a very important part of the drawing, and the correct "fit" of the pattern in work of this class often depends entirely on the accuracy with which the line of intersection is drawn. In fact, a development, or pattern, cannot be made until the drawing is complete in this particular. The principles governing the use of these lines are clearly shown in the explanation accompanying the problems, which the student should study carefully; for if he thoroughly comprehends the principles governing their use and exercises due care to see that lines are drawn from the same corresponding points in each view, he will have no difficulty in producing the correct lines of intersection for the surfaces of the solids represented on these plates, or, in fact, for the surfaces of any solid. The problems for this plate consist of the projection of intersecting solids having plane surfaces. The solids are shown in perspective in the illustrations accompanying each problem, and reference to the projections on the plate will be sufficient to show the method of finding the lines of intersection.

PROBLEM 22

92. To project views of intersecting prisms.

When the plane or curved surfaces of any solid so intersect as to present one continuous surface—that is, so that the surfaces meet "edge and edge" in the same plane—no line of intersection is necessary, since such surfaces are relatively in (and a part of) the same plane. When, however, the surfaces of one solid intersect a central portion of the surface, or surfaces, of another solid, it is necessary that the line of intersection—that is, the boundary lines of the surfaces of the intersecting solid—should be accurately drawn.

Case I.—*When the axes of the prisms intersect at an angle of 90°.*

EXPLANATION.—The solids for the projection of this problem are shown in perspective in Fig. 46, which represents

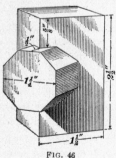

also their position in the intersection of Case I. The figure consists of an upright shaft in the form of a quadrangular prism with a horizontal octagonal prism intersecting, or "mitering," at right angles along the axial lines of the two solids. The projection and arrangement of the solids is seen in the drawings for this problem on the plate. It will be noticed that the octagons

FIG. 46

drawn in dotted lines in the figure do not form a part of the finished drawing, but are thus drawn to facilitate the projection, as the edges of the solids may thus be determined before the side view is drawn. It is often convenient to place portions of views temporarily on the drawing in this manner, as much labor is thereby saved. The plan is completed first and the remainder of the drawing finished in the usual way, as may be seen from the reduced copy of the plate. It is thus shown that the correct line of intersection is found by simple methods of projection, the position of the points in the line being determined by projection from the different views.

CONSTRUCTION.—Draw the plan $A B C D$ in its proper position, as shown on the plate, and next construct the elevation $A A' C' C$, thus completing the projection of the quadrangular prism as though that solid alone were to be represented. Draw a horizontal axial line (not shown on the plate) for the octagonal prism through both views, and at the left of the views thus drawn construct a full view of the end of the octagonal prism, as shown by the octagons in dotted lines on the plate. Next, draw the lines that represent the edges of the octagonal prism in both views. From the points of intersection of such lines in the plan with the edges $A B$ and $A D$ of the quadrangular prism, draw primary projectors to corresponding lines in the elevation. Draw connecting lines through the points of intersection thus determined in the elevation, as shown at $a' b' c' d'$ on the plate. This completes the projection of that view; the side elevation may then be projected by means of secondary projectors, as in former problems.

This plate is divided in the same manner as the preceding plate, and the projections for this case are drawn in the upper left-hand space.

Case II.—*When the axes intersect at an oblique angle.*

This projection is completed as shown on the plate. In this, as in the preceding case, the plan is first drawn; but

39—26

before it can be completed, a portion of the elevation has to be drawn in order to determine the outline of the octagonal surface in the plan (Problem 6).

CONSTRUCTION.—First draw the outline $A\,B\,C\,D$ in the plan and then construct the octagon shown in dotted lines at (a), from the points of which draw horizontal lines to the plan of the quadrangular prism, in the manner shown. Next draw the elevation of the quadrangular prism and locate the point x midway on the line $A\,A'$; the angle of inclination of the octagonal prism is in this case 45°, and a line at that angle is then to be drawn through x for the axial line of that solid. Construct the full view of the end of the octagonal prism at (b), and from the points e, f, g, etc. in that view draw lines of indefinite length towards the right; intersect these lines at a', b', c', and d' in the elevation by vertical primary projectors drawn from corresponding points in the plan, thus establishing the line of intersection in the elevation. The plan is then completed by drawing primary projectors vertically downwards from the edge view of the end of the octagonal solid in the elevation and tracing the outline of the inclined surface thus designated, as in Problem 6. The side elevation is next projected by the arc method of secondary projectors, as heretofore. Note that the intersection of the upper portion of the octagonal surface is to be represented in that view by dotted lines.

Case III.—*When the axes are at an oblique angle, but do not intersect.*

EXPLANATION.—The position of the solids is shown in the drawings on the plate, and the projections do not differ materially from those of the two preceding cases. The octagonal solid is in this case inclined at an angle of 30°, and its axial line $m\,n$, as shown in the plan, is drawn $\frac{5}{16}$ inch below the center of the quadrangular prism. The order of procedure is the same as that given for the drawing of Case II and will present no difficulties to the attentive student. It is necessary, however, to use extreme care in these projections, in order that the position of points in the different views may be located *in the same corresponding position with regard to one another.*

PROBLEM 23

93. **To project views of a prism intersected by a cylinder.**

EXPLANATION.—Fig. 47 is a perspective view of an octagonal prism intersected by a cylinder at an oblique angle, the axes of the solids not intersecting. The arrangement of the views, the dimensions, and the angle of inclination are shown on the plate. The projection of this problem is very similar to the last case of Problem 22. Note that the position of the two solids is such that the axis of the cylinder intersects the edge *D* of the prism. The circles that represent the end surface of the cylinder in each view are divided into a convenient number of equal spaces, and from the points thus located lines parallel to the axis of the cylinder are drawn on its surface. These lines are then projected in the same way as the lines that represented the edges of the octagonal prism in Problem 22. Since the surface of the cylinder is a curved surface, the line drawn through the points of intersection of the two solids will be a curved line.

FIG. 47

---

* Too much stress cannot be laid on this important statement; as the student progresses with the projection of the views, he will see the importance of this matter. The work must be done slowly, keeping the pencil points well sharpened; the position of the points in the drawing may then be accurately determined, if the views are constantly compared. If this is done, there will be no difficulty attached to any of the problems to follow in this section.

94. General Instruction Relating to Intersections.
When points are located on the full view of a surface
in a plan and elevation, as on the circles at (*a*) and (*b*) in
the drawings on the plate for the last problem, care must be
taken that the distinction between the different views is
maintained; thus, the point *x*, at (*a*) and in the plan, is
located at *x'* at (*b*) and in the elevation, both positions on
the drawing representing the same position on the solid.
Any other points thus located on an outline will be
changed in a corresponding way with relation to one
another. To project intersections of solids, all of whose
surfaces are bounded by parallel lines or on whose surfaces parallel lines may be drawn that will also be parallel
to the axis of the solid, it is necessary first to draw a
view that will show the intersect*ed* surface, or surfaces,
in one line—that is, "on edge." Such views have been
drawn in the plans of the preceding problems. The lines
of the intersect*ing* solid are then represented in this view,
and the points of their intersection with the upright
surfaces are projected to the elevation in the manner
described.

It will be seen that, if all the surfaces of any intersecting
solids are plane, their edges or outlines alone will suffice for
finding the lines of intersection. If the surfaces are curved,
it is merely necessary to locate a number of points on the
outline of the full view, through which to draw parallel lines
similar to those drawn on the cylinder in Problem 23. This
practically changes, or reduces, the cylinder to a solid
bounded by a number of plane surfaces. In the case of
Problem 23, the cylinder has really been treated as though
it were a prism having a number of sides equal to the number of spaces into which the circles were divided. This
would actually have been the case had straight lines been
drawn between the points thus located on the circles
at (*a*) and (*b*). Had this been done, the line of intersection would also have been represented by a series of short
lines drawn between the points located by projection
methods.

DRAWING PLATE, TITLE: INTERSECTIONS II

95. This plate is divided in the same manner as the preceding plate, and the problems occupy the same relative positions.

96. Intersections of Cylinders. — *The intersection lines of cylinders equal in diameter and intersecting one another in the same plane—that is, so that their axes also intersect—are always represented by straight lines in a view that shows the axes in their true length.* This is the case in the projections that are shown in Fig. 48, which represents

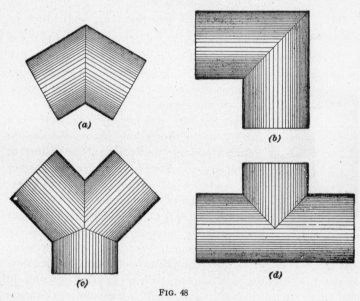

FIG. 48

objects that are familiar to all sheet-metal workers; namely, pipe angles (*a*), elbows (*b*), **Y**'s (*c*), and **T**'s (*d*). The same is also true of similar moldings "mitered" in a plane in which the true length of all members of such moldings may be shown. The line of intersection may always be found in such cases by bisecting the angle made by the pipe or moldings. Fig. 48 also illustrates an example of line shading often used by draftsmen to designate cylindrical surfaces on working drawings. When cylinders of different diameters intersect (or cylinders of the same diameter whose axes do not intersect), the lines of intersection in any view are curved lines, and are found in a manner similar to the projection in the last problem. The lines, however, that are drawn on any one cylinder must be projected to the intersecting cylinder, for it is at the intersection of lines thus drawn that points are established through which the curve of intersection may be traced. This is illustrated in Problem 24.

PROBLEM 24

97. To project views of intersecting cylinders of unequal diameters.

EXPLANATION.—Fig. 49 is a perspective view of a branch **Y** of occasional occurrence in blowpipe work. The arrange-

ment of the views and the method of projection are shown on the plate, and since it is similar to those of drawings that have been made on the preceding plate, no definite instructions are necessary. The diameter of the larger cylinder is 2 inches and that of the smaller 1 inch, while the angle of intersection shown in the elevation is 45°. The position of the two cylinders is such that the outline $r\,s$ of the smaller cylinder in the

FIG. 49   plan is tangent to the circle that represents the large cylinder. Note the position of points on the circle that represents the end surface of the smaller cylinder in the plan, at a, b, and c, and their corresponding location at a', b', c', etc. in the elevation (Art. **94**). Also observe that certain points on lines drawn on the surface of the smaller cylinder, as the lines $m\,n$, $p\,q$, and $r\,s$ in the plan, are projected to the front elevation, where they are represented as lines at $n'\,n''$, $q'\,q''$, and $s'\,s''$. These corresponding lines are in the same plane and are the lines drawn on the surface of the larger cylinder, as above mentioned. Through the points of their intersection with lines drawn from a' b', and c'

in the elevation, the curved line of intersection of the two cylinders is to be traced, thus completing the problem. Project the side elevation as heretofore.

---

98. To project views of a cone intersected by a cylinder, the axes of the two solids being parallel.

EXPLANATION.—Fig. 50 is a perspective view of a steam-exhaust head, a modification of which is in common use.

The drawing on the plate is a complete projection of the same, in which
the proportion of the cylinder C is increased, in order to show the method
of projection to better advantage.
Observe that the position of the object
is reversed, as the drawing is thereby
facilitated. The elevations on the
plate show that the lines of intersection of the two cylinders A and B with
the cone are represented by straight

FIG. 50

lines; this is always the case when a cylinder whose diameter is equal to a section of the cone intersects in this manner.

CONSTRUCTION.—First, construct the elevation of the cone in its proper place on the drawing and in accordance with the dimensions given on the plate. The cylinders A and B are then drawn as shown. Next, draw the plan and repre-sent the outline of the cylinder C in that view by a circle of the diameter indicated on the plate. Divide this out-line into a convenient number of equal spaces (in this case 8), as shown at a, b, c, etc., and through each of these points draw elements of the cone, as $O\,p$, $O\,q$, etc. Project these elements to the elevation and locate thereon by pro-jection methods the position of the points of intersec-tion a', h', g', etc. Complete the elevation by drawing the outline of the cylinder C in that view and tracing the line of intersection of the two solids through the points a', h', g' etc. Project the side elevation by the usual methods.

PROBLEM 26

99.   To project views of intersecting cones.

Fig. 51 is a perspective view of an object that illustrates

this problem. The cones are shown in a somewhat more convenient proportion for this problem in the projections on the plate. The construction of this problem must be followed very carefully, as a number of the operations are necessarily made over one another on the drawing and the student must be careful to distinguish each process.

CONSTRUCTION.—Describe a circle $2\frac{3}{4}$ inches in diameter in the plan to represent the lower base of the larger, or intersected, cone in that

FIG. 51

view; and from the same center describe a circle $\frac{7}{8}$ inch in diameter, to represent the upper base. Project the front elevation of this cone and define the frustum $2\frac{1}{4}$ inches high, as shown on the plate, producing the outlines until they meet in the vertex. Next, through the point F, Fig. 52, draw the axial line of the smaller, or intersecting, cone (the line $A B$, Fig. 52) at an angle of 45° with the base of the larger cone; locate the point A 3 inches from F, and, after fixing the point C 1 inch from F, draw $C D$ perpendicular to $A B$. Draw the outline of the upper base of the

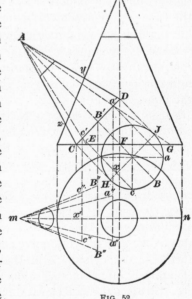

FIG. 52

smaller cone in the elevation parallel to C D and $\frac{3}{4}$ inch
from A. Draw the full view of the base of the smaller cone
at J B H; divide this outline into a convenient number of
equal parts, as at J, a, B, c, etc., and project these points
to the base C D.   Draw the elements of the smaller
cone, as shown in Fig. 52, and produce them until they
intersect the base of the large cone at E, F, and G.*
In the plan of this drawing, a series of sections of both cones
are now drawn as the sectional curves would appear if each
of the elements of the smaller cone shown in the elevation
were considered as a cutting plane, as in Problem 20.   The
sections of the smaller cone will in each case be a triangle
(Art. **86**), while the sections of the larger cone will be elliptical, parabolic, or hyper-
bolic curves, as the case may
be.   The point of intersection with the side of each
triangle and its corresponding sectional curve of the
larger cone is then projected
to the elevation and the line
of intersection of the two
cones traced through these
points.   The sectional triangles of the smaller cone
are shown in the plan of
Fig. 52.   Draw vertical
primary projectors to the
plan from points a', B',
and c', and on these projectors set off distances
from the horizontal center
line of the plan similar to

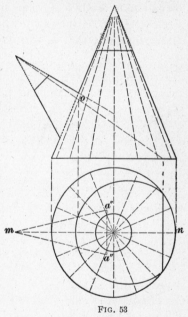

FIG. 53

the distances from H J in the full view of the base; that is,
make x' c'' equal x c, etc.

---

* In this case eight elements are represented, since it is not desirable
to complicate the drawing by using more, although in practical work
it will be found necessary to use a larger number of points in order
that the line of intersection may be more accurately traced.

It is not necessary to develop the sectional curves of the larger cone in their entire length, since all that is required is to find a point on each curve that is at the intersection of the triangular sections of the smaller cone. This is better illustrated in Fig. 53, in which is shown the projection of the point *o* in the line of intersection. A study of this figure will show to the student that the operations are similar to those of Problem 20; the process in the case of each point is merely a repetition of that here indicated and need not be further explained. The extreme upper and lower points *y* and *z*, Fig. 52, are the points of intersection of the central section and may be projected directly to the plan from the elevation, since the outline of the figure in the elevation is really a section on the line *m n* in the plan of Fig. 52. Fig. 54 shows the three sections produced by the above method; that is, the irregular curve *p q r*, Fig. 54,

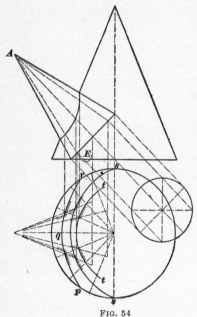

is a section of the larger cone produced by the intersection of the cutting plane *A E*; *s s* and *t t* are found as above described, the section lines being indicated in the figure by short cross-hatching. Project the side elevation as in former problems.

The student may at the completion of the drawing on the plate erase all the construction lines except those projectors shown on the reduced copy of the plate, those lines only being inked in that are necessary to show the outlines of

FIG. 54

the figure and the line of intersection in each view, as well as the outer projectors.

100. **To project views of a sphere intersected by a cylinder.**

When the position of these two solids is such that the axis of the cylinder passes through the center of the sphere, as shown in perspective in Fig. 55, the line of intersection is shown in a right elevation as a straight line. In the case of the solid shown in perspective in Fig. 56, the axis of the cylinder does not pass through the center of the sphere, and

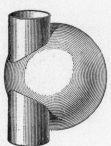

FIG. 55   FIG. 56

the line of intersection is an irregular curve, which may be found by the following method. Since the construction of this problem involves lines that must necessarily be drawn closely together in the small scale adopted for these drawings on the plate, a proportion is selected that does not admit of the entire figure being shown in the elevations; these projections are therefore finished by broken lines, as indicated on the plate.

CONSTRUCTION.—Draw the plan first and represent the view of the sphere by a circle 3½ inches in diameter. Draw a vertical diameter and from a point midway on the radius $a\,b$ describe a circle 1⅝ inches in diameter, to represent the end view of the cylinder, on the outline of which locate a number of points by spacing with the dividers, as at *1*, *2*, *3*, *4*, etc. Through these points, in the manner shown on the plate, draw vertical lines, as $a\,b$, $c\,d$, $e\,f$, $g\,h$, and $i\,j$, each of which will now represent a cutting plane. Sections of the sphere and cylinder on these lines are now to be produced in the side elevation.   These sections, as already stated, are circles and parallelograms, respectively, the diameter of the circles being ascertained from the view in which the cutting plane is shown on edge, as in the plan.   In this problem, the side elevation is next projected.   Describe arcs representing the sections in the side elevation, using the radii $a\,b$, $c\,d$, $e\,f$, $g\,h$, and $i\,j$, the radius $a\,b$ being the great circle of the sphere. By the aid of primary projectors, project the points from the cylinder in the plan to the side elevation, intersecting corresponding arcs in the side elevation.   Trace the irregular curve shown in that view on the plate through these points. Next project the front elevation, thus completing the problem.

101.   **Recapitulation.** — The problems of this plate have afforded the student an opportunity for careful study. Owing to the number of points necessary to be found in each figure, the problems may have had the appearance of more or less complication, but if the student, as previously cautioned, will carefully locate the points required, *one at a time*, not hurrying his work nor trying to grasp the entire problem at once, but keeping in mind the different principles in the order presented, and by referring, if necessary, again and again to the primary principles, he will experience no difficulty in making the drawings.   He will also be able intelligently to project any view of any object; in other words, he will be able to make any working drawing whatever, and, in addition to this, be able to read and understand any working drawing he may be called on to examine.

DEVELOPMENT OF SURFACES

INTRODUCTION

1. Definition of a Development.—A development is a drawing in which a full view of all the surfaces of a solid is represented. Whenever a development is to be drawn (except in the case of solids of very simple form), a projection drawing must first be made. This projection should show the solid in a *right* position. Since the location of the various points in a development is dependent on their corresponding position in the projection drawing, the importance of the projection and the necessity for accuracy in its construction are thus clearly seen. If a solid is bounded entirely by *plane* surfaces, its development can be accomplished by merely projecting their full views, as already explained in *Practical Projection.*

A solid is said to be developed when all surfaces composing it are represented on one plane and in such relation to one another that, if formed or bent up, they will constitute a solid similar to the one represented by the projection drawing from which the development was made. Such a representation is called a **development,** or a **pattern,** the process of laying out the pattern being termed *developing the surfaces of the solid.*

2. Relation of the Surfaces in a Pattern.—When it is desired to produce a pattern requiring a combination of several surfaces that are adjacent in a solid, such surfaces must be drawn in the same relation to one another in the

§ 17

development. The surfaces of a solid when thus combined in a pattern, or development, bear the same relation to one another that they would if they were considered as being *unfolded* or *unrolled*—the same relation that a paper wrapper would bear to the package from which it had been unfolded or unrolled. The paper wrapper is not always an apt illustration, as the metal worker seldom requires several thicknesses of his material. In the case of the familiar "square pan," however, the ends are folded on one another in precisely the same way as in the paper wrapper.

It will be seen from the foregoing that, were all solids bounded by flat, or plane, surfaces, the subject of developments would present no new problems; it would be necessary merely to study the relation of surfaces to one another, project their full views, and carefully redraw them in the pattern in the same relative position.

3. Projection Methods Used.—It has been shown in *Practical Projection* that a single surface is developed, or, as stated, its full view is drawn, by a modification of the same methods that are used to produce the different views of that surface. Many of the operations attendant on the development of solids are like those used in producing full views of single surfaces; or, if not, the principles involved may be traced to their origin in other methods used in projection drawing.

A thorough knowledge of projection is absolutely necessary that the student may understand the operations involved in developing the surfaces of a solid. The position of the several points located in a drawing and their corresponding location in an imaginary way on the object itself must be definitely fixed in the student's mind. Each line must be determined in its relation to the other lines of the drawing and its ideal, or imaginary, location definitely ascertained; the surfaces, also, must be treated in a similar way. The student must picture to himself the completed object as it will appear when the surfaces laid out on the drawing board in the development are formed up in their final relation to

one another. This imaginary part of the study is of even
greater importance in the case of developments than in projection drawing. As the student has already had some drill
in this part of the work, the subject he is now studying
should be found less difficult than would otherwise be the
case. In projection drawing, the surfaces of the solid are
represented as being in their proper position; in the development, the same surfaces are represented as being developed
or spread out on the surface of the drawing board.

GENERAL CLASSIFICATION

4. General Classification of Solids.—An accurate
development may be drawn for the plane surfaces of any
solid, or for surfaces having, when related to a given line on
such surface, a curvature in one direction only. In general,
it may be stated that any solid may be developed on whose
surfaces it is possible to lay a straightedge, in continuous
contact, in any one direction. To use in this connection
the illustration of the cylinder, it will be seen that, if the
straightedge is resting on the surface parallel to the axis of
the cylinder, it will remain in contact at all points. If, on
the other hand, the straightedge is resting on the curved
surface and is not parallel to the axis of the cylinder, the
surface will be in contact at a single point only. However,
the fact that it is possible to place the straightedge in continuous contact on the surface allows the inference that
such surface is capable of accurate development.

The same rule applies to solids of irregular form. The
methods of development, however, are not the same in certain variously formed solids, as will be explained later.
There are certain forms whose surfaces, owing to their
curvature in several directions, are not capable of being thus
laid out on a flat surface, i. e., not capable of being developed. On the surfaces of solids of this class—the sphere, for
example—it will be found impossible to lay the straightedge
in contact in any direction. For, if placed on such a surface,

there will be but one point of contact—that of the *tangential* point. Tangential contact indicates that development can be accomplished only in an approximate way. For purposes of development, then, it is convenient to separate all solids into two general classes according to the result obtained in developing their surfaces. These two classes are: solids whose surfaces admit of accurate development and solids whose surfaces admit only of approximate development. Approximate developments are, however, so nearly accurate for the purposes of the sheet-metal worker that the kind of solid is more clearly marked by the method of developing its surface than by the result obtained by the development. Therefore, in order to distinguish the kinds of solids, both accurately and approximately developed solids are divided into three main classes according to the method used in developing their surfaces. These classes are explained later.

5. Accurate Developments.—Solids whose surfaces are capable of accurate development are of frequent occurrence in the sheet-metal-working trades. To this class belong all prismatic, cylindrical, and conical forms, whether of regular or irregular geometrical form. It includes all articles or objects whose covering may be formed without being submitted to the operations known to trade workers as " raising," or " bumping." Any solid whose surfaces may be unrolled or spread out on a flat surface without " buckling " may be accurately developed. Although it is often necessary, especially when working metal of unusual thickness, to take into account the stretching of the material when producing patterns for many objects, these objects belong to accurately developed solids, providing that the metal does not have to be " raised," or " bumped," in order to form the object. It is, therefore, essential that the metal worker should thoroughly understand the nature of the material and be well informed as to the best manner in which to provide for all laps and edges used in the construction of the finished article.

It is the purpose of *Development of Surfaces* to define and illustrate *theoretical developments* and the means used by the draftsman in their production.

6. Approximate Developments. — The sphere and other solids whose surfaces have a curvature in two or more directions are examples of objects capable of only approximate development. The test by the straightedge is (with the exception of the helicoidal surface) a positive indication of the class to which any solid may be assigned. Patterns for the surfaces of objects of this class may be *approximated*, because it is necessary for the metal to undergo the operations of "raising," or "bumping," before it will conform to the exact surface represented in the drawing. It is necessary in these cases to make allowance in the pattern for the stretching of the metal. Since this part of the subject does not belong to theoretical development, it is not treated here.

SOLIDS THAT MAY BE ACCURATELY DEVELOPED

7. There are three distinct methods in common use, by means of which patterns are produced for solids whose surfaces are capable of accurate development. It is advisable, therefore, to separate the different varieties of these forms into three general divisions, in order that their development may be studied in a systematic manner. This classification may be made by studying the manner in which the covering of these solids—to use again the illustration of a wrapper—would be unrolled or spread out if done by rolling the solid on a flat surface.

8. Solids Developed on Parallel Lines.—A convenient illustration of the manner in which the surfaces of a solid will appear when unrolled as above indicated may be found in the following example, which serves at the same time to define a property peculiar to solids of a certain form. Let the continuously adjacent surfaces of the prism

39—27

shown in Fig. 1 (*a*) be carefully covered with thin paper, as at Fig. 1 (*b*). Denote each of the four surfaces by a letter, as *A*, *B*, *C*, and *D*, and further designate the edges of the prism by the letters *a b*, *c d*, *e f*, and *g h*. As the ends of the paper covering meet at the edge *a b*, that edge of the surface *D* may be denoted by the letters *a' b'*, as shown in

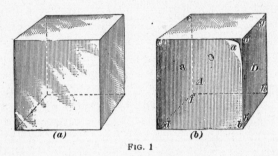

FIG. 1

Fig. 1 (*b*). Assume now that the prism is laid on the drawing board, the surface *A* face down, and the paper covering removed by turning the prism over and over, the paper remaining on the surface of the drawing board, as shown in Fig. 2 (*a*) and (*b*).

Two important principles relating to developments are demonstrated in these illustrations. *First*, as will be seen

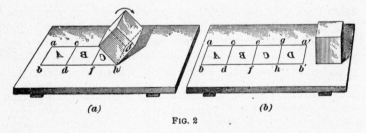

FIG. 2

from Fig. 2 (*b*), the edges *a b*, *c d*, *e f*, *g h*, and *a' b'* are all parallel to one another. This is true both in the development and on the solid, as may be readily seen by the student, the only difference being that on the solid certain of the lines are in different planes, while in the development they are all in the same plane. *Second*, it will be noted that, since the letters shown in Fig 2 are reversed, the *outer* surface of the paper covering in Fig. 1 (*b*) corresponds to the *under* surface in Fig. 2 (*b*). In a similar manner, it is learned from the second principle that positions indicated on any surface of a solid, as shown in a projection drawing, are reversed when shown in the development of the solid.

The same treatment of the cylinder is found to produce results closely resembling those shown in the case of the prism. The cylinder is represented in Fig. 3 (*a*) as covered

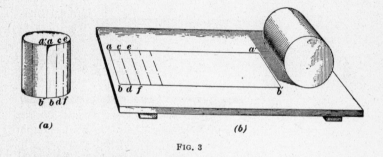

(a)   (b)

FIG. 3

with paper, a number of lines being ruled on the covering parallel to its axis, as shown at *c d*, *e f*, etc. The paper is shown unrolled in Fig. 3 (*b*), and it will be observed that not only the outer edges *a b* and *a' b'* are parallel to each other, but that all other lines parallel to the axis of the solid appear in the development parallel to one another and to the edge lines *a b* and *a' b'*. The student that has ever flattened out a piece of straight molding, as for cornice work, probably noticed a number of straight parallel lines on the metal where it had been bent in the brake. This is an illustration similar to that of the cylinder, the different members of the molding being considered as the various surfaces of an irregular solid.

Such illustrations indicate that parallel lines bear some relation to certain forms, and it will be shown that the patterns for these forms are developed by a method whose principles are based on this fact. Many solids may be at once recognized as belonging to this division. In general,

any solid whose edges are parallel may be located here.   In
the case of solids having curved surfaces, it may be stated
that, if it is possible to draw a series of parallel lines on
such surfaces, the development of the solid may be produced by the same methods given for this class.   The first
general division, therefore, comprises those solids whose
surfaces may be developed on *parallel lines.*

9.   Solids Developed on Radial Lines. — When the
test given to the cube and the cylinder in Figs. 1 to 3 is

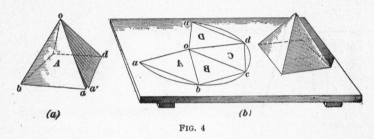

FIG. 4

applied to the pyramid, it is found that the lines indicated
on the paper converge to a point, as shown in Fig. 4 (*a*)
and (*b*).   It is noticed, also, that this point *o*, Fig. 4, defines
the position of the vertex of the pyramid.   The same may be
said of the cone, illustrated in Fig. 5 (*a*) and (*b*).   If lines

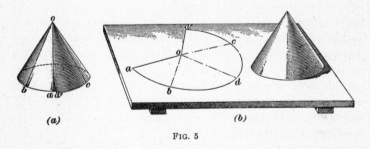

FIG. 5

are first indicated on the surface of the cone corresponding
to its elements, it will be found, when the covering is
unrolled, that these lines also converge to a point, as in the
case of the edges of the pyramid.

It was found possible to institute a system of obtaining developments based on parallel lines in the case of the prism and cylinder; in a similar manner, it is quite evident in this case that a system dealing with radial lines should produce like results. Since, in projection drawing, the elements of the cone are known to be useful factors in determining the position of points on its surface, it may readily be conceived that their use in a somewhat similar way may be adapted to developments. This is found to be the case; and a second general division of solids is thus made, consisting of those forms whose surfaces may be developed on *radial lines*. Included in this division are all regular tapering solids and such irregular forms as are derived from regular solids. The metal trades furnish many examples of solids belonging to this division; in fact, the writers of several works on patterncutting confine their instruction almost entirely to the development of solids of this character.

10. Solids Developed by Triangulation.—There are many forms of irregular surfaces to which the test of the straightedge may be applied and the conclusion thereby reached that their surfaces admit of accurate development. It may also be concluded that neither of the two former methods is applicable, for neither parallel lines nor a series of radial lines may be drawn on their surfaces. Many of these solids are not of such a shape as to admit of their being either turned or rolled on a plane surface. It is found, however, that on every such surface, series of two or more lines each may be drawn in certain directions, forming angles.

On such irregular surfaces it may happen that no two of the angles thus drawn on the solid, or represented—either correctly or foreshortened—in the projection drawing, will lie in the same plane or be equal to each other. Since it is possible thus to project these angles, evidently they may be reproduced on the flat surface of the drawing paper in their correct size. If this can be done, it may be reasonably assumed that the surfaces thus represented will be the same as the corresponding surfaces of the solid. An illustration of this principle, as pertaining to a plane surface, was given under another heading in *Practical Projection*.

In Fig. 6 an irregular solid of this kind is shown. It is the solid whose projection was drawn in Problem 19 of

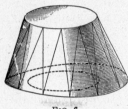

FIG. 6

Practical Projection. This figure illustrates in a general way the method used in arranging the triangles on the irregular surface of such solids. The triangles are represented in the figure in a perspective way, but they are, of course, always drawn in connection with the usual methods

of projection. The third general division, therefore, consists of those solids whose surfaces are developed by *triangulation*—that is, by means of triangles.

11. How the Division of Solids Is Accomplished. It is not to be understood that the draftsman actually applies the test of the straightedge in reaching a conclusion as to whether the surfaces of a solid may be accurately or approximately developed. Nor does he roll the object on the drawing board in order to determine whether the method by parallel lines or one of the other methods is to be used. As a matter of fact, he seldom has a model to work from, and, therefore, could not apply such a test if he so desired. But as he studies the drawings and imagines the position of the surfaces as they will appear in the completed object, he is enabled to apply the tests as effectually, in an imaginary way, as though the tests were made with a straightedge. In the same imaginary way, also, he assigns the solid to the general division to which it properly belongs, and thus decides as to the method he will use in the development of its surfaces.

A little practice will enable the student to classify the variously formed objects in this way and to select the method that shall be applied in any given case. A very important part of the patterncutter's acquirements consists in being able to recognize in various irregular objects those forms that may be only a portion of some regular solid. In other words, the student must learn to establish in his own mind the connection between complete and perfectly formed solids and those objects in which only a portion of the solid may be represented. The method of development is, of course, the same in both cases, but as a matter of fact,

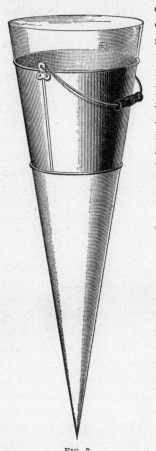

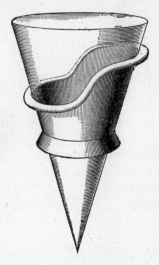

FIG. 7   FIG. 8

the operations are usually more complicated in cases where the incomplete solid demands the patterncutter's attention. Especially is this true of conical forms, or those developed on radial lines. Frequent illustrations of this principle may be found in commonly occurring objects. The flaring pail shown in Fig. 7 is seen to be a part (or frustum) of a cone, the completed cone being indicated by the light shading in the illustration.

The same is true of the sitz bathtub in Fig. 8. Here it is seen that the portion of the cone represented by the finished article is an irregular section of the cone; its development is, however, accomplished by the same methods to be shown for regular cones. Another instance is found in the measure shown in Fig. 9. Here are two intersecting cones: a regular frustum of one forms the body of the measure; and an irregular frustum of the other—an inverted cone—forms the lip of the finished article.

All the articles in Figs. 7 to 9 are thus shown to be frustums of regular cones, although varying in the regularity of their bases. In certain cases, as in the "oval" pan body

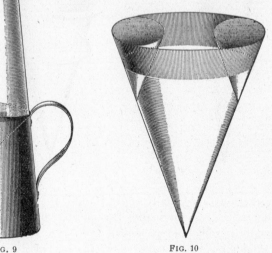

FIG. 9   FIG. 10

represented by the heavily shaded band in Fig. 10, the surfaces may be portions of the surfaces of different cones or of cones differing in size. The bases of this article are elliptical in outline. The ellipses are drawn by circular arcs. The vertexes of the different cones would be represented in a plan view by the centers from which the different arcs are struck. These cones are partially shown in Fig. 10, and in the relation required by the portions of their surfaces that compose the sides of the pan.

It is essential, therefore, that the student should possess a certain familiarity with the forms of the regular solids, to assist him in the classification of the objects that he will be called on to develop. It is with this end in view that a series of plates is to be drawn by the student. The instruction is in the form of problems, and several of the drawings of *Practical Projection* are reproduced for the purpose of showing the development of the surfaces of the solids there represented. The student's attention will first be directed to a consideration of those solids whose development may be accomplished by means of parallel lines.

DEVELOPMENT BY PARALLEL LINES

12. Importance of Certain Views.—It has already been stated that the making of a working drawing is the draftsman's first step towards obtaining a pattern for the surfaces of any solid. The solid in question should be shown in this drawing in such a position that measurements may be taken of its surfaces in all their dimensions. In order to accomplish this, several views may have to be drawn, although a right plan and elevation will usually be sufficient. In some cases there may be given to the mechanic a drawing in which the object is so shown that these dimensions may not be readily obtained. In such cases, operations in projection are required; with these the student is already familiar.

For purposes of development it is important that the view shown should be that one in which the lines of the solid are given in their true length, or, in other words, a *right view* of the solid. In addition to this view there must be given that view also in which the surfaces thus partially bounded by these parallel lines are shown as *on edge*. In some instances, as in the case of a simple solid of which all the dimensions are known, the latter view may be omitted; it is, however, understood as being drawn, for the draftsman knows all its dimensions. Generally, therefore, before the pattern can be produced, a plan and an elevation showing the solid in a *right position* must be drawn.

In drawing the projections in *Practical Projection*, the right views have first been drawn and inclined views have then been projected from them. This has been done in order to familiarize the student with the appearance of such drawings; but in every case the development of the pattern is to be projected from a right view. It is possible for the draftsman to become so expert by practice that in certain cases he is enabled to obtain, from foreshortened views, patterns for some surfaces. The beginner should not attempt this, however, since the operations involved are confusing, and should be resorted to only by the experienced pattern-cutter that thoroughly understands the subject.

13. The Stretchout. — As stated in the preceding article, it is essential that in all cases where the development of solids may be accomplished on parallel lines, the view showing certain surfaces as on edge should either be given or assumed. From such a view, the width of each surface may readily be ascertained. The total width of all these surfaces—the distance around the solid—is called the **girth** of the solid. In case the solid has a curved surface, its girth is found by spacing with the dividers the outline in that view. The girth of the cylinder, for example, is equal to the length of the circumference of a circle that represents the base of the cylinder.

When a distance corresponding to the girth of any solid is represented by a straight line on a flat surface, such a line is called a **stretchout** for the development, or pattern. This line is then marked off by a series of points, the points representing the places at which the line would be bent if formed up to correspond with the outline of the solid represented in the view from which the distances were taken. In the case of curved surfaces, a number of points are located on the outline, as previously indicated. This is usually done by dividing the outline into a number of equal spaces in the same manner as in projection drawing; an equal number of spaces is then stepped off on the stretchout line, whose total length is in all cases equal to the girth of the solid. An important point to be observed is that the points thus located on the stretchout must be (although reversed) in a position on the line corresponding to that relatively occupied on the solid.

14. Position of the Development.—The position in which the stretchout is placed on the drawing determines the position of the development. This line is always drawn *at right angles to the parallel lines of the solid* and from a view in which these parallel lines are shown *in their true length.*

In making a projection, then, from which to produce the patterns of any object, it is important that a sufficient space be left on the drawing, to one side or the other of that view. It frequently happens that this cannot be done, and in such cases it is a common practice to lay an extra piece of paper over a portion of the drawing, on which the development may be produced. When the latter method is adopted, the paper on which the development is made may be used in transferring the outline of the pattern to the metal, and the original drawing may then be preserved in perfect condition.

15. Development of the Cube.—For the purpose of explaining to better advantage the use of the stretchout, the development of the cube is presented, step by step, in Figs. 11 to 14, inclusive. A reproduction of this development should be made by the student in accordance with the following instructions, although the drawing is not to be sent to the Schools for correction.

The plan and the elevation shown in the left-hand portion of the figures are drawn first. The development could be produced from either view in this case, since in any right view the dimensions of a cube are equal. For the purpose of the illustration, the development is drawn from the elevation. At right angles to the parallel lines in the elevation draw a line as MN, Fig. 11. On this line locate a point at any convenient distance, as at w. This point may correspond to any of the upright lines or edges of the solid

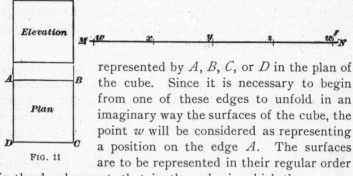

FIG. 11

represented by A, B, C, or D in the plan of the cube. Since it is necessary to begin from one of these edges to unfold in an imaginary way the surfaces of the cube, the point w will be considered as representing a position on the edge A. The surfaces are to be represented in their regular order in the development, that is, the order in which they appear on the solid itself; first, the surface represented in the plan by AB, then BC, CD, and DA, in their natural order as they are shown in the projection at the left of the line MN. The dividers may, therefore, be set at a distance equal to the length of the side AB, and since the sides of the cube are equal in length, the distances wx, xy, yz, and zw'—corresponding, respectively, to the sides represented in the plan by AB, BC, CD, and DA—are to be spaced off on the line MN.

16. Laying Off the Stretchout. — That portion of the line MN included between the points w and w' is called the *stretchout* of the cube. A stretchout may be drawn in any position on the drawing board, at the convenience of the draftsman, but it is invariably at *right angles to the parallel lines of the solid*.

Wherever the stretchout occurs in the drawings of this section, it is represented by a heavy line, as shown in Fig. 11. It is customary to draw a line of indefinite length quite near the view of the solid that is being developed, as in Fig. 11. When the stretchout is mentioned, the only part of the line referred to is that included between the extreme points w and w', Fig. 11, located to define the total width of the adjacent surfaces. This operation is called *laying off*, or *developing*, the stretchout. It will be seen that if a string equal in length to $w\,w'$ should be stretched around the cube in a horizontal direction, it would exactly reach the entire distance, and the ends would meet, in Fig. 11, at the edge A.

The next step is to erect perpendiculars to the stretch-out $M\,N$ that shall pass through the points w, x, y, etc. and be produced on both sides of the line. This is done by means of the triangle, in connection with the T square, as in Fig. 12. The lines thus drawn are called *edge lines*,

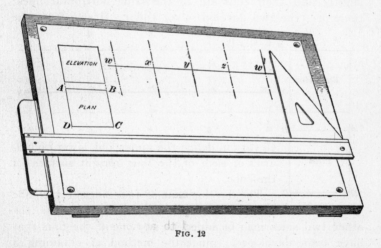

FIG. 12

since they represent, in the development, those portions of the surfaces that would form the edges of the solid if the pattern were to be cut out and formed up to the shape indicated by the projections. Edge lines are to be represented in these drawings by dash-and-dot lines, as shown in Fig. 12, similar to those used in *Practical Projection* for projectors.

Next, the length of each of the upright edges shown in the elevation is marked off on its corresponding edge line in the development.   This is readily done with the **T** square, and, since each of the four edges represented in the elevation is of the same length, the **T** square may be brought even with the horizontal lines in that view, and a line drawn from each across the development, as shown in Fig. 13. The lines thus drawn are called *developers*, and will be represented in these drawings by broken lines, as shown in Fig. 13. This name is applied to them for the reason that the length of the edge lines is determined—developed—when a developer is drawn from each extremity of the edge shown in the elevation to its corresponding edge line in the development.   In this case, the four upright edges of the cube, represented by the two vertical lines in the elevation, are of the same length, and their ends are in the same horizontal lines; therefore, the two developers pq and rs, drawn from the

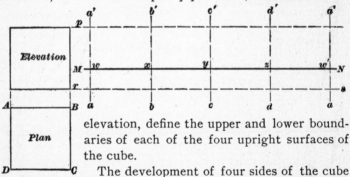

FIG. 13

elevation, define the upper and lower boundaries of each of the four upright surfaces of the cube.

The development of four sides of the cube is thus accomplished; and if desirable, the other two sides may be added to any one of the four that have been developed.   Since the method of obtaining a development, as it is now called, or a full view of any side or surface of a solid is already familiar to the student, no further explanation will be given.   In sheet-metal work it is generally preferable to make the ends (of forms similar to the cube) of separate pieces of metal, and, on account of the waste of stock, it will seldom be found desirable to combine all the surfaces of a solid in a single piece.   Should

such a case arise, however, the full view would be projected and afterwards copied into its proper place on the
development.

The development of any solid of this class, whose bases
are parallel and at right angles to its parallel lines, is always
a parallelogram; and, as in the development of the cube in
Fig. 13, this is divided into smaller parallelograms, each
representing a surface of the solid.

17. Finishing the Drawing.—In order to enable the
draftsman to distinguish the features of a development at a

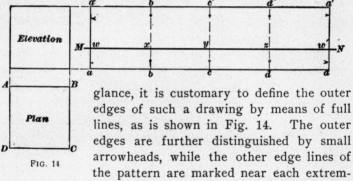

FIG. 14

glance, it is customary to define the outer
edges of such a drawing by means of full
lines, as is shown in Fig. 14.   The outer
edges are further distinguished by small
arrowheads, while the other edge lines of
the pattern are marked near each extrem-
ity by a small circle drawn by freehand methods, in the
manner shown, thus indicating to the mechanic that the
sheet is to be bent along this line.   It is sometimes desirable. as in detail developments for certain classes of sheet-
metal work, to designate the stretchout by a line drawn
with a blue pencil, thus readily attracting the draftsman's
attention.

The mechanic seldom resorts to the drawing board in
order to produce a development of a simple solid such as
the cube, since the same result may be accomplished with
the steel square, the sizes being marked out directly on the
metal.   The development of the cube, however, has been
shown in these illustrations, inasmuch as by the same principles any solid of this class may be developed.   It may also
be stated that the draftsman rarely represents developers

or edge lines by the particular lines used for that purpose
in this section. These distinguishing lines have been
adopted here solely for the purpose of fixing clearly in the
student's mind the principles on which these drawings are
made. After these principles have been mastered, the use
of such lines in practical work may be discontinued, and
the student may then, by the use of light pencil lines only,
proceed with the development of such other solids as he
may be called on from time to time to lay out. These
drawings, when inked in, should be completed in the manner shown in the illustrations.

18. Development of Intersected Solids.—In cases
where the parallel lines of a solid are interrupted by the

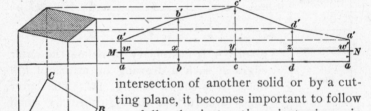

FIG. 15

intersection of another solid or by a cutting plane, it becomes important to follow
carefully the instructions just given; in
such cases it is of extreme importance
that an exact development should be
made on the drawing board. For examples of the development of such inter-
sected solids, we will refer to the figures illustrating the
cutting planes in their effect on the cube, which figures
have become familiar to the student from their use in *Practical Projection.* Fig. 15 is a reproduction of one of these
projections, showing the development of the parallel surfaces. Here it will be seen that the development can be
produced only from the elevation, since the cutting plane
has altered the solid in such a manner as to admit of parallel lines being drawn in but one direction.

The stretchout is drawn as before and the width of the
surfaces spaced off in the usual manner. It will be further
noticed that, since the edges of the cube are unequal in

length, it becomes more important to observe the order of the surfaces as they are being unrolled from the solid. After the edge lines are drawn in the development, the developers are drawn in the same manner as in Fig. 13, but with this difference: the lower ends of the edge lines are defined by a single developer as before, but it becomes necessary to draw a developer from the upper end of each edge in the elevation to its corresponding edge line in the development. If this is done carefully, it will be seen, from a comparison of the surfaces in the development with those on the solid in the elevation, that they are in the same relative position with reference to one another, although reversed. This is clearly indicated in Fig. 15 by the use of similar capitals and small letters for the corresponding edges and edge lines, respectively, in the projection and development. Thus, the edge line $a\,a'$ represents the edge A; $b\,b'$ represents the edge B, etc. It will be noticed, also, that those parts of a development that come together and form edges or seams are indicated by the same letters. A similar principle of lettering these drawings will be continued throughout *Development of Surfaces*, since, when once understood by the student, he can study the drawings intelligently and with less reference to the descriptive text.

In this drawing of the cube, another fact is presented that demands care on the part of the draftsman; that is, the outer edge lines in the development must be of the same length. It may seem unnecessary to call attention to a fact so obvious, since it is very clear that, as the outer edge lines represent the same edge of the solid, they *must*, therefore, be of the same length in the development. It is, however, a cause of frequent error, and is due simply to carelessness in drawing the developer to the wrong edge line. Great care must be exercised in this respect, since the accuracy of a development depends in no small degree on this feature.

A development similar to the one given in Fig. 15 is shown in Fig. 16. This development is made from the front elevation of the figure in *Practical Projection* that shows how

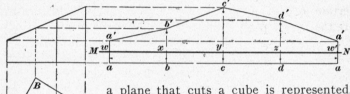

a plane that cuts a cube is represented. Fig. 15 shows a development made from the side elevation of the same figure. An excellent illustration is here furnished of the importance of all edges of a solid being defined in that view from which a development is made. The drawing in

FIG. 16

Fig. 15 represents the cube in such a position that the lengths of all its parallel edges are shown, while in Fig. 16, the length of the edge B is seen only by the aid of the dotted line. In drawings of this class, therefore, all edges should be indicated, whether on the side nearest the observer or not. In such drawings, however, it is customary to represent these hidden edges by dotted lines, in order to avoid confusion.

It frequently happens that the cutting plane so intersects the surfaces of a solid as to produce angles at points other than at the vertical edges of the solid. An example of this is found in Fig. 17. The method of obtaining the development is, in the main, similar to that used in the preceding cases. From the plan of the cube in Fig. 17, however, it will be seen that points are indicated on the lines $B\,C$ and $C\,D$ denoting the corners, or points, at the extremities of the line $K\,L$. The distances $B\,K$ and $D\,L$ must, therefore, be indicated on the stretchout $M\,N$, as shown at $x\,k$ and $l\,z$, the points in each case being located from $b\,b'$ and $d\,d'$ towards $c\,c'$. This is because the points K and L approach C in the plan in their distances from B and D, respectively; according to the foregoing instruction, it is necessary to define them in a position in the development corresponding to that represented on the solid.

Parallel lines must be produced through the points k and l in the same manner as the edge lines were drawn. In a certain way, these lines serve a similar purpose, since they are the termination of certain developers; but as it is not

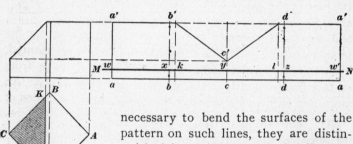

necessary to bend the surfaces of the pattern on such lines, they are distinguished from the regular edge lines by the term *interedge lines*. Interedge lines are as essential in determining the outline of a development as the edge lines themselves, and are to be distinguished on the drawings for this section by the dash-and-double-dot line. A comparison of the projections with the development in Fig. 17, made by looking for similar capitals and small letters in the figure, will enable the student to see clearly the manner in which the additional spaces are located on the stretchout, and also how this development is produced from the elevation.

FIG. 17

19. Importance of Accuracy.—The attention of the student has frequently been called to the necessity for accuracy in his drawings. If this is necessary in the case of projection drawing, it is doubly important in the case of developments. Too much stress cannot be laid on this very important feature of the patterncutter's training. Unless his drawings are accurate they are of no value; it is, therefore, of the utmost importance that the patterns for any piece of sheet-metal work should be carefully and accurately described. The draftsman may thoroughly understand all the principles involved in projection drawing and the development of surfaces; but if the work on the drawing board has been done in a careless manner, the pattern is as liable to be incorrect as though it had been "guessed at," or "cut and trimmed."

There are few solids whose development may be accomplished by the aid of the limited number of lines required in the case of the cube. The same principles, however, govern all solids of this class, and it is necessary merely to be careful and observe the form of the solid as it is shown in the projection drawing. The fact that the drawing contains many lines should not deter the student from recognizing each surface independently of the others, although it may require more care on his part to select the correct lines in each case.

20. The Imagination a Great Help.—The student's imagination will be found to be his best assistant in this work, and by the aid of the projections he should picture to himself a model of the object represented. Further, he will find it a valuable help in being able to imagine the surfaces as they would appear if a covering of the solid were unrolled and spread out on the drawing board for the development. In this way, the corresponding surfaces on the solid and in the development may be compared, and the student may be able to detect any errors that might otherwise escape him.

GENERAL RULES FOR OBTAINING PARALLEL DEVELOPMENTS

21. For the convenience of the student, and to aid him in the production of developments of solids by means of parallel lines, a general summary of the important features is here presented. This summary contains the substance of the foregoing instruction.

1. A projection must first be drawn, consisting of a plan and elevation, showing the solid in a right position.

2. The development is always obtained from that view in which the parallel lines are shown in their true lengths.

3. The stretchout is drawn at right angles to the parallel lines of the solid.

4.   To indicate the width and relative position of the surfaces, points are located on the stretchout corresponding to the place of those points in a view that represents the surfaces on edge.

5.   Edge lines and interedge lines are always drawn at right angles to the stretchout.

6.   Developers are drawn from each edge or interedge represented in the projection drawing to the corresponding edge line or interedge line in the development. The position of points located on these lines is determined in a similar manner.

7.   Interedge lines, when necessary for the development, must be indicated on the projection as well as on the development, and the same care exercised with the corresponding developers as with those drawn from edges to edge lines.

8.   The length of the outer edge lines in a complete development must be defined by the same developers.

These instructions should be carefully observed by the student, and if the work involved in the accompanying problems is done in accordance with the principles just enumerated, no difficulties will be encountered that may not be readily overcome by careful study and a comparison of the drawings with these rules.

DRAWING PLATE, TITLE: DEVELOPMENTS I

22.   For *Development of Surfaces* the student is required to draw five plates, which are the same size as those drawn for *Practical Projection* and in accordance with the same general instructions. The titles of the plates are given and are to be placed and lettered in the same manner as heretofore. The division lines between the problems are to be omitted, and in their place a general arrangement is to be followed which resembles the reduced copies of the drawings shown on the printed plates. The problems should first be drawn on separate paper to the given sizes.   The developments may then be drawn in such positions on the plates as to present an appearance similar to that of the reduced copies.

These problems consist mainly of developments of solids whose projection occupied the attention of the student in the study of *Practical Projection*.   They have been selected for this purpose because they are representative solids whose development affords an illustration of the principles involved in patterncutting.   The student that desires to pursue the study at greater length may find convenient illustrations in other objects of frequent occurrence.   Desirable practice may thus be obtained, and the practical application of the principles outlined will serve to fix them more definitely in the student's mind.   No insurmountable difficulties are likely to be encountered in developments thus undertaken. Additional work of this kind should be of the same class as the developments explained in the text.

PROBLEM 1

23.   To develop the surfaces of a pentagonal prism.

A perspective view of the prism is presented in Fig. 18.

The drawing is to be made on the plate to the size indicated by the dimension figures there given.   The completed development is shown at Fig. 1 (*a*) and (*b*) on the plate.   First draw the plan in the position shown and then the elevation, according to the given sizes.   Next, draw the stretchout *M N*, spacing off on its length, as previously instructed, the width of the surfaces; after this the edge lines are drawn, and finally the developers.   As before, indicate the edge

FIG. 18

lines, and finish this and all drawings in the manner described in Arts. **16** to **18**.

24. To develop the curved surface of a cylinder.

EXPLANATION.—No perspective figure is given for this problem, the cylinder being 1¼ inches in diameter and 1½ inches high. Since there are no parallel edges presented on the curved surface of the cylinder, it is necessary to assume them. When edges are thus assumed for the curved surface of any solid, the corresponding edge lines in the development are represented in the same manner as for the prism. It is unnecessary, however, to designate assumed edge lines by small circles, since there is no angular bending on such lines when the surface is formed to the shape indicated in the projections.

When it becomes necessary, on account of the intersection of another solid or plane with the cylinder, to represent intermediate lines, they are then treated as interedge lines, the same as for the prism. Edge lines and interedge lines, therefore, bear the same relation to the development of curved surfaces as to plane surfaces. But it is necessary to exercise more care in the development of curved surfaces, since these lines are not so readily distinguished from one another as in the case of prisms. Indicators may be marked on the outer edge lines; but, since the others are assumed merely for the purposes of development, the small circular indicators are omitted. In the case of a regular cylinder, as in this problem, it is unnecessary to project the edge lines to the elevation, and this work may be omitted in the construction of the problem on the plate.

CONSTRUCTION.—Draw first the plan and elevation shown on the plate at Fig. 2 (a), giving the figure the required dimensions. Next, divide the outline in the plan into a convenient number of equal spaces (in this case 16). Draw the stretchout M N as heretofore, and lay off on this line an equal number of spaces similar to those on the plan of the cylinder; draw the edge lines as shown, and complete the development by drawing the two necessary developers from the elevation. Then finish the drawing in the usual manner, as shown at Fig. 2 (b).

25. **To develop the surfaces of an intersected octagonal prism.**

Fig. 19 is a perspective view of the prism projected in *Practical Projection* in order to show an octagonal prism

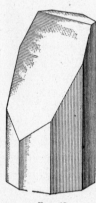

cut by a plane; the dimensions of the figure, however, are slightly changed, as may be seen from the plate. The drawing of the projections is similar to that in the problem referred to and may be completed as shown on the plate at Fig. 3 (*a*). This problem requires interedge lines, as in the case of the cube in Fig. 17; more developers, too, are needed than are used for preceding problems. Aside from these features, the drawing does not differ materially from those that have preceded it. After developing the stretchout, as in previous problems, and drawing

FIG. 19

the edge lines and interedge lines at right angles to the stretchout, developers are drawn from the several points indicated in the elevation; viz., E'', D'', C'', etc., as shown. Care must be used to terminate each developer on the line corresponding to each edge or interedge, as the case may be.

After this development is completed, the student may derive some assistance by cutting out a paper model according to the lines indicated and bending it to conform to the octagonal prism; he should then understand exactly what is implied by the operations that have been explained.

---

26. **To develop the curved surface of an intersected cylinder.**

Fig. 20 is a perspective drawing of the intersected cylinder required for this development; the dimensions in Fig. 4 on the plate indicate the size the drawing must appear thereon.

This problem is very similar to Problem 2, the only difference being that it is necessary to project the edge lines to the elevation in order to obtain the points of their intersection with the cutting plane. From these points developers are drawn to their corresponding edge lines in the development. The curve traced through points of intersection in that portion of the drawing is the upper outline of the development. This drawing being fully shown on the plate at Fig. 4 (*a*) and (*b*), the student should have no difficulty in completing the problem. Since the cutting plane in this problem is at an angle of 45°, the de-velopment may be used as a pattern for a two-pieced elbow.

FIG. 20

---

27. To develop the surfaces of two intersecting cylinders.

Explanation.—Fig. 21 is a perspective view of intersecting cylinders. Since the two cylinders are of the same diameter, their axes intersecting, the lines of intersection are represented on the drawing by straight lines.

Construction.—The projections shown on the plate at Fig. 5 (*a*) are first completed and an end view of the shorter cylinder projected as shown at (*d*). The outline of each cylinder in that view in which it is represented as on edge is then divided into a similar number of equal spaces (16 in Fig. 5). The points thus located for the purpose of representing the assumed edges are then projected from each view to the elevation. Stretchouts $M N$ and $M' N'$ are then developed, and edge lines are drawn perpendicular to the stretchout in each development. Developers may now be drawn from the ends of all assumed edges in the elevation

FIG. 21

to their corresponding edge lines in the developments. Note that in the development of the vertical cylinder the outline of the intersection of the horizontal cylinder is projected to any set of edge lines desired, the position of the outline of the opening being optional with the draftsman.

The development of the intersecting cylinder could be drawn from either the plan or the elevation in this case, since the true length of the parallel lines of that solid is shown in either view; for the sake of the appearance of the drawing, it is developed from the elevation.   The development of the intersected solid is here shown to be a parallelogram having an irregularly curved portion outlined in the central part of the figure.   It may be seen that the plan of the cylinders is not absolutely necessary for this development, since the edge lines from each circle intersect in the same points on the line of intersection of the two cylinders. In the practical work of such developments, therefore, one of the full views may hereafter be omitted.

28.   Recapitulation.—These five problems are to be copied on the plate in the relative positions indicated on the printed copy.   Care should be exercised that the figures when completed occupy central positions on the plate, and an equal distance should be left on all sides of the drawing. The plate will then present a neat appearance, and the developments may be easily distinguished from one another. When finishing these drawings on the plate, the various features are to be represented as follows:

Represent the boundaries of figures and all visible parts of solids by light full lines.   ————————————

Hidden edges and hidden intersection lines should be represented by light dotted lines.   — — — — — — — —

Projectors, as heretofore, are to be indicated by dot-and-dash lines.   —— · —— · —— · —— · —— · —— · ——

Edge lines are indicated by dot-and-dash lines, used also for projectors.

Interedge lines are indicated by dash-and-double-dot lines. ——··——··——··——··——··——

Represent developers by broken lines. —— —— —— —— —— ——

Represent the stretchouts by heavy full lines. ————

DRAWING PLATE, TITLE: DEVELOPMENTS II

PROBLEM 6

29. **To develop the surfaces of two intersecting prisms.**

The prisms developed in this problem are the octagonal and quadrangular solids whose projection was given in *Practical Projection* in order to show views of intersecting prisms.

CONSTRUCTION. — The development of Case I of that problem is shown in Fig. 22. Note that interedge lines are required for the development of both solids, their positions being found by projectors drawn from the different

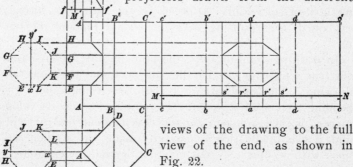

FIG. 22

views of the drawing to the full view of the end, as shown in Fig. 22.

Case II of the problem referred to is developed in a similar manner. A drawing of the latter will form the first development for this plate, and the projections

are accordingly reproduced as shown at Fig. 1 (*a*) of this
plate.   In order to avoid confusion of lines, projectors are
sometimes drawn as shown on this plate; that is, only their
starting points are indicated, as between the two views of
the octagonal prism in this drawing.   Next, develop the
stretchouts for the two solids, as at *M N* and *M′ N′*, and
draw edge and interedge lines through their respective
points.   The positions of the interedge lines are found by
projecting the point *A* in the plan across to the full view,
as shown at (*d*), afterwards locating the points *x* and *y*
at *x′* and *y′* in (*d′*); thence, they are projected to the elevation and carried to the development in the usual manner,
the resulting figures at (*b*) and (*c*) completing the development of the solids.

The development of Case III of the problem in *Practical
Projection* forms the second part of this problem.   These
projections are reproduced in Fig. 2 on the plate at (*a*).
In this case, the axes of the solids do not coincide, and the
problem has an appearance of greater complication than
the drawing in Fig. 1.   It is necessary to trace out the line
of intersection very carefully, and if this is done, the drawing of the remainder of the problem will be comparatively
easy.   The interedge lines are determined in the same manner and are shown on the plate by similar letters.   The
method of procedure is precisely the same as already
explained, the resulting developments at (*b*) and (*c*) completing the problem.

In drawings of this class, the student will perceive that
the true length of the parallel lines is found by projection
drawing.   The application of the rules found under the
heading " General Rules for Obtaining Parallel Developments " is then sufficient for the development of any solid;
and if this application is carefully made, the student will
meet with no obstacles that may not be readily overcome.

30.   Development of Intricate Solids.—In the process
of developing intricately formed solids, it becomes necessary to exercise diligence and caution in the observance

of the regular order of unrolling the surfaces on the stretch-out and carefully to draw the developers to their corre-sponding edge lines in the development. Note that in order to obtain the outline of the development for the inter-secting solid at Fig. 2 (c), a separate developer is required in the case of each edge or interedge of the solid.

DRAWING PLATE, TITLE: DEVELOPMENTS III

PROBLEM 7

31. **To develop cylinders that intersect irregularly.**

This problem is a development of the cylinders projected in *Practical Projection* to show views of intersecting cylin-ders of unequal diameters.

CONSTRUCTION.—The principles are the same as those governing previous developments, but since many lines are required for the drawing, the student should carefully fol-low the directions in the order stated. Draw, first, the projections as at Fig. 1 (a) of this plate and carefully indicate the line of intersection of the two solids. The development of the smaller cylinder is then made. Space the outline of the full view as at (b) and (b'), using 16 spaces; number these points in a corresponding manner, as shown, and project them to their adjacent views. Designate the intersections in the different views by similar numbers, to avoid confusion. Develop the stretchout M N in the usual way; draw edge lines and, afterwards, developers, as shown on the plate. The development at (c) is thus completed, the irregular outline there shown being the pattern for the surface of the smaller cylinder. This part of the work may be completed without reference to the larger cylinder. In fact, it may be considered as a separate drawing, and the student should take no notice of any other lines on the drawing except those pertaining to the smaller solid. In this way he will accustom himself to working on drawings that overlap one another.

A saving of the draftsman's time is often effected by thus making developments over other portions of the drawing, for if this were not done, a separate projection would be required for each development.   The large number of lines on the drawing is, however, apt to be confusing to the beginner, and is frequently a cause of error when the drawing is transferred to the metal.   Unusual care must therefore be taken in such cases.

The development of the smaller cylinder being completed, attention is directed to the larger solid.   It is evident that the outline of the development of the larger cylinder will be a parallelogram having an irregularly outlined portion in some part of the figure.   Reference to the plan indicates that the edges assumed for the smaller cylinder intersect the surface of the larger at *9, 10, 11, 12, 13, 14, 15, 16,* and *1,* the total distance from *9* to *1* being one-quarter of the length of its outline.   These points may now be assumed as the edges for that portion of the surface of the larger cylinder, the remainder being spaced off in the usual manner, as *A, B, C,* etc.   Any convenient point on the outline may be taken as the starting place for the stretchout, the extreme upper point of the plan at *A* being selected in this case. Since the intersections occur only on the assumed edges that are indicated by the *numbered* points, the drawing of the edge lines in the development may be omitted through the *lettered* points, the outer edge lines alone being necessary to define the size of the parallelogram.   Developers are then drawn from the same points of intersection in the elevation used for the development of the smaller cylinder, care being exercised that they extend to their corresponding edge lines in the development of the larger cylinder, as shown on the plate at Fig. 1 (*d*). *

---

* It will be noted during the drawing of this development that the stretchouts of these cylinders are measured as chord distances.   The lengths in (*d*) for the large cylinder, therefore, will be slightly different as measured from *a* to *1* when comparison is made with the length *1* to *9,* and, correspondingly, from *A* to *H*. The student should understand that in actual shop practice these chord distances are equally spaced in all quadrants in order to overcome this difficulty.   The difference is, however, so slight in this drawing that no allowance is necessary.

32. To develop an octagonal prism and an intersecting cylinder.

EXPLANATION.—The projections given in *Practical Projection* to show views of a prism intersected by a cylinder are redrawn for this problem.   The development of the cylinder is very similar to that of the smaller cylinder in the preceding problem, as shown at Fig. 2 (*c*).   Note that the edges *1* and *9*, assumed on the surface of the cylinder, coincide with the edge *C* of the prism ; this simplifies the development, and the student will have no difficulty in completing the work at (*c*), it being similar to that described in the preceding problem.

CONSTRUCTION.—Since the development of one-half of the prism will serve to illustrate the principles of this problem, four sides only need be laid out on the stretchout.   In this case, the edge lines are to be drawn and indicated as such, in order that the distinction between them and the inter-edge lines may be clearly marked, in accordance with the instructions given under the heading "Development by Parallel Lines."   After developing the stretchout as shown at (*d*), the completion of the development is made in the same manner as heretofore.

33. To develop the surfaces of a cylinder intersecting a sphere.

EXPLANATION.—The projections of the sphere intersected by a cylinder that were drawn for *Practical Projection* are here reproduced at Fig. 3 (*a*) on the plate, but to a smaller scale.   This problem introduces no new element in the development of solids by parallel lines.   It is given a place in this instruction merely to show the student that, while the task of finding the line of intersection of parallel-lined solids with solids of other classes may depend on various principles of projection drawing, their development after this line has been produced is the same in all cases. After the completion of the projections, the outline of the cylinder, as shown in the plan, is divided into spaces by locating a convenient number of points; this number is always optional with the draftsman, it being customary to take as many as are required for accurate development; for, of course, the more points there are, the greater will be the accuracy.

CONSTRUCTION.—In this case, as in the case of all symmetrical solids, it is necessary to locate points on but one-half of the outline, since their projectors, if produced, will fix corresponding points on the remaining portion of the outline. The assumed edges are then projected to the elevation and their intersections with the sphere carried by developers to the development at (*b*). A similar development may be completed at (*b'*) by producing the edge lines to that figure and drawing developers as shown, completing the problem.

The stretchout line has been prominently used in these problems. In many cases it may be convenient to develop the stretchout on one of the lines used for developers, thus avoiding an additional line on the drawing. Generally, in sheet-metal work, it will be found preferable to give the stretchout line the same prominence as in these problems, for reasons that will be apparent in the student's later work.

DEVELOPMENT BY RADIAL LINES

34. Relation of the Pyramid to the Cone.—We now come to the second general division of those solids whose development may be accurately accomplished—that is, solids developed on *radial lines*. It is here proposed to show the relation borne by the pyramid to the cone, since the methods of development of both solids are similar. In the development of the cylinder, its curved outline was divided by points into a number of equal parts. These points in the plan were then projected to the elevation and there considered as assumed edges; in other words, the cylinder was treated as a many-sided polygonal solid, this solid appearing inscribed within the cylinder. In a similar manner we shall now consider the pyramid as an inscribed solid in its relation to the cone. This may be better understood by reference to Fig. 23 (*a*), (*b*), and (*c*).

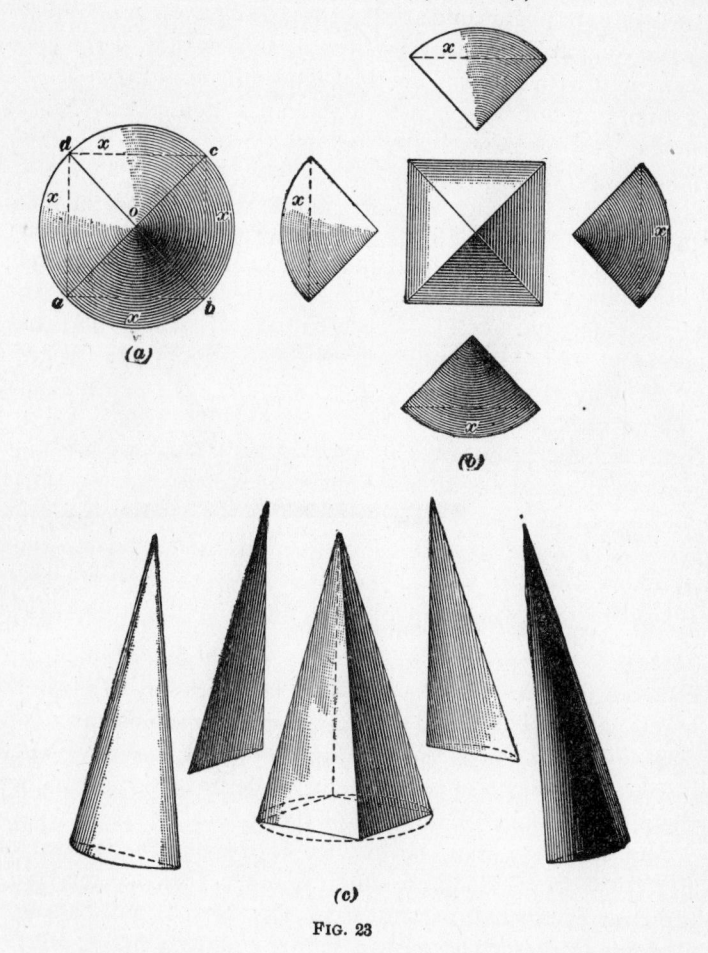

FIG. 23

The removal from the cone at (*a*) of the pieces marked *x* leaves a solid that may be recognized as a quadrangular pyramid—better shown at (*b*), the pieces being removed and shown in an adjacent position. The illustration at (*c*)

39—29

is a perspective elevation of the parts shown at (*a*) and (*b*), and is introduced for the purpose of showing the relation between the cone and the pyramid to better advantage. Comparing these two solids in the figure, it will be seen that the edges of the pyramid at (*b*) correspond to certain elements of the cone at (*a*). Further, it will be seen that, if the cone is covered with paper, as in Fig. 24, and the position of the elements noted, the paper afterwards being unrolled as shown, the elements may be imagined as leaving their imprint on the paper, as at $o\,a$, $o\,b$, etc., Fig. 24. The position of these imprints will correspond relatively to the location of the elements on the surface of the solid. A figure similar to the unrolled covering may be described by the aid

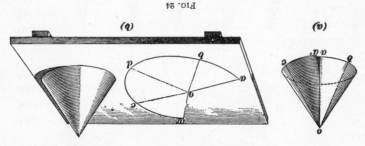

Fig. 24

of the compasses, the boundaries of the development being defined by the position of any element chosen at pleasure, notice being taken of the first and last contact of such element with the drawing during a single revolution of the cone. The *radius* of the arc thus described is always equal to the true length of an element, while its *length* is equal to the circumference of the base of the cone.

Suppose, now, that the surface of the pyramid shown at Fig. 23 (*b*) is covered in a similar manner, the covering being afterwards unrolled as shown in Fig. 25. It will be found that an arc described with a radius equal to that used for the development of the cone in Fig. 24—that is, equal to the true length of an edge of the pyramid—will pass through the points *a*, *b*, *c*, *d*, and *a'*, representing the lower extremities of the upright edges of the pyramid. These points are

equally distant from one another as measured on the arc.
This may be proved by setting the dividers at a distance
equal to the length of the base edge of the pyramid and
stepping off the spaces on the arc. The only difference
between the developments for these two solids lies in the fact

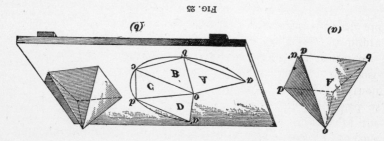

Fig. 25

that, for the *cone*, the development is defined by the circular
arc, while in the case of the *pyramid*, straight lines are
drawn between the points a, b, c, etc., as shown in Fig. 25.
These developments will be completed in a later problem.

35. Stretchouts for Radial Solids.— Since the distance around the bases of the cone and the pyramid may
be measured on an arc whose radius is equal to the length
of one of the elements of the cone (or, in the case of the
pyramid, to the length of one of its upright edges), such
an arc may be described for the stretchout of these solids.
The measurement around the solid being taken on a particular line, or base plane, it may here be observed that any
real or assumed base plane of a cone or pyramid may be
treated in a similar manner. The length of the radius by
which the stretchout is described must in all cases be
equal to the true length of the elements in that portion of
the solid.

This is illustrated in Fig. 26, the cone $O A B$ being developed along a stretchout described with the radius $O B$. An
assumed base may be taken at $C D$; an arc is then described
from the center O with the radius $O D$ ($O D$ being the true
length of the elements of the cone $O C D$). If the width
of a space between the elements on the assumed base $C D$

(measured on the plan) is taken in the dividers and spaced off on the arc DF, the spaces will be found to coincide with the intersection of the elements in the development drawn from the arc BE. The same will be found true for any right base that may be assumed for the cone. As a matter of precaution, it is customary, when drawing developments of the radial solids, to de-

scribe the stretchout with as long a radius as possible, usually not exceeding the length of the elements or edges shown in the draw-ing. For reasons that will be shown during the construction of the problems, it is con-venient to locate the center for describing the stretchout at the vertex of the solid.

36. Revolution of Radial Solids.— During the study of projection drawing, it was learned that meas-urements for all dis-tances and the posi-tion of points on the

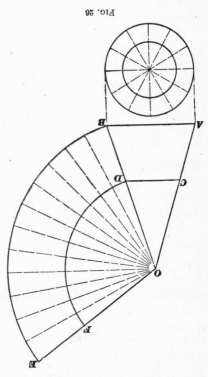

Fig. 26

surfaces of cones and pyramids—radial solids—are deter-mined by means of their radial lines, or elements. The same principle must be adhered to when developments of such solids are produced. It is essential, therefore, that these lines should be shown in their true lengths on drawings from which such developments are produced. This will necessi-tate much work on the part of the draftsman, especially if the surfaces are in any way irregular or are intersected by other solids. To overcome the necessity for drawing a number of views, advantage is taken of a principle that may be observed during the revolution of the solid. This revolution is effected in a very simple way on the drawing board, and an illustration of the method used is furnished in Fig. 27. The student will understand, from an inspection of that figure, that if the cone $O A B$ is revolved on its axis in the direction of the arrow, the motion of any point on its surface will be indicated on the elevation by a horizontal line. When any elements of the cone are in the positions occupied by the elements $O A$ and $O B$, their true lengths are shown on the elevation, and measurements may, therefore, be taken from such lines or from any points located on these lines. Lines in this position may be called *true edge lines*, their use under this name being peculiar to the radial solids.

When developing the surfaces of pyramids shown in certain positions, it is sometimes necessary to draw this true edge line independently of the figure. A problem illustrating this principle is given on the following plate. Since the elements of a cone are equal in length, the position of any point that may be located on any of these elements (as x, located on the element $O C$, Fig. 27) may be projected in a horizontal direction to the true edge line at x'', and its correct distance from the vertex O be there ascertained. The point x, therefore, could be projected to either element $O A$ or $O B$, but the supposed revolution is generally represented as being made towards the true edge line that is nearest the point whose location it is desired to determine, although in Fig. 27 the point x is moved in the opposite direction. Thus, in Fig. 27, if it is desired to determine the exact distance of the point x from the vertex O, the

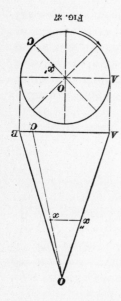

Fig. 27

horizontal line $x\,x''$ is drawn in the elevation, and the distance from the point O to the point x'' is then the exact, or true, distance between the two points. The same result would be obtained if an elevation were drawn showing the element $O\,C$ in its true length; but as seen from the foregoing explanation, the method here explained is much shorter and better adapted to the wants of the draftsman.

37. Use of Construction Lines.—In the development of radial solids, the same construction lines are used as in obtaining the developments for parallel solids, although in a slightly different manner. Since the stretchout line has been shown in its adaptation to the development of these solids, it may be represented in a similar manner on the drawings. Developers also are indicated by the same kind of broken lines used in the preceding class, but, like the stretchout, they are described in the form of arcs, and must be produced from an element or edge that is shown in its true length. In a similar manner, these developers are drawn to the development, arcs being described extending from points on edges or interedges, as the case may be, to their corresponding edge lines or interedge lines in the development. When edge lines and interedge lines occur, they converge to a point, and are the radial lines by which this class of solids is distinguished. Such edges and inter-edges are represented by lines similar to those used for the same purpose in parallel developments and refer to the same corresponding portions of the solid.

GENERAL RULES FOR OBTAINING RADIAL DEVELOPMENTS

38. A slight modification of the rules for obtaining developments on parallel lines is here applied to the develop-ment of radial solids. In connection with the foregoing instruction, a comparison of the two sets of rules will enable the student to understand the principles by which these developments may be accomplished.

1. A projection must first be drawn, consisting of a plan and elevation and showing the solid in a right position.

2. The development is always obtained from that view in which the axis of the solid is shown in its true length (since the revolution of the solid may not readily be shown in any other view).

3. The stretchout is described with a radius equal to the length of the true edge of the solid. Its center may be conveniently located at the vertex.

4. To indicate the width and relative position of the surfaces, points are located on the stretchout corresponding to the position of those points on the outline of a sectional or base view. This view must be taken at right angles to the axis of the solid, the distance from the vertex being determined by the length of the true edge lines in the elevation.

5. Edge lines and interedge lines are always radii of the stretchout arc.

6. Points located on the surface of the solid must be projected to the true edge line by projectors drawn at right angles to the axis.

7. Developers are described with radii equal to the distances on a true edge line from the vertex to the points projected to such edge line. Each developer extends thence to its corresponding edge line or interedge line in the development.

8. Interedge lines, when necessary for the development, must be indicated on the projection as well as on the development. Points located on such lines are projected to the true edge lines and thence developed in the usual manner.

9. The lengths of the outer edge lines in a complete development of a solid must be defined by the same developers.

The application of these rules will be made apparent to the student in the construction of the following problems, which involve the development of radial solids.

DRAWING PLATE, TITLE: DEVELOPMENTS IV

PROBLEM 10

39. To develop the surface of a cone.

CONSTRUCTION.—Draw a plan and an elevation of the cone, as shown at Fig. 1 on the plate. The cone is there shown in a right position, the dimensions being 1¼ inches in diameter at the base and 2 inches high. The true length of its axis is shown in the elevation, and the development is therefore made from that view. Divide the outline of the base in the plan into a convenient number of equal parts (in this case 12); from the vertex O' of the cone as a center, describe the stretchout arc $B'a'$ with a radius equal to the true length of the elements of the cone (that is, the distance $O'B'$ in the elevation). With the dividers, take the length of one of the equal spaces in the plan, and, starting at a convenient point on the stretchout, as at a, step off spaces equal in number to those on the plan, thereby making the length of the stretchout equal to the circumference of the base of the cone. From each of the points thus located on the stretchout, an edge line may be drawn to the vertex O'; but since there are no points on the surface of the cone that it is desirable to locate in this instance, only the outer edge lines $a O'$ and $a' O'$ need be inked in on the drawing. These lines are to be further indicated by means of the small arrowheads (as in the case of parallel solids) illustrated on the plate in Fig. 1. This completes the development.

PROBLEM 11

40. To develop the surfaces of a quadrangular pyramid.

CONSTRUCTION.—This development is shown on the plate at Fig. 2, the right plan and elevation being first drawn according to the dimensions given in the figure. It will be seen that the true length of the edge is shown in the elevation; the stretchout may, therefore, be described as in the case of the cone in the preceding problem. After setting the dividers to the width of one of the base edges shown in the plan at AB, Fig. 2, begin at a and step off on the stretchout line spaces equal in number to the base edges of the pyramid. Thus, points are located at a, b, c, d, and a'. Draw lines connecting these points in the manner shown, and draw other lines from each of these points to the vertex O'. In this case the edge lines must be drawn in the development, since there are actual edges on the solid; besides, it is necessary to define those portions of the development as indicated on the plate. Complete the drawing in the manner shown, the outline $O'a'bcda'$ being the development of the pyramid.

PROBLEM 12

41. To develop the surfaces of an octagonal pyramid.

EXPLANATION.—The base of the pyramid whose dimensions are given in Fig. 3 on the plate is not a true octagon, the alternate sides only being equal. It will be seen, however, that the octagon may be circumscribed by a circle; that is, a circle may be described in the plan from the center O with a radius OA, whose outline will pass through all the points A, B, C, D, etc.; therefore, the development of the solid may be accomplished by this method.

CONSTRUCTION.—The true length of the edge lines is not shown in either view presented, and it is therefore necessary to draw a line that will represent the true edge in the elevation. This is found as follows: From O as a center, with the radius OH, describe the arc HH', intersecting a line OH' (drawn parallel to the base line of the front elevation) at H'; project the point H' to the base line of the elevation (extended) at H''; $O'H''$ is then the true front elevation of an edge of the pyramid, and is, at the same time, the length of the stretchout radius. Next, describe the stretchout with this radius from the vertex O' as a center; then space off the width of the surfaces shown on the base in the plan, as at a, h, g, f, etc., and complete the development as directed in the preceding problem.

PROBLEM 13

42. To develop the surfaces of an irregular frustum of a hexagonal pyramid.

Construction.—The projections shown in Fig. 4 on the plate are first drawn in accordance with the dimensions there given, thus producing a right plan and elevation of the frustum. In this and all similar developments, it is desirable to extend the edges of the pyramid to the vertex of the solid. Since the drawing does not show the true length of the edge, this must first be found by the method described in the preceding problem, and produced as shown in the elevation at $O'a$. The points in the upper portion of the solid, at B', C', D', are then projected to the true edge line at B'', C'', and D''. The stretchout is next described from O' as a center with a radius $O'a$; the widths of the surfaces are then laid off at a, b, c, d, etc., and the corresponding edge lines are then drawn. Developers are now described from B'', C'', and D'', as previously directed, the intersections with their corresponding edge lines being noted at $b'a'$, $c'f'$, and $d'e'$. Complete the development by drawing its full outline and adding the indicators in the manner shown.

PROBLEM 14

43. To develop an irregular frustum of a cone.

Two developments are required for this problem, one of them being fully described and the other to be drawn by the student as a test of his advancement.

CONSTRUCTION.—The projection drawings for the first development are shown on the plate at Fig. 5, that portion of the cone representing a parabolic section being presented for development. In this, as in the preceding case, the completion of the figure, as shown by the broken lines, must first be made. Proceed then as if the complete cone were to be developed; that is, divide the outline of the base in the plan into a number of equal spaces, observing that certain of the points fall on the ends of the parabolic curve (as at F and B in the plan, Fig. 5). The elements of the cone are then produced in the elevation, their intersections with the edge of the frustum at b'', c'', d'', etc., being then projected as before to the true edge line. As in former problems, the stretchout is next described and spaced off, and edge lines are drawn. Developers may now be described as shown on the plate and the development completed in the usual manner. The irregular curve is now traced through the points thus determined. The projection drawings for the second development of this problem are shown on the plate at Fig. 6, and, since the methods used are the same as in the case just described, the development may be completed by the student without further instruction.

PROBLEM 15

44.   To develop the surfaces of intersecting cones.

The projections for this problem are shown on the plate at Fig. 7. They should first be carefully drawn by the student, the line of intersection being accurately determined by the method for finding the intersection of two cones that was given in *Practical Projection*. After this line has been found, all construction lines used in the projection should be erased from the drawing; if this is not done, confusion is liable to result.

CONSTRUCTION.—The development of these surfaces does not differ materially from those in the preceding problem, as an inspection of Fig. 7 will indicate. First draw the development of the surface of the smaller cone; extend the edge lines in the elevation to the vertex O', as shown; extend them also to the assumed base $a e$ and produce the full view of the base in the manner indicated by the broken lines at (n), using only one-half of the circumference. The semi-circumference is then spaced off as at a, b, c, d, and e; b, c, and d are then projected to the base line $a e$; and the elements $b' O'$, $c' O'$, and $d' O'$ are drawn as shown. The intersections of these elements with the line of intersection of the two solids are then projected to the true edge of the smaller cone, at a'', b'', etc. A stretchout for this solid is next described from the vertex O' as a center with a radius $O'e$; the points a, b, c, etc. at (b) are located by spacing the stretchout; and the distances $a b$, $b c$, etc. are taken from the full view at (n). Next, draw the edge lines $a' O'$, $b' O'$, $c' O'$, etc. at (b); and from points a'', b'', etc. describe developers in the manner shown. The irregular curve at (b) is then traced, completing the development for this solid.

As a matter of convenience in this case, the development of the larger cone, or, rather, as much of its surface as will show the opening made by the intersection of the smaller cone, may be drawn to the right of the projections, as at (c). Now draw the horizontal center line in the plan and from the center of the plan draw a line tangent to the line of intersection of the cones, marking the point where this line meets the base $4'$. Divide $1'$–$4'$ into a convenient number of parts (in this case 3) and project the points $1'$, $2'$, $3'$, $4'$ to the elevation. Draw elements from O'' to the projected points and mark the points where these elements cross the line of intersection of the cones 1, 2, 3, 4, 5, 6, and 7. The points $1'$, $2'$, $3'$, $4'$ in the plan establish the width of the spaces that shall be stepped off on the stretchout. Describe the stretchout from the center O'', as shown at (c), and on this line set off the spaces determined in the plan at $1'$, $2'$, $3'$, and $4'$, and repeat them on both sides of the edge line $1 O''$, as indicated at (c). Project the points 1, 2, 3, etc. to the right-hand true edge line of the elevation and carry them thence, by developers, to the drawing at (c), completing the development as there shown.

The student will readily perceive that if the line of inter-section of the two cones is not correctly drawn, the true development cannot be produced, since the drawing depends entirely on the line thus determined. If these points are incorrectly located, the development is necessarily wrong. The importance of having a correct projection is thus evident.

45. How to Recognize Radial Forms.—Since many objects of frequent occurrence in the trades are portions of the cone or pyramid, the student should familiarize himself with the appearance of such frustums. Many objects represent a combination of the surfaces of cones of unequal sizes, and at first sight it might appear that their development should be produced only by triangulation. But an experience in the projection of cones and conic sections will often enable the student to refer such sections to the appropriate form, in many cases thereby avoiding a tedious process of development.

The representation of the elements of the cone in both plan and elevation will determine the method to be used in the development of a given solid. In a certain case, a number of vertexes may be defined; each cone is then to be traced out carefully and the development of its surface made, or as much of that surface as is required for the object in view, the operation being similar to that of the preceding problems.

TRIANGULATION

46. Elementary Principles. — Triangulation — the process by which the development of solids belonging to the third general division is accomplished—is generally regarded by sheet-metal workers as particularly intricate and difficult. It is, on the contrary, a very simple method of development, and should, to the student that thoroughly understands the principles of projection, present no serious obstacles. This process depends for its results on two general principles, both of which have been mentioned in this section: *first*, to find the true length of all lines, real or assumed, appearing on the surfaces of the solid; *second*, having determined the true length of such lines, to construct triangles similar in form and relation to those shown on the solid.

Certainly, the construction of a triangle whose three sides are given is not a difficult problem; and the task of finding, from the projection drawing, the true lengths of its sides involves nothing but the elementary principles of that study. Having found the true lengths of the sides of such triangles as are involved in a development, nothing apparently remains but to show the method of arranging the triangles in their proper relation to one another on the different surfaces of the solids. Since this is naturally suggested by the shape of the solid itself, several solids are presented in the accompanying problems, from the study of which the student should learn to apply the principles to the development of any solid of this class.

47. Illustration of Methods Used.—This method of development has been previously mentioned, and while this principle of patterncutting is usually applied to solids having curved surfaces, it is best illustrated by its application to a solid having plane surfaces. Such a solid is shown in Fig. 28, where a perspective view is given of what may be termed a *transition piece*—that is, a piece used to connect openings of different sizes, as in pipework. Both bases are rectangular and in this case parallel, but diagonally arranged in their relation to each other, as may be seen from the figure.

Fig. 28

It is at once seen that none of the methods described under the headings of parallel- or radial-lined solids will apply to the development of the lateral surfaces of this solid, although it is possible to project a full view of each of the surfaces shown in the figure. Since this would require an

unusual amount of work on the part of the draftsman, the
following process, admitting of more rapid application, is
presented.

48. Determining the Triangles.—Clearly, a reproduction of these triangular surfaces on the flat surface of
the drawing board, in the same corresponding relation with
reference to one another, will be a development of the solid.
Apparently, the only difficulty that presents itself is the
fact that, in certain cases, the sides of the triangles are not
shown in their true lengths. It is necessary to determine
the true lengths of all lines, in order that the triangles may
be constructed of the same size as they are on the surfaces
of the solid.

As in all cases where a development is desired, a right
plan and elevation must first be drawn. This is shown in
Fig. 29, and from that illustra-
tion it is seen that all lines of
the solid that appear on either
base are shown in their true
lengths. It is therefore necessary, before the triangles may
be produced, to determine the
true lengths of the remaining
lines of the solid. As mentioned
in *Practical Projection*, this is
most readily accomplished by
constructing in each case a
right-angled triangle whose base
is equal to the length of any
foreshortened line in the plan,
and its altitude to the vertical
height of the same line, as shown in the elevation. The
hypotenuse of such a triangle will then be equal to the true
length of the line. In this case, the lines $A H$, $D H$, $A E$, $B E$,
etc., foreshortened in the plan, are all represented by lines
of the same length. The vertical height M, Fig. 29, is the
same in the case of each line.

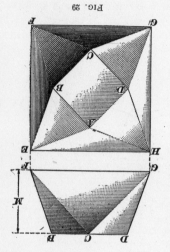

Fig. 29

A single triangle constructed by the above method, therefore, will be sufficient to indicate the true length of all lines
not shown in their true length in Fig. 29.

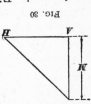

Fig. 30

Such a triangle is constructed in Fig. 30;
the base of the triangle $A H$, Fig. 30, is
equal to the length of $A H$, Fig. 29, the
altitude M being the same as M, Fig. 29.
The hypotenuse of this triangle is therefore
the true lengths of the lines $A H$, $D H$, etc.,
as shown in Fig. 29. The true lengths of all lines border-
ing the triangular surfaces of the solid shown in Fig. 29
having been found, the triangles may now be constructed
on the drawing, care being observed that the adjacent
triangles are completed *in the same order* as they are shown
on the solid. Any edge of the solid may be assumed as a
starting place for the operation; the true length of such an

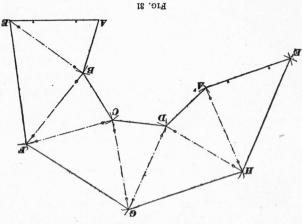

Fig. 31

edge is then laid off on a line as at $A E$, Fig. 31. The triangle $A E B$, Fig. 31, is first constructed; the length of the
side $A E$ being laid off, and $B E$, Fig. 29, being of the same
length, an arc may be described in Fig. 31 from E as a center, with a radius equal to $E A$. Intersect this arc at B,
Fig. 31, with one described from A as a center, with a
radius equal to $A B$, Fig. 29. Draw $A B$ and $E B$, thus

developing the triangle $A E B$, Fig. 31, which is the correct development of the surface $A E B$, Fig. 29.

The adjacent triangle $E B F$, Fig. 31, may next be constructed. Since $B F$ is equal to $B E$, Fig. 29, an arc may be described in Fig. 31 from B as a center, with a radius $B E$; this arc is then intersected by an arc described from E as a center, with a radius equal to the length of $E F$, Fig. 29, thus developing the triangle $E B F$, Fig. 31, which corresponds to the surface $E B F$, Fig. 29. In like manner, each surface of the solid is developed, due care being observed that adjacent triangles are placed in corresponding positions in the development.

49. Completion of the Drawing.—The completion of the drawing is made in a manner somewhat similar to parallel and radial developments; that is, the edge lines may be indicated as in those methods, the outer edges being denoted by full lines and those lines on which bends are to be made when the flat surfaces are formed up being designated by the customary indicator circles. It will thus be seen that no new principles are required to produce developments by this method. A careful observance of the different portions of the drawing is required, since an object as simple as that shown in Fig. 29 is seldom met in practice. The same methods are used, however, and should be readily understood by the student and applied to the drawing in the same manner as has been shown.

DRAWING PLATE, TITLE: DEVELOPMENTS V

50. Several problems relating to the development of solids by triangulation are given on this plate. The same principles that were shown in connection with the development of the transition piece in Figs. 28 to 31 are used in these drawings; but, owing to the different shapes assumed by the solid selected for each problem, slightly different constructions are given in each case.

Particular attention should be paid to the manner in which the triangles are located on the irregular surfaces, care being exercised that similar points in each view shall be taken as a basis for finding the true length of each line.

PROBLEM 16

51. To develop the surface of an irregular solid having parallel bases.

The solid shown in perspective in Fig. 32 is the same as that used in *Practical Projection* for the projections of views of an irregularly formed solid and a sectional view from a given cutting plane.

CONSTRUCTION.—The first step is to draw a right plan and elevation, as shown at Fig. 1 (*a*) on the plate. Draw the horizontal diameter *a m* through the plan, thus dividing the solid into symmetrical halves. It will now be seen that, if a development is made of the upper portion of the solid, as seen in the plan, a duplication of the resulting figure will be the complete development. In order to locate the sides of the triangles that are to be assumed on the surface of the solid, the outline of the bases is divided into the same number of equal parts (in this case 6), as at *a*, *c*, *e*, etc. on the lower base and *b*, *d*, *f*, etc. on the upper base.

Draw, in succession, lines alternately from the points on the upper and lower bases; *a b* being on the line of the diameter, draw *bc*, *cd*, *de*, etc.

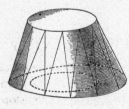

FIG. 32

Project these points and lines to the elevation, and represent them by dot-and-dash lines, as used in preceding developments to designate edge lines. The surface of the solid is thus divided into a number of triangles that may be better understood by the student from an inspection of Fig. 32. This is a perspective view of the solid, showing in the full lines the triangles that have been assumed on its surface. The lengths of the sides bd, df, ac, ce, etc. may be taken as chord distances directly from the plan, since they are there shown in their full length. A construction of right-angled triangles is necessary, however, in order to find the true lengths of the lines bc, cd, de, etc., Fig. 1 of the plate; and in order to construct them, the base line $a'm'$ of the solid in the elevation, Fig. 1, is extended indefinitely towards the right of the drawing to m'', as shown at (b).

At a convenient distance from the elevation locate a point on this line, as at b' in Fig. 1 (b) on the plate. Take the distance bc, as shown in the plan, and set it off with the dividers, as at $b'c'$; in like manner, make $c'd'$ equal to cd, as shown on the plan, and proceed to copy all the distances there shown until the point m'' is reached. It will be seen from an examination of the projections that the lines $a'b$ and $m'n$ are shown in their true length in the elevation, and a triangle is, therefore, not required for those lines.

Since the bases of the solid are parallel, the vertical height of the triangles at (b) is the same in all cases, and may be projected from the elevation as shown on the plate. The true lengths of all lines now being determined, the triangles may be constructed as shown at Fig. 1 (c). Draw the line ab, making it equal in length to the corresponding line in the elevation—that is, $a'b$; next, describe an arc from a as a center, with a radius ac, taken from the plan at (a); intersect this arc by an arc described from b as a center, with a radius equal to the length of the hypotenuse of the triangle whose base is $b'c'$ in (b). This completes the triangle abc at Fig. 1 (c). The triangle bcd is next constructed in a similar manner, and the completion of the development is accomplished by a continuation of the methods described. Small arrows are introduced in Fig. 1 (c) to indicate the location of the centers of the corresponding arcs. Thus, the arrowhead on the line bc is pointed towards b, and indicates that the center of the arc, by means of which the point c is determined, is located at b; c in like manner is similarly shown to be the center of the arc described through (d). Since there are no edges to be bent angularly when the surface is formed to the shape shown in the plan and elevation, the circular indicators are omitted; but arrowheads indicating the boundary edges of the development may be added as heretofore, completing the problem.

PROBLEM 17

52. To develop the surface of an irregular solid having inclined bases.

A perspective view of this solid is shown in Fig. 33; it is a modification of the solid used for the preceding problem,

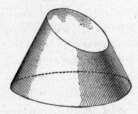

and may be drawn as shown on the plate at Fig. 2 (*a*). The outline of the lower base is drawn as in Fig. 1, and the center of the semicircle at *o* is also the center of the circle that represents the inclined upper base, the angle of inclination being 45°.

FIG. 33   CONSTRUCTION.—Draw a line (not shown on the plate) vertically upwards from *o* and fix the point *h* 1½ inches above the lower base of the solid. Through this point draw the line *b n* at the given angle; and at right angles to *b n* describe the circle representing the full view of the upper base, as shown. Next, locate the points shown on the semicircle and, by means of the temporary full view shown at *b' h' n'*, project the inclined view of the upper base in the plan. These points are then used, as in the preceding problem, for the purpose of defining the triangles. Divide the lower base of the solid, as shown in the plan, into an equal number of parts, and draw lines representing the sides of the triangles, as in Fig. 1, producing them in the plan and elevation, as *b c, c d, d e*, etc. Fig. 2 (*a*).

The manner of determining the true lengths of the lines *b c, c d, d e*, etc., is slightly different from that used in the preceding problem, since the vertical distances are not the same in all cases. Produce the lower base *a m* to the left, as shown at (*b*) on the plate, and on this line set off the lengths of the lines bc, cd, de, etc. as they appear in the plan at Fig. 2 (*a*). The vertical heights are then projected from the elevation in the manner shown, taking similar points in each case.

The true lengths of all lines now having been determined, the development may be constructed as shown at Fig. 2 (*c*). In this case, as in all instances where the solids are uneven and irregular in their form, it is preferable to begin the development from the longest edge that is shown in its true length. The line mn is, therefore, copied as shown at (*c*), and the triangle nml constructed as in the preceding development, taking the lengths of the radii nl, lj, jh, etc. from the full view of the upper base, and the lengths of the radii ml, lk, kj, etc. from their respective triangles as formed at (*b*), while mk, ki, ig, etc. are taken from the full view of the lower base as shown in the plan at (*a*).

PROBLEM 18

53. To develop the surface of an irregular solid whose upper base is rightly inclined and whose lower base is a portion of a cylinder.

This solid is shown in perspective in Fig. 34, and the triangles that are to be located by the student in the projections are represented in the drawings shown on the plate.

CONSTRUCTION.—As may be seen from Fig. 3 (*a*) on the plate, the projections do not differ materially from those of the preceding problems. First draw the oval in the plan as in the two preceding problems, noting that, in this case, the outline is a foreshortened view of the real surface. Next, draw a line vertically upwards from o, the center of the semicircle, to the point h in the elevation, which is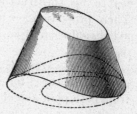

FIG. 34

3 inches distant from o. Through h draw bn at an angle of 30° with the horizontal; at right angles to bn project the full view of the upper base, which, as in Problem 17,

is a circle. Through the plan draw *a m* and bisect it at *x*; with *x* as a center and a radius of $1\frac{13}{16}$ inches describe in the elevation the arc *a g m*, representing that view of the lower base.

As in the preceding problem, project the foreshortened view of the upper base, and, as before, designate the positions of the six spaces. Since the view of the base in the plan is foreshortened, it is necessary to project its full view, in order to ascertain the true distance around the outline. Divide the foreshortened outline of the lower base shown in the plan into six equal spaces, at *a, c, e,* etc. First, however, draw the center line *a m*, as in previous cases, and then project to the elevation the points thus located. To produce the full view, as at Fig. 3 (*c*), extend the line *a m* in the plan towards the left as far as to *m'*, and on this line lay off the stretchout of the lower base, as shown in the elevation; thus that portion of the solid is treated as a surface developed by means of parallel lines. Draw edge lines perpendicular to the stretchout, as on the plate, and produce developers from the points *a, c, e, g,* etc. in the plan to *a', c', e', g',* etc. at (*c*). The light curve shown at (*c*) is then drawn and represents the true outline of the lower base of the solid; measurements may now be taken from points on this outline, as *a' c', c' e',* etc., for the radii of the arcs required in that portion of the development at (*d*), their true lengths thus being shown. The true lengths of the lines shown in the projections at *b c, c d, d e,* etc. are obtained as before by constructing diagrams of triangles at (*b*), (*b*). Their projection on both sides of the elevation is done to avoid confusion from having a number of lines cross on the drawing.

Note the varied heights of the triangles, hence the need of extreme care; for if corresponding points are not taken from both plan and elevation, it will be difficult to trace the resulting errors. The true lengths of all lines having been determined in (*b*), (*b*), and (*c*), the development at (*d*) may be constructed by methods precisely like those used in Problems 16 and 17.

Since *m n* is the longer true edge shown in the elevation, the development should begin from that line by making *m n* at (*d*) equal to *m n* in the elevation at (*a*). With a radius *n l* (taken from the full view of the upper base), and with *n* in (*d*) as a center, describe an arc as shown, and intersect it at *l* with an arc described from *m* as a center, with a radius equal to the hypotenuse of the triangle *m l* at (*b*)—the true length of the line *m l*, as shown at (*a*).

This completes the triangle *m n l* at (*d*). Next, describe an arc from *m* as a center, with a radius *m′ k′* taken from the full view of the lower base at (*c*), and intersect this arc at *k* with an arc described from *l* as a center and a radius equal to the hypotenuse of the triangle *l k* at (*b*). The triangle *m l k* is thus completed, and the remainder of the figure at (*d*) is constructed in a similar manner. The development at (*d*) is one-half of the irregular surface of the solid shown in Fig. 34.

It should be noted that, in the practical work of laying out patterns by this method, a sufficient number of points should be located on both bases of the solids to insure accuracy in tracing the curved line of the development.

54. Importance of a Correct Projection.—It will be seen from the foregoing problems that in each case the first operation is the drawing of a correct projection. The true lengths of all real or assumed lines that may have been shown in such a drawing of the solid are thus ascertained, and the draftsman is then enabled to determine which of the three general methods is to be applied in order that a development may be produced. The views to be drawn are in all cases those that will represent the solid in a *right* position, since the true length of any line is most easily obtained from such drawings. The ease with which this is accomplished is clearly shown in the foregoing examples; and if the student will devote his attention to the projection of a variety of commonly occurring trade subjects, he will quickly acquire a facility obtained only by constant practice.

Particular attention is directed to the imaginative feature of the projection, as mentioned in *Practical Projection;* for a correct conception of the actual position of the various lines as they will appear in the completed object can be acquired in no other way, and it is of extreme importance to the draftsman desiring to become proficient in the production of developments. If a student is expert at "reading" drawings, he will experience no difficulty in applying the various principles that have been given for producing developments of surfaces.

55. Employment of Modified Methods.—In producing the developments given in the last three problems, the triangles are not always projected from the views in the manner shown on the plate. Short methods are often used; but since in such cases there is more chance for error, the student will do well not to attempt any other method than

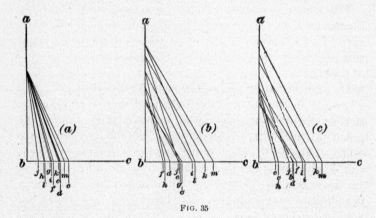

FIG. 35

that just described—at least, not until the principles are firmly fixed in his mind. As the drawings from which such developments are made are often too large to permit the projection of the triangles in the manner shown, the construction given in Fig. 35 is often applied. In this figure the triangles for Problem 16 are shown at (*a*), and those for Problems 17 and 18, at (*b*) and (*c*), respectively. A single right angle is first drawn, as *a b c* ; the lengths of all lines shown in the plan are then set off with the dividers on the side *b c*, while the vertical distances taken from the elevation are set off on the side *a b*. A number of slanting lines are then drawn between the points thus located, each forming the hypotenuse of its respective right-angled triangle. Unusual care must be observed when this method is adopted, since the points are located close together and are very apt to be mistaken for one another.

When many lines thus appear in the drawing, the student is very apt to become confused and to consider the drawing as complicated. If due care is used and ample time taken, this confusion will be avoided, for the drawings themselves depend on the simplest of principles—principles that may readily be understood by any one willing to give the time necessary for mastering this work.

56. Scalene Cone.—The development of this solid illustrates a short method of triangulation applicable to a number of solids, particularly to those represented by transition pieces one of whose bases is a polygon. A right view of such a cone is presented in Fig. 36 (*a*), and an inspection of its elements will show that they are of unequal length. This inequality, combined with the fact that a section taken at right angles to the axis of a scalene cone is not a circle, precludes its development by the method applied to radial solids, although the process is a combination of that method and triangulation. In accordance with instructions given hereafter, a drawing of this development should be made by the student, although it is not required to be sent to the Schools for correction.

After drawing the right plan and elevation as in Fig. 36 (*a*), the base is divided into a convenient number of equal parts (12 in Fig. 36). Next, the elements are drawn in both views, and it may then be seen that the surface of the cone is divided into a number of triangles whose common apex is at *o*, the vertex of the cone. In the elevation, the elements *o g* and *o a* are the only ones shown in their true length. In order to determine the true lengths of the remaining elements, the drawing shown at Fig. 36 (*b*) is constructed.

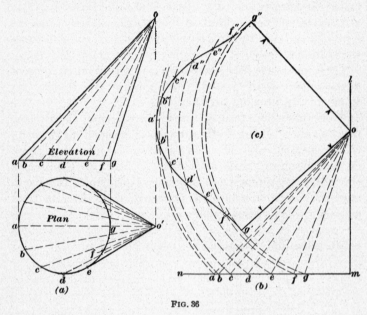

FIG. 36

Draw the right angle *l m n* and set off *m o*, the vertical height of the cone.

The length of each element shown in the plan at (*a*) is now set off on the line *m n*; thus, make *m g* at (*b*) equal to *o′ g* in the plan at (*a*), *m f* at (*b*) equal to *o′ f* at (*a*), etc. Draw *o g*, *o f*, *o e*, etc. at (*b*), thus producing the elements of the scalene cone in their true length, the method used, as will be seen by the student, being similar to that used in the other triangulation problems.

From *o* as a center, with *o g*, *o f*, *o e*, etc. as the respective radii, describe arcs in the manner shown in Fig. 36 (*b*). At a convenient point locate *g′*, and draw *g′ o* as indicated at (*c*). This line (*g′ o*) is one edge of the development, which may be completed by making *g′ f′* at (*c*) equal to *g f* in the plan at (*a*), *f′ e′* at (*c*) equal to *f e* at (*a*), etc., the compasses being set at this distance and similar arcs described as the successive points are located. Proceed in the manner shown until the point g'' is reached, when the development is completed by drawing $o\,g''$ and tracing the curve through points at the intersection of the arcs. The outer edge lines of the development may be further noted by the use of indicators as before described.

There are many irregular solids to which this method of development may be applied. The student should therefore work out this drawing very carefully, that the construction may be well understood and the method of its application readily seen. Where convenient, models should be made of these developments. These models may be cut out of paper or thin sheet metal and afterwards formed up to represent the solids described in the particular projections accompanying each problem. A better idea of the solids and their respective developments will thus be obtained. Should any errors arise in the course of the work, they may frequently be detected by this means.

APPROXIMATE DEVELOPMENTS

57. The Sphere.—The sphere is the most prominent example of the many solids whose surfaces admit of approximate development. The methods used with solids capable of accurate development must be applied to solids of approximate development. Since solids of approximate development may be resolved into parts resembling those capable of accurate development, it is clear that the same general methods are easily applicable. Thus, in the case of the sphere, that solid is resolved into a number of frustums of cones, in the manner described in the next article.

As already stated, it is necessary to submit the covering for these solids to the operations of "raising," in order to conform the metal to the profile of the solid itself; an allowance is therefore required for the consequent stretching of the stock. This allowance varies with the thickness and quality of the material; hence, no general rules can be given here. The mechanic must be acquainted with the nature of the material in order to determine the allowance required in each case.

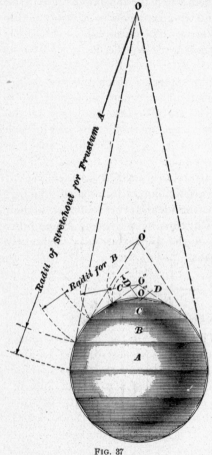

FIG. 37

58. Development of the Sphere.—It has been stated that each solid of *approximate* development must be referred to one of the three classes of solids capable of *accurate* development. It is first necessary, therefore, to determine which of the regular solids the irregular solid to be developed most resembles. The blanks, or patterns, produced by these methods are, as has been observed, flat, or plane, surfaces; and since it is necessary to "raise" these surfaces by hammering, the draftsman must imagine the surface desired in the final form. The principle by which these solids are classified is illustrated in Fig. 37 by the perspective of the sphere and its resolved cones. After the sphere has thus been resolved into cones—or rather, frustums of cones—their developments may be produced in the regular way, each frustum being separately treated, in the manner shown. This is called *development by zones*, and may be applied to a number of irregular solids resembling the sphere.

Another method of treatment is shown in Fig. 38, certain
sections of the sphere being here considered as portions of
the surface of the cylinder. This
method is referred to as the *develop-*
ment by gores; the patterns are
developed, as with any portion of
the cylinder, by means of parallel
lines.

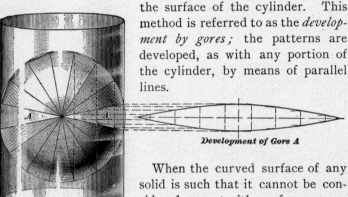

Development of Gore A

FIG. 38

When the curved surface of any
solid is such that it cannot be considered as part either of a cone or
of a solid with parallel lines, it is
customary to determine a series of
sections in a regularly occurring order and apply the
method of triangulation as shown in Problems 16 to 18.
Such surfaces are then formed up as nearly as possible to the
shape of the solid and are then submitted to the operations
referred to for "raising" to their proper shape.

INDEX

ix